The Regions of the World

EDITED BY

H. J. MACKINDER, M.A.

READER IN GEOGRAPHY IN THE
UNIVERSITY OF OXFORD

THE REGIONS OF THE WORLD.

EDITED BY H. J. MACKINDER, M.A.

Each complete in one volume,
Large Crown 8vo.

BRITAIN AND THE BRITISH SEAS.
By the EDITOR.

CENTRAL EUROPE. By JOSEPH PARTSCH,
Ph.D.

THE NEARER EAST. By D. G. HOGARTH,
M.A.

INDIA. By Colonel Sir THOMAS HOLDICH,
K.C.I.E., C.B , R.E.

THE FARTHER EAST. By ARCHIBALD
LITTLE.

NORTH AMERICA. By ISRAEL C. RUSSELL,
LL.D.

LONDON : HENRY FROWDE.

*

THE NEARER EAST

THE
NEARER EAST

BY

D. G. HOGARTH, M.A.

FELLOW OF MAGDALEN COLLEGE, OXFORD
LATE DIRECTOR OF THE BRITISH SCHOOL AT ATHENS

With Maps and Diagrams

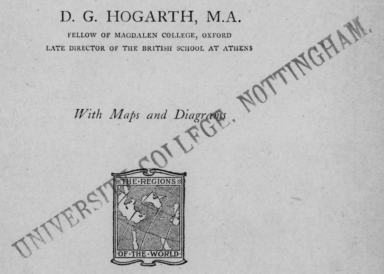

HENRY FROWDE
LONDON, EDINBURGH AND GLASGOW
1905

EDITORIAL NOTE

Owing to Mr. Hogarth's absence in Crete at the time when it was necessary that this book should go to press, a few errors have unfortunately remained uncorrected. These he has noted on page xvi.

H. J. M.

PREFACE

THE aim of this volume is to present the causative influence of geographical conditions upon Man in a
certain region. As the operation of the same physical
feature may often be traced in diverse aspects of human
life, the same idea has to be expressed more than once in
other, and sometimes the same, words in such a treatise
as the following. The public for which this series is
designed by its promoters is so various, that the first
essential is to be generally intelligible. In the matter of
the orthography of proper names, therefore, I have at-
tempted no scholarly precision. Philological translitera-
tions of, *e.g.*, Arabic or Turkish words are eschewed. Such
recognised conventions as " Bedawins " are retained. To
the unfamiliar Asiatic names the Royal Geographical
Society's compromise system has been applied ; but
familiar names, *e.g.* in the Holy Land, or those usually
transliterated on a familiar system, such as the Latin
rendering of Greek, have been left alone. It is useless to
write Evvia for Eubœa, if Piræus is not to be Pireéfs.
As a guide to pronunciation, an accent has been placed
on the stress syllable of the less familiar names on their
first occurrence.

D. G. H.

CONTENTS

FIRST PART

SECOND PART

LIST OF ILLUSTRATIONS

MAPS

DIAGRAMS AND MAPS

The Coloured Maps in this volume are by Mr. J. G. Bartholomew; the Diagrams and black and white Maps by Mr. B. V. Darbishire.

ERRATA

Page 12, line 35, *for* 'animadversing,' *read* 'animadversion.'

    ,,   31, line 34, *for* 'Saihun,' *read* 'Sihun.'

    ,,   34, line 24, *for* 'Western Asia,' *read* 'Asia Minor.'

    ,,   38, line 1, and p. 40, l. 7, *for* 'outcrop,' *read* 'intrusion.'

    ,,   40, line 8, and p. 52, fig. 10, *for* 'Sa. Savelan S. Sahend,' *read* 'Sa. Sahend S. Savelan.'

    ,,   41, line 31, *for* 'little lake of Balik . . . Ararat itself,' *read* 'range of Ala Dagh.'

    ,,   42, line 1, *for* 'Bitlis,' *read* 'Melasgird.'

    ,,   43, line 5, *for* '17,300,' *read* '17,000.'

    ,,   43, line 19, *for* 'This hollow spine . . . 'Bingiol,' *read* 'The southern limb, which makes a hollow spine between Perli Dagh and Tandurek.'

    ,,   43, line 28, omit 'The southern limb . . . northern limbs; but . . .

    ,,   65, fig. 12.   Main Karun flows to the Shatt, not the Gulf.

    ,,   84, line 8, *for* '1805,' *read* '1801.'

    ,,   95, line 21, *for* 'Assuan,' *read* 'Aswan.'

    ,,   150, fig. 39.   The last reference should read 'Under 5.'

    ,,   172, fig. 40, title, *for* 'Racial,' *read* 'Social.'

    ,,   187, note, line 6, *for* 'Greek map,' *read* 'Ethnological map of European Turkey, &c., with copious introduction, compiled in conformity with Greek views and . . .'

    ,,   190, fig. 42*a*.   Millet should be indicated in the Nile valley.

    ,,   194, line 23, *for* 'hardly,' *read* 'hardily.'

    ,,   198, line 1, *for* 'goat,' *read* 'goats.'

    ,,   211, line 25, *for* 'a quarter of a million,' *read* 'three-quarters of a million.'

    ,,   213, fig. 45.   Route S.E. from Aleppo should hug Euphrates. The railway to Kars should be shown in Trans-Caucasia.

    ,,   215, line 11, *for* 'by a large body of troops . . . repulsed,' *read* 'for an invasion of Persia since the inroad of . . .'

THE NEARER EAST

FIRST PART

CHAPTER I

AREA AND POSITION

THE Nearer East is a term of current fashion for a region which our grandfathers were content to call simply The East. Its area is generally understood to coincide with those classic lands, historically the most interesting on the surface of the globe, which lie about the eastern basin of the Mediterranean Sea ; but few probably could say off-hand where should be the limits and why. The land-marks towards the West are somewhat doubtful and apt to be removed. Fifty years ago the author of *Eothen* saw the portal of the East in the walls of Belgrade. To-day the western visitor, though conscious that the character of the life about him has undergone some subtle change since his train steamed over the Danube bridge, would not expect to find himself in the " East " until he should sight the minarets of Adrianople, or, at earliest, the three mastoid hills of Philippopolis. For want of an effective natural division, the north-western limit of the East depends largely on political conditions. Where centres of the superior civilisation of the West lie so near at hand as to exercise an intrusive influence in any case, occu-pation by a Power, which does not derive its origin from the East, quickly decides in favour of the West. How greatly even a temporary western occupation will modify the border-line, despite a strong natural barrier, may be

A

judged from consideration of Corfu, still Italian in type, though within cannon-shot of Albania.

At the end of this century, therefore, when the Austrian occupation of Herzegóvina, Bosnia, and the *sanjak* of Novi-Bazar, and the creation of independent Servia and Rumania, and an all but independent Bulgaria, exposed to the predominant influence of Central Europe, have won the basin of the Lower Danube for the West, we must set the north-western limit of our " Nearer East " at the Balkan water - parting ; but somewhat arbitrarily and without begging the question that there East and West are divided in any very obvious manner, or will long continue to be divided even as obviously as now. Upon the west the southern Adriatic supplies a natural frontier, not seriously impaired either by the increasing western influences on the Albanian shore or the decreasing western survivals in isles of the Ionian sea. Thereafter opens out the eastern basin of the Mediterranean ; and the Nearer East may be said in very general terms to comprise those tracts that are set in its waters and those that lie about them, measured inland up to certain strong physical frontiers.

Our region, therefore, will embrace all south-eastern Europe below the long oblique water-parting of the Balkans ; all the islands eastward of Corfu and Crete, which themselves are included ; all of the north-eastern corner of Africa that is fit for settled human habitation ; and all of Asia that lies on the hither side of a truly distinctive natural boundary. That boundary is not to be found before what is loosely called the " Medic " or " Indian Isthmus," which is that Waist of Asia, reduced to 700 miles' breadth, which lies between the Caspian and the Indian Seas, and is composed as to two parts of marsh and tremendous mountain, as to one part of sterile tract, kept alive here and there by outflows from the foot-hills and as to four parts of one of the most forbidding deserts that exists in the world. By the great salt hollows of Central Persia and the shifting sands of Persian Beluchistán, where Alexander left great part of the force which

he led from Sind, the Nearer East is parted from the
Farther East. That looks to western centres of civilisation with however faint and purblind a vision. This has
had from immemorial ages, and still in large measure
retains, its own springs of development.

Such communications as man, born in this region,
adolescent and wishing to expand, but bound in early
stages of his growth to follow the line of least resistance,
would establish with other regions have led him westward. And still after a century which has made greater
changes in the world's ways than all the sum of the centuries before it, the points of easy access to the Nearer
East are for geographical reasons to be sought on its
western flank. The natural difficulties of the land approach by way of the Waist are almost as prohibitive
as ever, and will so remain till railways shall have
been constructed from Meshed to Teheran and Kerman.
The southern Beluchi belt, in which the early Islamitic
invaders of India saw a resort of damned souls, was only
traversed by Captain Sykes and his small party in 1896, on
their way to join the Delimitation Commission of British
Beluchistan at Kuhàk, by the help of much provision made
by the friendly governor of Kerman. On the next belt to
the north, the sands and salts of the Dasht-i-Lut, no one
but the most hardy, mounted on the best of camels, ever
venture themselves. Small caravans, content to drink foul
water at rare intervals, carry Bombay goods from Yezd
to Seistan and Meshed by a line of sorry oases on the
sandy ridge which divides the Dasht-i-Lut from the Dasht-i-
Kavir, and some day is to be traversed by a Russian railway. The Kavir is the bed of an ancient sea, whose
bottom lies 2000 feet below the general level of the Irak
Plateau, salt beyond all hope of reclamation. In most
parts it is described as having for surface a "swollen,
puffed up glazed crust with innumerable pock-marks large
as a man's head," and being absolutely devoid of vegetation. In other parts it is covered by a glittering ice-like
sheet of salt efflorescence on which rest pools of brine,

intensely blue. Under the crust lurks water, and round its edges is a foul and dangerous slime.

This fearful tract stretches almost to the foot-hills of the southern chain of the Elburz, leaving scanty room for a narrow passage which, running by way of stony plains and black undulating ridges and isolated oases, fed by springs more perennial than the common in Persia, is, and has always been, the single trunk road from western to eastern Asia. It passes out of the former on leaving Teheran (as in earlier times on leaving Rhey) and debouches in Khorasan, whence it forks to Merv and to Herat. This difficult roadway is not better kept now, probably is less well kept, than when the last Darius fled over it for his life; but since the Russian conquest of the Tekke Turkmans, it is no longer traversed by caravans in such haste and fear as used to be the case. On the north above this road hangs the ruddy wall of the Elburz range, crossed in its eastern part by only two or three lofty passes, and falling northward to the marshes and forests which fringe the sand-choked lagoons and shoaling waters of the south-eastern Caspian shore.

The approaches on the south and north are not so impracticable as on the east, but being in the main by way of sea, they are open to predominant western influence. They are, however, at best but bad. The southern shore of the Caspian is only more ill provided with harbours than the southern shore of the Euxine; and both seas are skirted at short distance by continuous and lofty ranges, which completely cut off the interior, save where man has tardily blasted and levelled his own arduous ways of access. Steam may do much in the near future to modify these prohibitive conditions. The Russian rail-head has now been pushed far south in Transcaucasia, and it will surely be advanced ere long into Azerbaiján, and open a northern way into the Nearer East more effective than the new cart road from Resht to Teheran (also Russian), or the older and worse kept ways which lead from open roadsteads at Trebizond, Kerasúnd, Únieh, Ordu, Samsun, and Inéboli into Turkish Asia.

Nor is it much easier as yet to penetrate from the south. The starved Makran coast invites none to land. Indifferent ports on the Persian Gulf from Bunder Abbas to Dilam can only be reached from the interior by mule-tracks of much difficulty. The great estuary of the Shatt-el-Arab at the Gulf head, once its bar is passed, admits to three great waterways, navigable by steamers of shallow draught,—waterways of which the shortest, the channel of the Karun to the Ahwaz reef (Bund-i-Naziri), is over one hundred miles in length. But Nature, which has spread her wastes on either hand of the Euphrates and Tigris for nearly half their course, and predatory Man, Arab, Kurd, and Lur, who infests the caravan routes of the upper country, combine to render these great water-ways too little frequented. The huge peninsula of Arabia may be dismissed from the case. No trunk road to the heart of the Nearer East lies, or in all likelihood will ever lie, from its shallow and reef-blocked harbours across the torrid coast belt and ring of desert, set about its ill-watered uplands. And finally the Nile valley, the one route from central to north-eastern Africa possible for anything but a very well equipped caravan of camels, has yet to be developed as a serious avenue of trade.

There remains then only the western access. And here the peculiar facilities which Nature has granted for communication have been a theme for all who have treated of the growth of the early civilisation of Europe. A great inland sea, incapable of oceanic violence, which washes its deep waters on shores so frequently indented that they develop a coast line five or sixfold the flight of a bird from point to point of the periphery ; a sea tideless, and not prohibiting access in reasonably fair weather even to such harbourless shores as the Syrian ; a sea fringed by harbours from Avlóna and Corfu to Port Said and Alexandria, among which many, Corfu itself, Navarino, Piræus, Suda Bay, Milos, the Gulf of Volo, the Darda-nelles, Smyrna, Marmarís, Kékova, will bear comparison with any ports in any lands ; a sea festooned with islands, that tempt timid mariners from its western to its eastern

shores ; a sea giving access to fertile, well-watered tracts
that lie about the harbours, and to the great valleys of the
Vardar, the Maritza, the Porsuk, the Greater Ménderes,
and the Nile, conducting to the interior of the continents
—these signal advantages have made the Levant a favoured
resort of seafarers in all ages ; and now the opening of a
continuous waterway from its south-eastern angle to the
Indian Ocean has established it as the greatest thoroughfare of shipping in the world.

There are disadvantages to set on the other side
of the account, but they leave a large balance to credit.
There is not a single river that is navigable by large
craft from the sea to any useful distance.   Among
all the European and Asiatic streams, the Boyána will
admit light draught steamers to the Skútari lake, and
the Sihun in flood time can be ascended to Ádana—
voyages of small mileage and beset with undetermined
difficulties.   The Nile, whose Rosetta mouth is impracticable for steam craft of any tonnage, can be entered over
the Damietta bar by no ocean-going ship.   In fact, the
construction of the Barrage at the Delta head, and of new
main canals, has put a finishing touch to the decay of the
Lower Nile as a waterway of foreign trade.   There must
be added to this defect of navigable estuaries the blocking
of harbours by river-silt, which is an evil most difficult to
combat in the Levant.   For the rivers which fall into that
sea flow through tracts where long dry summers, that dis-
integrate the soil and destroy vegetation, are followed by
swift torrential rains.   Trickling torrents, which for two-
thirds of the year need but narrow and shallow beds, will
rise and sweep at large over broad tracts of dusty unbound
earth.   Therefore insignificant Levantine streams, carrying
annually to the sea a silt out of all proportion to their
volume of water, afford some of the most astonishing examples of land building in the world.   The rocky knobs,
which the sailor sees far back in the plain behind the
Menderes mouth, were islands off the deep port of Miletus
in the time of Christ.   The river is pushing forward this
coast about forty feet a year.   A little to the north, the shallow

sea at Scala Nuova washed in the third century of our era up to the walls of Ephesus which now stand high and dry five miles inland; and all the new tract has been formed by the Kuchuk Menderes, the little reedy Cayster of antiquity. The next stream on the north, the Gediz Chai, the famous Hermus stream of Lydian history, has filled up all the vast bay between Phókia and Mount Sipylus, and until a new outflow was cut in 1886 it was reducing the depth of the navigable entrance to Smyrna by about three centimetres a year.

The Nearer East is still imperfectly and unequally known to the West. The inhabitants have produced no first-rate surveys of any of their territories, not even Greece; and only certain districts of special interest to enterprising European Powers have been thoroughly mapped (Fig. 1). Such are the Mediterranean, Euxine, and Persian coasts surveyed and re-surveyed by the British Admiralty; Cyprus, Palestine, and Sinai mapped by British engineers; the Nile flats, originally triangled by the French, and re-surveyed with part of the northern deserts by the present occupying Power; the Morea, whose lines were laid down by the French; the Caspian coast surveyed by the Russians; Eastern Rumelia by Russo-Bulgarians; and various isolated strips on either hand of lines of railway, such as the Vardar and Porsuk valleys by Austrians; the Menderes and Lycus valleys by Britons; the southern Lebanon by Frenchmen; or the route from Resht to Teheran by Russians.

All the rest of the map, within the outlines fixed by the British Admiralty Survey (not over accurate on the Red Sea and South Arabian coasts), and by the limits of Austrian and Russian surveys on the north, is a sketch of greater or less fulness and accuracy in the several localities, according as fewer or more points are fixed astronomically, as European military consuls have or have not been stationed and able to survey, and as European travellers have been many, unhampered, well-provided with instruments, and capable of using them, or, on the other hand, few, jealously watched, compelled to journey empty-handed, or unable to use instruments profitably.

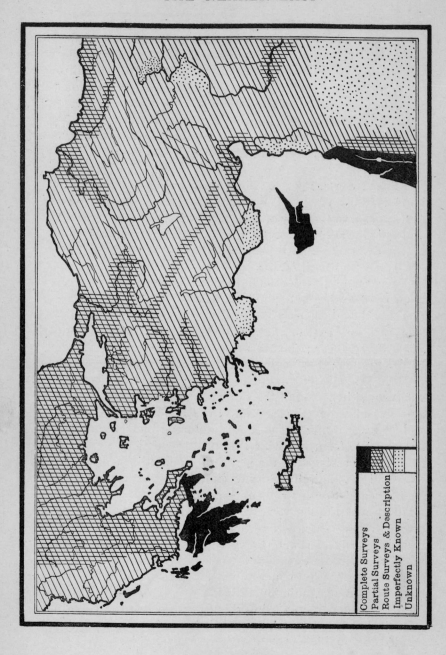

FIG. 1.—The Progress of Survey in the Ægean and Anatolian Regions.

Complete Surveys
Partial Surveys
Route Surveys & Description
Imperfectly Known
Unknown

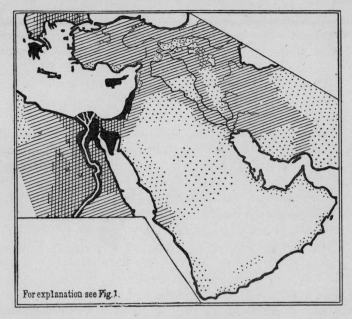

For explanation see Fig. 1.

FIG. 1a.—Arabia.

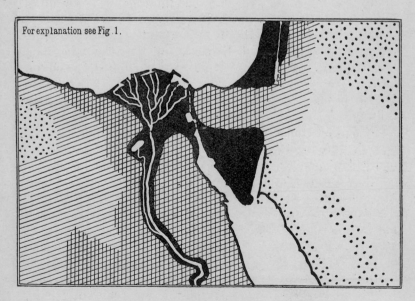

For explanation see Fig. 1.

FIG. 1b.—Egypt.

The map of the Balkan Peninsula and Isles falls below Surveys but in the first class of Sketches. Built on a framework of triangulation, it is correct in all main features, and only falls short of a first-rate survey in accuracy of minuter detail, *e.g.* of hill contours. This result is due mainly to Austrians in the western, and Russo-Bulgarians in the eastern districts. The cartography of the interior of Crete, northern Albania, and the upper valleys of the Mesta and Struma is still, however, nebulous. The east Armenian highlands, Azerbaijan, and the Caspian littoral find a place in the same leading category, thanks to Russians ; but for no other large district, not already mentioned, can the like be claimed except doubtfully for the border deserts and oases of Egypt, where much detail remains vague, even within sight of the Nile. Narrow strips along the lower courses of both Euphrates and Tigris may also be included.

The map of Asia Minor and its islands opens a second class. Here we have many fixed towns for check points, and a great deal of triangulation in isolated districts or along roads, together with a great number of route notes more or less accurate. But the observations having been made independently without system and unofficially, large lacunæ, especially in hill districts, and irreconcilable data are frequent. The Ottoman provincial charts, based on most perfunctory surveys, are little use ; but, thanks to British military consuls, to British, Austrian, and German railway engineers, and to archæological explorers of all nations, the Peninsula is now mapped with broad accuracy, though little detail, in its eastern half. At the same time many blank patches meet the eye, even in the west country, on the best maps, and the detail actually given is often not reliable. In the same class may be ranked now the southern Armenian highlands, central and southern Persia (the map of which, revised for Lord Curzon's book, owes much to British telegraph officials and Europeans in the Persian service), even the mountainous western borderland, since the work of Sawyer, and de Morgan in Bakhtiári-land and Luristan, and the west Syrian fringe north of Palestine. But within or beside these regions wholly unsurveyed districts exist. The southern Lur country and Laristan, as well as the central Persian deserts, the wilder parts of the Kurdish mountains, *e.g.* the Dersim, and the northern Lebanon, Jebel Ansaríyeh, and the region east of the Nahr-el-Asi, would naturally fall into the third class.

This last class will include those large areas where no triangulation worth mention has been effected, very few astronomical observations have been taken (and those usually unconfirmed), and the map must be filled in from the reports of a few solitary wayfarers concerning distances, covered under varying and uncertain conditions, and local features observed cursorily ; in short, where many unknown personal equations have to be reckoned with in the result. The Syrian and Mesopotamian steppes, with the more fortunate parts of the Arabian fringe, Yemen, Hádramut, and Eastern Oman, are the best circumstanced lands in this class. Travellers there, though few, have been comparatively free to observe, and most main routes have been traversed more than once. Some roads, *e.g.* in part of the Hadramut, have even been triangled. The central plateau and deserts of Arabia, however, and Midian, Hejaz, Asir, Western Oman, and the Turkish territories on the Gulf, must stand at the bottom of the list as the least known regions in our area. Fully half the huge southern peninsula has not been seen by any European eye, and most of the other half only by ill-equipped or disguised travellers passing covertly along main caravan tracks. Scientific route notes were taken in Jebel Shammar by Huber and Euting; on eastern roads to and from Riad by Pelly ; and from Katif to Medina and Jidda by Sadlier. Less elaborate notes were published by Ali Bey and Burckhardt for the Hejaz ; but what are these in so vast an area ? Unfortunately those who, like Palgrave and Doughty, have covered the most ground in Arabia, were the least equipped, qualified, or concerned to take scientific observations.

Note on Maps.—For a general atlas of the Nearer East, Stieler's, albeit old, should be used.

Albania : The best available map is that of the Austrian General Staff, which may be used also for **Macedonia** and **Greece** ; but in the former land it is less recent than the fine sheets issued from Philippopolis (by Ch. G. Danoff, 1892), and in the latter land see Philippson's **Morea,** based on the French Survey. Special Austrian map of **Attica** and one of **Thessaly** and **Epirus** in Philippson's book. For **Ægean Isles,** see British Admiralty charts. All maps of **Crete** based on same, made by Spratt. **Rumelia** best in the Bulgarian sheets.

Asia Minor : Coastal and western districts in the fifteen sheets, H. Kiepert's crowning effort (*Specialkarte v. Westl. Kleinasien*) ; but for the interior and for north **Syria** the smaller French map, by Kiepert (*Service Géog. de l'Armée*). **Cyprus :** British Survey. High **Armenia** and half **Persia :** sheets issued by the Imp. Topogr. Institute of St. Petersburg are much the best ; a reliable general map of Persia will be found in Lord Curzon's book, about to be revised. Special localities in Houtoum Schindler's articles (*Irak*), and Sawyer's *Bakhtiari-land* (*G. J.*, December 1894).* Also good maps of Irak, Elburz, and Central Persia in A. F. Stahl's *Reisen*, &c. Southern **Kurdistan** and **Mesopotamia,** both the Russian and French sheets, and for the **Euphratean Delta** and **Gulf Coasts** the Indian Government Trans-Frontier sheets.

Palestine has been surveyed by the British Exploration Fund. So also **Sinai** ; but of inland **Arabia** no decent map exists. That accompanying Doughty's "Arabia Deserta" shows the north-west. A new survey of Upper Hadramut and parts of the S. coast appears in Bent's *S. Arabia.*

Egypt : All based on the French Survey and the Public Works Department irrigation charts. The Nile Valley good in Murray's *Egypt ;* but for the Deserts we must await publication of the official survey in progress.

Note on General Authorities.—Superfluous to cite the great compendium of Elisée Reclus for individual chapters. The section on Persia has perhaps been of the most service to me ; those on the Balkans (slight and out of date), and Egypt (spoiled by political animadversing) of the least. A. H. Keane's Compendia in Stanford's series, and Ritter's *Erdkunde*, are also most valuable. V. Cuinet's *Turquie d'Asie* is an authority for a great part of the " Nearer East," but being largely based on Ottoman official records, and the reports of Christians in the Turkish service, needs critical use.

---

* The following abbreviations are used in these notes to chapters :—
   G. J. = Geographical Journal.
   P. M. = Petermann's Mittheilungen.
   B. S. G. = Bulletin de la Société Géographique.

CHAPTER II

THE BALKAN BELTS

THE character of man's life is determined primarily by the Relief of the land, exercising a various influence, especially through the climatic conditions. In treating, however, of any region in a Temperate Zone, we must bear in mind that its own Relief will not be the first cause of its climate, but will act only as a secondary agent upon contending influences of extreme zones on either hand. The cold currents in the atmosphere of the Nearer East are drawn from the Russian and Siberian steppes : its warm airs originate in Equatoria. The seas, which lie wholly within its boundaries, are not its main reserves of moisture, nor are those of its tracts like the Persian Desert and the Arabian Plateau, which experience tropical heats, the main determinants of its aridity.

This influence of local Relief on the races of mankind is modified by their recollection of other regions, in which they may formerly have dwelt, and yet more by the influence of other groups living under different physical conditions. It will be, therefore, necessary to glance in passing both at the origin of races and the causes of their present distribution, and, further, at their natural opportunities for communication.

The better to survey the superficial aspect of the Nearer East, we will envisage our region as part of a relief model of the globe, which we are to clothe in imagination with proper soils and organic life.

The eye, which having surveyed Central Europe has been attracted down the great depression of the Danube and up to the remotest sources of its right bank affluents, is arrested by a continuous curving swell of the land. High, precipitous, and very broad at the north end, the mountains which compose this swell shrink greatly both in height and breadth as the curve turns south-eastward, then rise again into an imposing pyramid, only to drop once more as the bend swings round to true east. Thereafter the elevation rises steadily, with one slight check, to a broad ganglion of peaks, whence, after a last dip, it is carried high and almost straight eastward, till it falls by a steep stairway to the Black Sea. This swell is the Balkan watershed. The mountain mass at the end of the curve is the butt of the North Albanian Alps, which throw huge fibres through Montenegro to the Adriatic, to complete the partition of the Peninsula. The pyramid, which springs up between two depressions, is the mighty northern slope of Liubótrn, the butt and crown of the Shar range ; the second ganglion, which closes a gradual rise to the east, is the syenite group of Vitocha and the Rila Dagh, south of Sophia ; and the straight continuation thence to the Black Sea is the " Hæmus" or proper Balkan system. On the outer face of this great curve begins the " Nearer East," as for present purposes we are to understand that region.

Here is a continuous parting of waters, but not, orographically, a continuous mountain range. For the swell, so far as its composition is known, is made up of a succession of oblique chains radiating to south-west and south-east, as from a common centre in the north-west. And though their foothills interlock to make an unbroken horizontal watershed, the integral ranges themselves, prolonged to the south, give a vertical, not a horizontal, direction to the main structural lines of the Balkan Peninsula, dividing the land into long Belts, which may communicate more readily with what lies to north or south of them, whether sea or land, than with one another (Fig. 2).

The westernmost of these vertical Belts bears the general name Albania, being, as to its northern part, all

the territory that intervenes between the main range of
the North Albanian Alps and the start of a main vertical
Spine in the Shar Mountains, and as to its southern part,
such land as divides that Spine from the Adriatic Sea,
into which the original ganglion, continued by the Monte-
negrin system, runs round the head of the Skutari Lake.

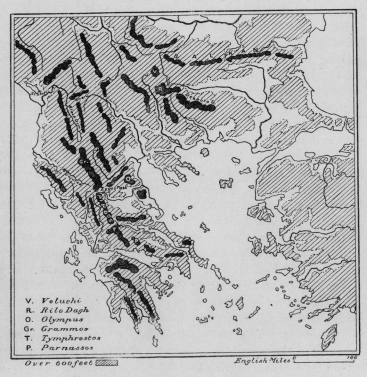

V. *Veluchi*
R. *Rilo Dagh*
O. *Olympus*
Gr. *Grammos*
T. *Tymphrestos*
P. *Parnassos*

Over 600 feet ▨▨▨   *English Miles* 0 _____ 100

FIG. 2.—The Balkan Peninsula, showing the general scheme
of the Mountain Ranges.

The largest part of the Albanian Belt is mountain,
being the western half of the complex system of the
Spine, which, originated by the single and lofty chain of
Shar, runs due south to the extremity of the land.

This long limestone Spine, which assumes bolder and
barer outlines as it runs southward to the metamorphic

systems of Greece, is orographically not very well known. Lateral pressure, exerted from the Adriatic side, has crumpled up the ridges in crabbed confusion. But the broad fact may be stated, that it throws off at constant intervals great ribs which, on the eastern side especially, tend to curve upwards against the course of the main Spine, and, mingling their roots, to lock the intervening valleys. Hence there are found on the Macedonian flank a succession of low basins of greater or less extent, some still occupied in part by lakes, others, of which the plains of Monastir and Thessaly are the most considerable examples, now drained almost dry by natural outflows.

On the western or Albanian side the ribs are equally frequent and perverse. They do not, however, recurve so much towards the Spine, but make long alignments of river valleys trending northward, rather than enclose lake-basins. From the Black Drin to the Voyútza, Albania is disposed in deep and narrow grooves, denuded at one end of the soil which is to make marsh at the other. These disastrous conditions are modified, however, in the south of the Belt, coincidently with a change in the direction of the rivers. For those that spring in the ganglion of Mézzovo follow more faithfully the general trend of the Spine, whose lateral chains are hardly to be called any longer ribs, but a thickening of the Spine itself. Amid the lower hills to the west appear upland lake-basins and plains, such as that of Jánina, which drains by a subterranean outlet. The parallels of the Spine align the sea, throwing out short spurs, which form breakwaters, leaving less room for marshes. The coasts are sheltered by the long island line of Corfu. But the land is still terribly broken, and the ranges which compose the central Spine are not less high and steep, and are more barren, than the northern Grammos or Shar. The rivers, in their natural state, serve to impede man far more than to aid him ; for during the most of the year, owing to the heavy rain and snow falls of this Adriatic slope, they sweep along with currents too full to be forded, while they are never at any part navigable, always dry when most

100

500
800
1000

1000
1000

500
100

40

REFERENCE
TO COLOURING

METRES		FEET
2000		6562
1500		4921
1000		3281
500		1640
200		656
100		328
SEA LEVEL		SEA LEVEL
100		328
200		656
500		1640
1000		3281
1500		4921
2000		6562

HEIGHT OF LAND

DEPTH OF SEA

35

Scale = 1 : 60
English Mi
10   0   20   40
Kilometre
25   0   25   50   75

The Edinburgh Geographical Institut

needed, and sunk too deep in their limestone troughs to be turned upon the thirsty lands of their banks.

Such is Albania, closed at the lower end by the shallow inlet of Arta, which leaves only one narrow passage under the face of the Spine—a Thermopylæ of Western Greece—to admit to the southern extremity of the Belt, which is politically Greek. This in its structure is not different to south Albania, being disposed in a series of moderate valleys enclosed between not lofty lateral offshoots of the neighbouring Spine, and containing lacustrine deposits and a chain of actual lakes, about which agriculture is possible and profitable, though small in extent.

Parallel to its coasts and to the general trend of its ranges, the south end of this western Belt has a chain of mountainous but fertile islands, which are in intimate geographical connection with it, sharing to the full its sheltered immunity from the north-easterly scourge of Greece, and its copious Adriatic rainfall, but free from the maleficent influence of the Albanian rivers and the south-westerly exposure of the Albanian shores. In every other physical respect Corfu is a favoured fragment of lower Albania. The other five larger isles, with their dependent islets, Santa Mavra excepted, have less continental character, and group more fitly with the southern sea-girt prolongations of the Spine. Kefalónia, the largest of the group and set farther than the others into the sea, possesses so much higher a relief than any other point either of the islands or the nearest mainland, that it is largely responsible for its own frequent rains, and enjoys greater variety of climate than its fellow-isles. Zante, again, though much smaller, is hardly less an independent unit, blessed with a broad deep plain and a fair port, but cursed with too frequent earth-tremors, of which its bitumen springs afford constant warning. The rest of the Seven Isle group are no better than small dependent rocks, Cérigo not being reckoned into the account. For that island has no connection with the group other than is due to a tradition of political union. It is a prolongation of the

Málevos range, and a visible link in its chain of connection
with the Cretan highlands.

The Spine of the mainland has been already summarily
described, but it may detain the eye a moment longer as
we pass to the second vertical Belt. For this is the most
important, because the longest, structural line in the
European part of the Nearer East, and its course is not
exhausted on the mainland, but is carried on by half
drowned peaks from the Morea even to Crete.

It starts, as we have seen, in the huge Shar range,
whose highest peak, Liubotrn, though never yet accurately
measured, may be taken to overtop by some hundreds of
feet all other points of the Balkan Peninsula, even Musallá
in the Rila group, or the majestic Olympus. Itself impassable, the Shar is easily rounded on the north by way
of the two depressions that appeared in the Swell, when our
eye first scanned the concave curve of the Balkan Divide ;
and through these is conducted the northernmost of two
great roads, which cross the Peninsula from east to west.
From its southern butt, below the Vardar head, the Shar
throws off a great eastern spur, which, running obliquely
south-east to the elbow of the Vistritza, leaves space between itself and the main Spine for the lake-basins of
Presba, Malo Jézero, and Kastória, and throws up one
superb peak, Peristéri, the dominant feature of the plain
of Monastir. Subsidiary ranges, leaving this again on the
east, bound the Monastir plain and enclose the lake-basin
of Óstrovo ; and of these one, running to the Vardar at
the Iron Gate, and another, which does not die down till
it reaches the Vardar plain, north of the Vistritza estuary,
define the main divisions of western Macedonia.

The main Spine keeps due south, first as Galichica,
then, when it enters a Greek-speaking land, as Grammos,
leaving on its right the gorge of the Black Drin, wherein
lies Dibra, the lake of Óchrida, and the low-lying basin
of Goritza, and throws off westward spurs between the
Albanian rivers, of which the most noteworthy towers
above Berat into the great Tomar, nearly 8000 feet high.

But the main Spine rises to a yet higher peak, Samarína, far seen as a glittering point from the block-houses on the Greek frontier, ere it falls at the north-westernmost angle of Thessaly to the Zygos or Mezzovo gap, whence part more races, rivers, and ranges than from any other point in the Peninsula. Of the ranges which thence trend westward we have spoken above, though not by name—of Vrádeton, better known under its ancient title of Tymphe ; of Mishikelí, which, curving round the Drynos head, swells into the group whose " vast Acroceraunian walls " close the northward prospect from Corfu ; and of the lower ranges, which, declining towards the Gulf of Arta, contain the gloomy subterranean waters of Acheron and Cocýtus, and the much sung rock of Suli. But the most famous off-shoot of Zygos is that which starts from the eastern slope, and, after a low interval of rounded sandstone hills, bends north-eastward as a succession of short oblique ranges to the mighty many-peaked group of Olympus and the eastern sea.

From the southern butt of Shar to the Zygos knot the Spine itself is not so formidable but that it might be crossed by many other trunk roads than that single ill-kept track from Monastir to Durazzo by way of Ochɪida and Elbassán, which is the old "Egnatian Way," were it not for the savage character of its eastern slopes, which has formed and fosters the rude nature of the men of Dibra and Goritza. And when, south of Zygos, the ridge domi-nates a softer prospect, at the same time it becomes itself more rugged and abrupt. The limestone parallels, abruptly folded and diagonally cleft by the Aspro river, which constitute Pindus, are very difficult of passage. There are only two fairly practicable summer tracks in all the length, and no easy pass until the ganglion of Velúkhi is left behind and two lateral chains are thrown off right and left ; of which the last, famous in history as Othrys, bends round the Gulf of Volo to Pélion, and after forking south by way of the Magnesian tongue to the chain of islands of which Skíathos is the first, is joined to Kíssavos (Ossa), and divided only by the narrow cleft of Tempe from the roots of the Olympus system.   The right-hand offshoot of Velúkhi forms the Acarnanian group, east and south of the Gulf of Arta.   Thereafter the Spine opens out a low *col*, west of Karpenísi, giving easy traverse ; but immediately beyond, trending south-eastward and changing its constitution to metamorphic, it throws up Óxia, a rocky ganglion, whence chains radiate on all hands, west to Arabokéfalon and Varássova of the Ætolian group, south to the peak of Kióna, highest point on Greek soil, and eastward in the long oblique line of Oeta, which ends, as Ptoon, above the Bœotian basin, only to emerge again in the high Euboic chain and the islands of the eastern Cyclad group.   The Spine itself continues at a great elevation through a series of storied peaks, whose old Greek names are more familiar than the Romaic— Vardúsi (Corax), Liakúra (Parnassus), Palæovounó (Helicon), to the lower range of Elátea (Cithæron).   Here is the last important fork.   The main Spine, keeping its direction, falls rapidly through the Attic hills, re-emerges, and at last dies away in the western chain of Cyclad isles.   But a right-hand offshoot, which has declined through the famous Geraneian heights almost to sea-level at the Corinthian Isthmus, springs up again in the many-peaked semi-island of the Morea, which is nothing but a single mass of mountain, most uniformly uplifted in the north, hollow in the centre, and ribbed vertically on either hand of its heart by four ridges, which all start from the ganglion of the North Arcadian Alps.   Of these the first and easternmost runs down the Argolic Peninsula into the islands of Hydra and Spetsae ; the second fringes the hollow heart on the east, and under many names, of which Malevos or Parnon stands for its highest point, continues to the sea at Cape Málea and re-emerges in Cerigo ; the third skirts the west of the hollow and rises into beautiful Taýgetus ere falling to Cape Matapán; the fourth and westernmost is that chain of many names which passes through Elis and Messenia to enter the sea at Cape Gallo.

    Continued from Cerigo by way of Cerigotto and a sunken reef, the Spine emerges for the last time in Crete.   This long island must originally have been three units, of which the first is represented now by the lofty chains of the White Mountains, Kedros, and Psiloríti (Ida); the second by the group of Lasíthi (Dicte) with Kófina; and the third by the so-called eastern Lasithi, or mountains of Sitía. The three *massifs* are divided now by low tracts, upheaved by a pressure working from the south-west, whose not exhausted travail may be gauged by the fact that the ancient quays of the western city of Sélinos are now nearly twenty feet above the water-mark.

The other islands that depend on the Spine of the Peninsula or its offshoots, the northern Sporades, and all the Cyclades, need only be mentioned, for they are too small to be affected by their own Relief so much as by the Relief of the mainlands about them.

In enumerating the recurving chains thrown off eastward by the Spine, we have noted already the most significant feature in the relief of the Second Belt, namely, its series of basins. As the eye travels southward over the model of Macedonia, it must follow four grooves, more or less parallel (Fig. 3). On the extreme right, and still on the Albanian flank of the Spine, the long gorge of the Black Drin, widest below Dibra, leads at last to a deep basin, filled wholly, except for the black Struga strand, by the blue waters of Ochrida. The rib which hems the lake on the south, bounds on the north a second basin not less wide, but occupied only in small part by the Malik Lake. This is the rich and populous vale of Goritza, crossed by the Devol not far below its source above Biklista. Next in order is a short groove lying immediately under the Macedonian slope of the Spine, and hemmed in on the east by its main lateral offshoot, which holds the lakes of Presba, Malo Jezero, and Kastoria, each with a broad northern and eastern strand of fat soil, and carries southward the headwaters of the Vistritza. Third comes that most important groove, which determines the character of the whole Belt. Opening under the southern flank of Shar, from the gentle water-

shed between the Moráva and the broad head valley of
the Vardar, it is continued beyond a rugged belt by
the largest of the Macedonian basins, the rich plain
of Monastir or Vitólia, drained entirely by the greatest
tributary of the Vardar.   With hardly an interval this
passes on the south into the smaller basin of Ostrovo and
Kailer, still filled in part by a lake, and beyond the

FIG. 3.—Macedonia.

Vistritza and the low Cambunian range it is resumed
by an immense expanse girt on every hand by hills
(Fig. 4).   The lake, which once spread over all this
Thessalian plain, and flowed out to sea through rifts on
each side of Ossa, has shrunk to a little mere in the
south-east corner, leaving the southern outflow dry;
but the northern rift, deep-wooded Tempe, still passes

the drainage of the upper plain down the channel of the Salamvría. A broad belt, formed by the eastern off-shoots of the Velúkhi and Oxia *ganglia*, and fringed on the east by small deltaic tracts, shuts off the last hollow in this central groove, the basin of Bœotia, once filled as to its northern part with the Copaic marsh, but now drained by the energy of French and English engineers, who have re-opened and enlarged old subterranean out-

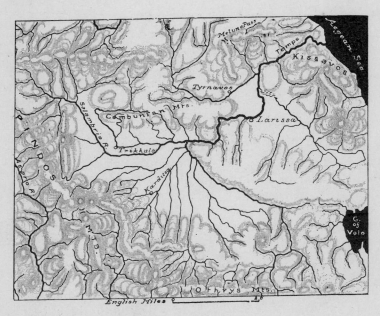

FIG. 4.—Thessaly.

flows, partly natural, and given the Hellenic kingdom its largest arable area outside Thessaly.

The eastward curve of the Spine to the sea closes this long chain of basins, and with them the second main Belt; but in its northern part there remains yet to be noted on the east a fourth parallel groove, traversed in all its length by the greatest stream of the Peninsula. Swift and much broken by rapids in all its upper course, choked by sands in its lower reaches, the Vardar affords no through waterway ; but its long and gently inclined valley, only once narrowed to a gorge, conducts an easy land-road to the heart of the Peninsula, and spreads out on the south into an immense deltaic flat which, united to the alluvia of the Vistritza, rivals the basin of Monastir in extent. These two broad plains, lowland and upland, the Emathian and the Pelagonian, made the great Macedonia of the past, and will be the determinants of its fate in the future.

East of the long Vardar valley three ranges start from three *ganglia* on the Balkan Curve and run south, penning between their respective spurs two large rivers, the Struma and the Mesta. This mountain tract may be taken to be the third Belt of the Peninsula, corresponding in political nomenclature to eastern Macedonia, and the western part of Rumelia. Its three vertical ranges increase in scale from west to east. The first, known under many names, but chiefly as the Plashkavitza, Kursha Balkan, and Beshik chains, falls on the south into a low alluvial plain filled by a line of marshy lakes, draining to the Gulf of Réndina. But it rises again in an interlaced group of minor chains ; and these run out southwards in three long promontories, of which the two on the west are low, but the third, ere it sinks below sea, throws up the 6000 feet of Athos. On its eastern flank the main range puts out long spurs, which, confronted across the Struma by others of the second and higher range, as the Perim and Boz mountains, break up the valley into three basins. The valley of the Mesta, lying beyond the peak of Perim, whose shape and position make it not less imposing than its loftier neighbours in the Rila and Despóto groups across the stream, is narrower and wilder and, therefore, more exclusively pasture and forest than that of the Struma. The Perim range falls on the south, like its western parallel, to a low plain, and likewise also, ere reaching the sea, rises again in the Bunar group, and sinking once more reappears in the island of Thasos. Last and highest of the three main ranges of this Belt is that which, starting from the syenite rocks of Vitocha,

reaches its greatest elevation in the Rila group, and is continued by the broad and shaggy mass of the Despoto chain,
anciently Rhodope, and by three islands, Samothrace, a
solitary peak 5000 feet high, Imbros, low and rocky, and
Lemnos, still lower but volcanic, plain and arable.

All the length of the coast below the butts of the
three main ranges, extends a low tract of varying width,
and for the most part both fertile above measure and
genial because sheltered from the north, which permits
of easy passage from west to east. But, being fringed
by almost continuous sea-marsh, this malarious strip
hardly permits sea access between Dedeagách and
Kaválla.

The eye which, since it left the Vardar, has been
arrested by ridge upon ridge each higher and wilder
than the last, comes suddenly over the bare peaks of the
Despoto chain upon a very different prospect. Spurs,
densely wooded, fall abruptly to an immense lowland,
roughly triangular, with apex lying high up on the
left, between the Rhodope and the Hæmus, which
are its nearly equilateral sides. The sea forms a base,
which would trend fairly straight north-eastward from
the Dardanelles to the lagoons of Burgas, were it not
for an intrusive mass of plutonic rock, a detached bit
of Asia, which breaks the line half-way, carrying Constantinople on its low crest. This triangle is the fourth
and last main division of the European Nearer East—
those fat Rumelian plains of the Maritza basin, which are,
so to speak, the vast home-farm of whatever Power may
chance to rule in the capital city of the Eastern Empire
(Fig. 5). Seen from the top of its mighty western wall
the triangle seems one unbroken plain ; but in reality it
is crossed horizontally by a low swell, through which the
Maritza breaks at Harmanlí ; and this, connected with
a shaggy group of hills which align the Black Sea, and
continued on the Marmora coast into the Gallípoli Peninsula, separates the basin of the river into upper and lower
parts, centred respectively on Philippopolis and Adrianople,

and constitutes now a political frontier. The northern
wall of the triangle is less savage than the western ; for
a lower range, made up of the Sredna and Karajá
chains, which starts independently from the Rila ganglion
and lies parallel to the main Balkan, graduates the
rise from the south and interposes the deep vales of
Kárlovo and rose-growing Kasanlík below the abrupt
fall of the watershed. For the rest the immense treeless
basin, drained by slow-flowing earthy streams, varies its
monotonous fertility with little but occasional marshes,
even from its apex at Ikhtimán, where the most impor-

Fig. 5.—Rumelia.

tant gate of the Nearer East admits the Sophia railway, to its natural outlets of Ænos and Dedeagách by
the Maritza mouth. But so insignificant and narrow
is the rise which divides from the Marmora coast the
low headwaters of the Erkené, the main left-bank affluent
of the Maritza, that Rodosto and the Golden Horn serve
for ports to Rumelia as well as those to which the right-
bank railway conducts directly from Demotiká ; and Constantinople draws its supplies from European cornlands
as easily as from the gardens of opposite Asia.

Such is the so-called Balkan Peninsula, the north-
eastern part of which is, perhaps, more properly to be

counted part of the continental mass of Europe. The true peninsular dependency begins to south of a line drawn from the head of the Gulf of S. Juan di Médua to that of Salonica through the low basin region of western Macedonia, which is continued by a deep marine trench from Olympus to Gallipoli.

The relief of most of the western part of the Balkan Peninsula is treated thoroughly by A. Tuma in his *Griechenland, Makedonien und Sud Albanien*, an official commentary on the Austrian Staff Map. There is no similar authority for the Eastern part, but much may be gleaned from the geographical chapters in C. Jiriček's *Furstenthum Bulgariens* as to all but Turkish Rumelia. For that, as for N. Albania, I know no comprehensive authority. One must rifle the travellers. Murray's *Constantinople* describes the capital and its environs excellently. The Thracian Islands are well dealt with in H. F. Tozer's *Islands of the Ægean*.

Of less known districts Middle Albania and Epirus have been illuminated by the work of Baldacci and Hassert, botanists (*P. M.*, 1897, pp. 175, 198), and the Macedonian side of the Spine by that of geologists, Cvijic, *Die Macedonischen Seen* (Mitth. d. Ung. Geogr. Gesellschaft, 1900), and Oestreich, *Reisen im Vilajet Kosovo* (Verh. d. Ges. für Erdkunde zu Berlin, 1899). The Thessalian border chains equally by the travels of Philippson (*Thessalien und Epirus*), and the Ætolian by those of Woodhouse (*Ætolia*). For Greece proper there is a good deal that is useful in Dr. Clon Stephanos' *La Grèce au point de vue physique*.

Crete awaits a geographical monograph. Spratt is still the best authority. But several of the smaller islands have received special attention of late, *e.g.* Kefalonia from A. Issel (Mem. d. Soc. Geog. Italiana, 1896). Cerigo from R. Leonhard (*P. M.*, Ergänz, 128). Milos from Ehrenburg (*Inselgruppe Milos*). Santorin from Hiller von Gärtringen (*Thera*).

CHAPTER III

THE ASIAN ASCENT

THE ferry across those marine rivers, the Bosphorus or the Dardanelles, lands the traveller in a new continent, but not in any sense in a new geographical world. The shallow cut, which divides the Castle of Europe from the Castle of Asia, pierces a mass of plutonic rock on which Stambul and Skutari alike stand ; and opposite cliffs of the Dardanelles show the same stratification. Two submarine ridges connect the European and Asiatic isles of the Ægean, the one making a chain of shallows from Skyros to Chios, the other bounding the central deep-sea trench on the south with a line of continuous shoal from the northern Cyclades to Nikária and Samos. Moreover, as we shall see, the general trend and character of the Asia Minor mountain ranges are not other than the trend and character of the south-eastern ranges of Europe.

As the student of the relief model would see it, the land, over which his eye has been travelling south-eastward, sinks to an almost imperceptible streak of sea, which, starting from one great land-locked basin, broadens out into a second and smaller pool and again narrows to a thread. Beyond this the land rises again rapidly and forms a great blunt-headed Peninsula, whose western front supplies a third side to the oblong sea which contains the Archipelago. On the north its coast continues the northern land limit of the Nearer East. On the south it carries to eastward the line of the islands which, from Cerigo through Crete to Rhodes, set a southern limit to the Ægean shallows and a northern limit to the profounder eastern basin of the Mediterranean, the true Levant.

The continental shelf of the European Peninsula, as we have seen, here and there emerges from the eastern sea in insular peaks, trending obliquely from WNW. to ESE., and these islands, becoming uniformly larger as they approach the Asiatic shore, are for the most part separated therefrom by very narrow and not profound straits. Mitylene, Chios, Samos, and Rhodes are all more extensive, and more varied, than the western islands, except Eubœa. Happily compounded of mountain and plain, they are enabled to make use of their own waters instead, like the Morea, of losing the most part in the sea at the foot of the steeps, and they are protected from steppe winds by the high mainland which overhangs their eastern roadsteads. Smaller islands, steep crests of submerged mountains, not rising high enough to affect the general climatic conditions, form the links of the chain.

All these islands, as well as the Rumelian coast range, are connected structurally with ribs of the great mainland mass of Asia Minor, whose general trend from E., bending to ESE., throws them out in long westerly promontories (Fig. 6). The Ægean coast of the Peninsula is as frequently indented with deep and narrow gulfs, as the north and south coasts, to which the chains lie nearly parallel, are without inlets. The south coast of the Black Sea has but two natural harbours, Sinub and Vona. The north coast of the Levant is hardly better provided. For, after the turn of the land at Kékova, there are no ports better than open roadsteads, the most part, like that of Mersína, lamentably shallow. Nor does the direction of the structure give the west coast preference in the matter of ports only; for upon it open deep and spreading valleys, up whose long easy slopes lead the natural routes to the interior of the Peninsula. The north has only the small neighbour plains of Bafra and Charshembé thrown out by the waters of the Kizil and Kalkid rivers, which debouch from almost impassable gorges in ridges, stretched across their courses, and to be traversed only by high passes. The south has likewise only two considerable deltaic plains, the Pamphylian strip from New to Old Adália, and the

broader Aleian levels of eastern Cilicia, joint gift of
the Sihun and Jihun, whose beneficent waters emerge
from stupendous cañons in the Tauric wall.   While, therefore, on the side of the Marmora and Ægean Seas the
Anatolian Peninsula is a land of many harbours admitting
between its ribs to broad and long lowland valleys, main
avenues, and themselves sources, of its products, it presents
little towards the Black and Levant Seas but lofty parallels
of hills.   In themselves these ridges are not unproductive,

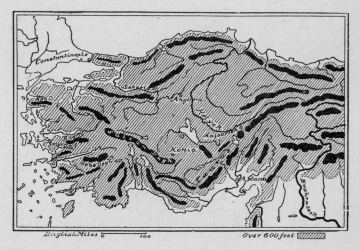

FIG. 6.—Asia Minor, showing the general scheme of the
Mountain Ranges.

but they are neither easily to be approached nor easily to
be passed.

Asia Minor has a general upward tilt towards the
east; and its upheaval has been of a more gigantic and
general sort than that of the Balkan Peninsula.   The bulk
of the Anatolian Peninsula is elevated in one great mass,
sloping from a mean of 2000 feet above the sea at
its western and north-western edge, through a hollow
heart, above 3000 feet, to a mean of over 4000 feet
at the western roots of the Pontic and Armenian Alps.
The axial swell of this gable-shaped plateau divides

the Peninsula longitudinally into two nearly equal parts. Starting in the ridge of the Murad mountain the swell flattens as it trends upwards slightly south of east, and becoming concave, holds the closed basins of the Phrygian lake-marshes, and the greater expanse of the " Axylon " plain, which now drains only to its own salt centre, and not, as formerly, into the Sakária basin. Continuing due eastward, the axis throws up the lofty volcano of Erjiés, whose waters drain to closed lake basins on either hand, and bends north along the steppe of Uzun Yaila and round the great elbow of the northern Euphrates, till, by way of the mountains of Erzerum, it reaches the crowning groups of Bingiol and Ararat.

The course of this ridge in the Anatolian roof has been insisted upon because, though often much less noticeable than the higher ribs which run north and south of it, it determines the parting of all the waters, and they do not. The Plateau is indeed traversed longitudinally by several ridges of an elevation superior to its general mass ; and while the centre is comparatively open, such ribs rise one beyond the other towards the north, and decline like hollow steps to the Black Sea. On the south a series of oblique southeasterly ranges join their foot-hills to form a long and lofty wall, geographically known as Taurus. Asia Minor is usually likened to a great cup with an encircling rim, or to a narrow-brimmed hat with hollow crown. Neither simile is really just. The mountainous rim is made up of a multiplicity of ranges disposed in echelon, not in line, which open out freely towards the west ; and the declivity behind them takes up again towards a farther crown. All the great streams of the north and south rise at the back of the " Rim,"—the Yeshil, Kalkid, and Kizil rivers, the Sakaria and Porsuk, the Saihun, together with all its main tributaries, and the Jihun. And although the tremendous cañons by which most of these streams break through the hills afford in their natural state no possible roads, when the engineer comes to make artificial ways from the coasts to the Plateau, he will find

the great border barriers ready cut ; and by such service
to communication, the larger Anatolian rivers may redeem
in the future their uselessness for navigation.   Rails have
actually been laid up the valleys of the Porsuk, the Gediz,
and the Menderes ; and the gorge of the Kizil river (Halys)

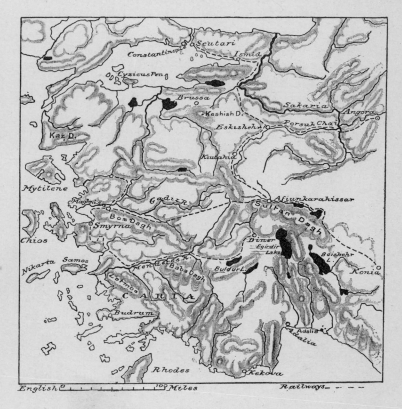

FIG. 7.—Western Asia Minor.

has been surveyed by engineers in quest of a railway route
up to and over the Plateau.

    Seen in bird's-eye view from the west, the Anatolian
Peninsula would present in the foreground a series of
small deltaic plains, divided one from another by bold
and shaggy mountain masses whose roots advance far
into the sea (Fig. 7).   The plains are deep, marshy, and

malarious, and the sea is shallow in the hollow of the bays, by reason of immense deposits of silt brought down by the rivers. In their steep upper courses these last cut such deep gorges and even subterranean conduits in the limestone formation of the Plateau that they both are useless for irrigation purposes and also overdrain their basins ; and in the rainless season a terrible sterility results on the lower western uplands. But from the point at which the gradient begins to grow easier the valleys are fed with such rich spoil of the Plateau, both of earth and water, that, basking in a sub-tropic climate behind unbroken screens to north and east, they are luxuriant beyond other lands in the Levant, save certain similar coastal plains of Syria.

At its north-west corner the edge of the Plateau is somewhat less steeply inclined than elsewhere. Both the Sakaria and Porsuk have long valleys which lead without too abrupt steps to a high level, and have in all ages facilitated communication between the Bosphorus and inland Asia, by routes of which one is followed more or less closely by the modern railway to Ángora. But on all its western face the central mass falls abruptly, and the main sources of the streams lie much lower than on the north. The headwaters of the Menderes, for instance, issue 1000 feet below the general western level of the Plateau, and the great natural road up its valley, thus far broad and easy, must climb an abrupt slope to the heart of the country. But in compensation for this disadvantage, the traveller, who has turned either butt of Sultan Dagh, one of the most imposing of the chains that trend north-westward in a direction slightly oblique to the general lie of the southern ribs, will find himself in the most open and naturally fertile region of the Peninsula.

The general edge of the Plateau level, however, is set much further back on the west side than on the north or south ; and the mountainous region between it and the sea, formed by the prolongations of its ribs, is of much greater extent. Four mountainous projections, distinguished broadly, are thrown out to the west by the Central

Mass between three lowland districts, more or less accidented by subsidiary swells. The first and last of these
four are rather systems than single chains, being direct
continuations of the multiplex northern and southern
border ribs of the Plateau. The northernmost system,
which is also the least lofty and abrupt, is that which runs
to the sea through three main Spines, of which the first
ends in Boz Burun on the Bosphorus; the second at the
Cyzicus Peninsula, having thrown up the peaks of Keshish
(Mysian Olympus) on its way; and the third after passing through the Kaz Dagh (Ida), reappears in northern
Lesbos. The southernmost system is a tangled continuation of the "Taurus" ribs, the general trend of whose
ranges is slightly to south of west after they leave the
central mass. This system is of greater elevation: point
after point approaches or passes 10,000 feet; and as seen
from Rhodes or from shipboard in spring, the wild Lycian
region supplies the most impressive coast scenery of the
Levant. Between the spurs of the "Taurus" system and
those of the third projection of the Plateau, the chain of the
Baba Dagh and Mount "Latmos," south of the Menderes
valley, a series of elevated basins is enclosed, of which
two, Egerdír and Beishéher, contain the only large fresh
water seas in western Asia. As it declines westward this
southern lowland belt, the Caria of antiquity, opens to a
wide sea frontage, and with better government would
become one of the best agricultural areas in Asia Minor.
The next belt in order is the fat Menderes basin, bounded
on the north by the second projection of the Plateau,
best known as the range of Boz Dagh ("Tmolus" of
Lydian history), which runs out south of the Smyrna
Gulf to Mount Elias in the island of Chios. The wide
undulating third belt, that remains to be placed between
Tmolus and the northern system, is largely volcanic in
character, the "Katakekaúmene," a region of extinct cones
and crater-shaped lakes about the town of Kula, which
throws up the Mánisa range (Sipylus) by the sea, and is
connected, like the hot springs of the Menderes basin,
with a focus of subterranean activity which often shakes

the city of Smyrna, destroyed Chios, and has latterly worked terrible ruin in the upper valley.

The heart of the Peninsula is a rolling steppe, maintained at a mean level of some 2500 feet, but falling slightly on its northern edge towards a bottom choked by a great salt swamp. Its northern and southern ribs, both trending alike to the eastern Armenian ganglion, begin presently to converge towards each other, the "Taurus" especially throwing up a series of ridges of which the Bulgar and Ala ranges, the highest of the eastern members of the system, define sharply the southeastern limit of the great level. Behind them rise the "Anti-Taurus" ranges in parallel alignment, running to the upland of Uzun Yaila. On the north the rolling Haimané hills merge east of the Kizil river into the Sivas highlands, which will eventually become the Pontic Alps. But the "Áxylon" level is prevented from filling up the angle between these converging systems by a great eruptive intrusion first seen in the extinct volcanoes of Hassan Dagh, and continued through a contorted igneous region, known in part as Soghanlí Dere, to a culminating point, the dormant cone of Erjies, loftiest peak in Asia west of Euphrates.

Concerning the mountainous belts on either hand of the Central Plains, and concerning the coasts of the Black and Levant Seas, something has already been said. The hilly region on the north is disposed in long parallel hogbacks trending almost due west, of which the highest attain to a little more than 8000 feet without presenting any grandeur of aspect. The general decline, where the central Plateau is fully developed, being more northwards than westwards, each parallel valley is lower than the last, and the streams, breaking their way between the butts of the ranges, descend from level to level across the general lines of land structure. Thus the upper valleys of the infant Yeshil, Kalkid, Kizil, Sakaria, and Porsuk rivers, and those of their tributaries, lie for the most part east and west, broad and open, with long slopes on either hand. But as the main streams, always seeking means to follow the more cogent northward slope, gain volume, they force their passage by a succession of precipitous gorges through the transverse lines. Since, therefore, all these silt-laden streams, of which two, the Kizil and the Sakaria, are over 300 miles long and pour out of their estuaries more than 100 cubic metres per second, come out upon the Black Sea, that coast is furnished with a few deltaic plains of great richness, thrown out, not as in the west, between projecting ranges, but outwards from the flank of the coastal ridge; and these, creating shallows, render access to the harbourless shore yet more difficult.

The southern mountain region, as has been stated already, is narrower and less complex than the northern, but seen both from the interior and the coast it is far more Alpine and imposing. The short echeloned chains which compose it drop opposite the centre of the Plateau to a mean height of not over 7000 feet, but both to west and east they erect serrated walls to 10,000 or even 11,000 feet. There is here no system of parallel valleys, and the rivers must begin at once to thread their way through the ridges by gorges, not less impassable and more tremendous than those of the northern streams. But the volume of the southern streams is less, and their deltas are smaller, with the single exception of the Aleian Plain. For the rest the most part of the coast line is as rocky and abrupt as on the north, but more indented by reason of the oblique trend of the mountain ribs. Small craft find many places of partial shelter, and, if they can work up stream, may still enter the estuary of the Sihun in time of flood, as once they could enter that of the neighbouring Cydnus, now lost in marsh.

The margin of the profound marine abyss which skirts Rhodes and the Lycian coast line, trends sharply south-eastward from Cape Khelidónia, leaving only a shallow sea along the remaining coast of the Peninsula; and dry land emerges again from this shoal bottom at a distance of about fifty miles, in two elevated ridges, which follow the general trend of the Tauric system, and are united by a low alluvial plain. These form the island of Cyprus, once two mountainous units, now single, and the largest piece of sea-girt land in the Levant. The northern ridge, a chain of hard limestone peaks, which fall steeply on both hands, and are not at their highest much above 3000 feet, runs down in a rocky tail to the north-east, forming the long promontory of the Carpas. The southern ridge, of eruptive character, springs up somewhat farther west to 4000 feet, in a chain most steeply inclined to the north-east, and presently rises to its culmination in the massive hog-back of Mount Tróodos, the official hill-station of the island. Falling to 5000 feet, it is continued due east, maintaining its elevation for about twenty miles, and there-after falls quickly to the low gypsum formations, which end in Cape Greco. On the long southern slopes of the higher chain lie the green hill cantons of Baffo and Limassol, and below the seaward face of the northern ridge stretches a beautiful but rugged coast strip. The low eastern tails of both the ranges have their rich slopes and hollows ; but it is between the higher opposing flanks that the most arable soil has been washed down into that Mesaoría plain, which extends right through the island from Morphu to Famagusta. Cyprus has no good natural harbours, since its coasts lie parallel to the mountain spines, and rise out of a shallow shoaling sea. The joining of a low island to the coast by the deposits of the Kuri river, west of Limassol, has given partial pro-tection to the roadstead of the latter port; but Larnaka lies open to every southerly gale, and no other actual har-bour of the island is better than a sea-lagoon or a shallow pan in the rocks. The deeper soundings of the Levant lie a long way to the south, but the gulf (whose existence they reveal) bends north again to the eastward of Cyprus, dividing the isle effectually from the mainland, and mark-ing the fact that its ridges are geographically connected, not with the Syrian coast range, but with the Anatolian Taurus.

Looking beyond the " Axylon," we have noted already that the structural axis of the Peninsula bears north and

east from the volcanic outcrop of lower Cappadocia
through the highlands south of Sivas along a line marked
for all, who travel the great trunk road to Malátia, by the
col of Deliklitásh. This elevated country, unbroken by
any formidable chains, but seldom or never plain, slopes
gradually up to east-north-east, its mean level being about
1000 feet higher than that of the "Axylon" basin. To
the south it is especially steppe-like, where the undulating
sheep-runs of Uzun Yaila stretch east of the cone of
Erjies, to the northern butts of the Anti-Taurus ranges,
where are the headwaters of south-flowing rivers, the Sihun-
Zamanti, and Jihun, and also of the Tokhma Su, and other
streams which reach the right bank of Euphrates, just
before that great river begins to break through Taurus on
its way to the Commagenian and Syrian lowlands. On
the opposite quarter, however, the Sivas highlands break
up into the same alignments of hog-backed ranges, which
characterise all the north of the Peninsula, rising about
2000 feet on an average above wide valleys, down which
flow westward the upper reaches of the broad and shallow
Kizil Irmak (Halys), and the more torrential Yeshil and
Kalkid rivers, which will mingle their waters ere reaching
the Black Sea.

But, as the central mass narrows towards its north-
eastern crown it also rises more rapidly, and the Plateau
formation breaks up into bold mountain ranges, converging towards an eastern ganglion. The steeper
declination of the whole roof being to northward, the
streams flowing off it to the eastern end of the Black
Sea have short and much impeded, but very full and
violent courses. The Choruk falls 7000 feet in fifty
miles. But down the long southern slopes, fed by much
wider catchment-areas, descend the greatest rivers of
Western Asia, the Kara Su and Murad (western and
eastern Euphrates), and the Dijla, or Tigris, and its upper
left-bank feeders, notably the Batman and Bitlis-Botan
waters and the two Zabs. It will be noticed that all these
great streams radiate fan-wise from the central mountain
group. The two parent rivers of Euphrates must obey

at first the general westward declination of the whole Peninsula till strong enough to break through the ribs, and follow the more imperious influence of the southward slope. The Dijla and its affluents lie too far east to feel the attraction of the western decline, and rush straight to the south.

The converging ranges, which rise rapidly from the south of the Cappadocian steppe and attain an Alpine character in the Dersim or Merjan group, meet between the head-springs of the two streams of Euphrates in the broad bulk of Bingiol Dagh ("Mountain of a Thousand Lakes"). And since this *massif* is connected also through the ridges which contain the Erzerum plain and the head-waters of the Kara Su on the east, with the Black Sea coastal ranges, and even the Pontic Alps (a high chain which trends towards the Caucasus) it is looked upon as the orographic centre of the Armenian Alps, from which the southern and eastern chains containing the volcanoes of Nimrud and Sipan, and the huge Egri or Masis (Ararat), the pinnacle of the whole, are to be held to radiate (Fig. 8). Containing, as it does, the source of the Aras, Bingiol stands at the beginning of the eastern fall to the Caspian. The two branches of Euphrates rise in western and eastern prolongations of it, but the springs of the Tigris lie in a more southerly swell, which trends eastward independently to join a second ganglion, embracing on its way the deep lacustrine basin of Van.

Whether this salt sea is to be regarded as itself a feeder of the Tigris is a moot point, depending first on the existence or absence of a subterranean western outflow, and secondly on the direction of that outflow—does it escape north by the Kara Su to the Murad, or south by the Bitlis river to the Dijla ? If ever such an outlet existed it would appear to have been blocked these fifty years past, perhaps by lava, for the level of the Van Lake has been slowly rising all that time with much detriment to the valley of Arjish at its head. But should the lake begin again to fall, it ought not to be difficult to determine whether its waters, so strongly impregnated with carbonate and sulphate of soda, are issuing in any of the western springs.

The eastern limit of the Armenian Crown is defined, more or less clearly, by a horseshoe of volcanic peaks of which those on the south and east have been alluded to under the names Sipan and Egri-Masis. The volcanic outcrop is continued westward to a series of long extinct craters north of Erzerum, and also northward by Alagiúz to Transcaucasian Russia, and eastward by the great cones of Sahend and Savalán in Azerbaijan. No member of

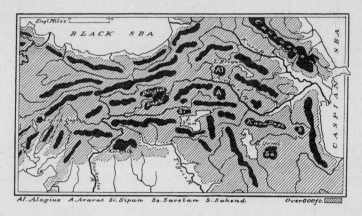

FIG. 8.—Armenia, showing the general scheme of the Mountain Ranges.

this group is active, but some peaks, for example the Greater Ararat itself, are not quite extinct, and retain symptoms of inward fires in hot springs, geysers, and intermittent tremors.

So greatly elevated is the whole region about the Bingiol group, that for fifty miles as the crow flies in any direction, and for more than that towards east or south-east, there is no spot of ground where an aneroid will record a lower altitude than 5000 feet. The whole *vilayét* of Van lies under snow for three months. The level of the great lake is 5300 feet : the average level of the Erzerum plain is about the same,—these two localities being one hundred miles apart, and neither quite on the uttermost fringe of the Crown.

It is down these high Alpine valleys that the first beginnings of the great Mesopotamian rivers flow (Fig. 9). The northern branch of Euphrates, usually regarded as the main stream, and still often called "Frat," has its remote source, as we have seen, high up on the flank of the northern wing of the Bingiol *massif;* but it is fed also by abundant springs north-east of Erzerum, and from that town westward is become a full river, not fordable except in an exceptionally dry midsummer. So long as it flows east it maintains an average width of some 200 feet, and a mean speed of about four miles an hour down an open valley, flanked on the south by the black peaks and snow-fields of the Muzur range in the Dersim group; but on reaching the western end of this wall it turns sharply south, and plunges in a series of rapids between perpendicular walls, Dersim on the left and Sarichichék mountains on the right, which only recede sufficiently now on one hand, now the other, to allow a terraced town or village to approach the stream. Henceforward the "Frat" takes a reddish hue, apparent even after the confluence of the clear Murad has taken place just above the point when the long gorge opens out on both sides. The last bridge spans the stream in the narrowest of the gorge below Egin, and thenceforward passage is only effected by primitive horse-ferries or by rafts buoyed upon inflated skins.

The southern branch, the Murad or Palu Su, which has come in at Keban Maden, rises still farther east in the little lake of Balik, "The Fishery," situated in the range of Ararat itself; and it is more distinctly a snow-fed river, deriving most of its waters on the right bank from the high streams of Bingiol Dagh and of Merjan in the Dersim, which are ice-bound a third of the year. Its beginning is more wild and torrential than that of its northern fellow, and the scenery of its right bank continues to be of savage character almost to Palu; but on the left bank, after it has grown to the estate of a river, it drains a less tremendous country, the wide upland basins of Bitlis, Mush, Palu, and Kharput.

The combined " Frat " opens out to a majestic, slow moving flood as it enters the Malatia plain, at an altitude of not more than 2500 feet ; but ere it can escape to the southern plains and an unimpeded course it must break through the Tauric chains.   Contracting to a deep swift stream it enters the hills below Ísoli, where a bridge has long been desired to carry the Diarbékr road, and for above a hundred miles rushes down rock ladders till it

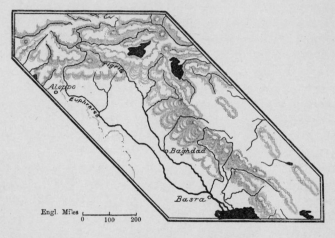

FIG. 9.—The Euphrates and Tigris Rivers.

emerges at last above Samsat, a vexed tumult of eddies which are gradually appeased ; for the great river has henceforth only 1000 feet to fall in the 1800 miles of its lower course.

The Dijla, or Tigris, does not greatly concern us yet, for it soon reaches the plains.   Its origin is usually traced to the little mere of Gioljik, situated south of Kharput on the southern flank of the eastern Tauric system, and a feeder of the Murad also ; but the Bitlis and Botan springs, on the south slope of the Van mountains, supply the greater head of water.   At the point of junction of the affluent that they form with the main stream below Diarbekr the broad and swift Dijla is already clear of any mountains, except the lower spurs of the Hakkiári country on the left and the Mardin hills on the right ; but these, though of no great elevation, suffice for forty miles to pen the stream into an impassable gorge which, shortly above the boat bridge of Jezíre, opens into the Mesopotamian lowland.

The central mass of Bingiol is continued due eastward by a ridge which, falling to 7500 feet, allows the passage of caravans from the headwaters of the Aras to those of the Murad, but springs up immediately to nearly the elevation of Bingiol itself, and forks left and right. The northern limb runs on eastward at an even height and suddenly shoots up to its supreme height of 17,300 feet in the massive volcano of Mount Egri, or Masis, the "Greater Ararat" of our tradition, divided by a *col*, where the three realms of Russia, Persia, and Turkey meet, from its south-eastern pendant the sharp cone of "Lesser Ararat." This hollow Spine between Ararat and Bingiol may be called the hinge of the west Asian relief. For it is prolonged north-westward through the Palantóken range to the mountains north-east of Erzerum, and thence to the Kur watershed ; and also southward through the ganglion of Tandurék to the Zagros. The levels fall away from it west and east, and streams on the one hand drain all to the Black Sea or the Persian Gulf, on the other all to the Caspian Sea and the Persian lakes and swamps. The southern limb of the fork, therefore, is not a main watershed, but is broken through by the upper course of the Murad, whose headwaters lie in the vale of Alashgird enclosed between the southern and the northern limbs ; but it displays a series of summits not less lofty than those of the northern ridge, the Ararats alone excepted. The Ala, Gerdagiól, and Kori peaks, which separate the springs of the Murad from the eastern feeders of the lake of Van, and form a chain, which runs, like the northern limb, to Tandurek, are none of them much under 10,000 feet.

Reunited, the single axis of the structure trends south-eastward from the Crown, but it will be seen to lose again almost immediately its simple character, and finally to split up into long parallel alignments of distinct chains, with intervening half filled valleys, running south-eastward nearly one thousand miles. For all that distance its members buttress up the south-western edge of that eastern continuation of the general West Asian upheaval, which we call the Iranian Plateau, while their western roots are set 3000 feet lower in the Tigris basin.

On the farther slope of Ararat begins the eastern stage of our survey. There are ranges yet to be considered as high as any seen already, and one peak that overtops even the Greater Ararat, but there is no large district found in Asia up to the confines of India so Alpine as the Armenian highlands.

There is no final and comprehensive description of Asia Minor. More accurate detail is embodied in Sir C. Wilson's Handbook (Murray, 1895) than any other single volume ; but research in it is necessary if any general idea is to be obtained. So, too, in Ramsay's *Historical Geography*, and his *Cities and Bishoprics of Phrygia* (2 vols.) ; in Radet's *Lydie;* and in that part of V. Cuinet's *Turquie d'Asie* which deals with the Anatolian provinces. Of late the archæological explorers, who have done much for knowledge of the modern geography, have been supplemented by representatives of other sciences, mainly Germans, *e.g.* Märcker, who has explored the Kizil Irmak valley (*P. M.*, 1893), and the geologist, F. Schaffer, who has examined the eastern Taurus, the central volcanic area, and Anti-Taurus.

Of the islands, Cyprus has not been thoroughly described. Rhodes is the subject of a good monograph by C. Torr, and Nikaria of an exhaustive article by L. Bürchner (*P. M.*, 1894). For the Armenian and Kurdish relief one depends on travellers. H. F. B. Lynch is about to produce a general work, but one may doubt if the *data* are sufficient. Wilson and Cuinet need supplementing from Maunsell, Tozer, Lord Percy, and other recent visitors.

CHAPTER IV

THE CENTRAL UPLAND

THE eastern foothills of Ararat and Tandurek melt, before they have fallen within 5000 feet of sea-level, into a billowy tableland, which stretches to the mountain fence of the Caspian, maintaining its general elevation over an oblong area roughly 200 miles west to east by 150 north to south. This tableland is a part of the Iranian Plateau, but by one step higher than the central plain, marked off from it by a swell, which runs north-east from the border ridges north of Hamadán, and through Sultaníeh, to join the Elburz above Kasvin. South of this line the general level drops presently 1000 feet, and the traveller from the north finds himself in Irak Ajémi, or Iran proper.

The upper step, corresponding in the Persian imperial economy to the province of Azerbaijan (with a strip added on the south), has not the monotonous uniformity of the lower. The long spurs of the Armenian highlands run far down to the south-eastward, enclosing north and south a broad and rich basin, filled in part with a shallow expanse of salt water of greater superficial area than any other inland sea of West Asia, the Caspian and Aral of course excepted, but of much less cubic content than Van. This Lake of Urmi, or Dária-i-Shahi, too salt to nourish any life but certain crustaceans, has, unlike its western fellow, been shrinking slowly for some years past, exposing ever-widening tracts of sour slime ; but whether this phenomenon is due to subterranean leakage, or to the supply of water by reason of a decreased rainfall and the extension of the irrigated area ceasing to counter-act successfully the evaporating action of the sun, the doctors are not agreed.

On the north descend contorted spurs of Kara Dagh,
physically a part of the highlands of Russian Armenia
or "Lesser Caucasus," beyond the Aras, which themselves are attached to the Ararat system. On the east is
felt the influence of the Caspian wall ; and this sends into
the south-eastern angle of the Plateau an oblique offshoot
sloping up to the summit of Ak Dagh, 13,000 feet high.
On the south is a line of volcanic peaks, of whose
number is the conical Takht-i-Balkis, overlooking the
famous fire temple of "Solomon's Throne." Nor is this
all ; for in the heart of the tableland itself those forces of
upheaval which have cracked the crust in many parts of
this region and brought ruin on Tabriz about three times
in a century, have thrown up two mighty volcanoes, now
quiescent, the many-peaked Sahend south of the city, and
the still huger Savalán, whose long ridge, connected with
Kara Dagh, attains to nearly 15,500 feet above the town-
ship of Ardebíl.

In the area of all this upheaval it is natural to find
earth-waves crossing and recrossing ; and, in fact, Azerbaijan is far from a level land. But being nowhere abrupt
or rocky, while everywhere well watered by springs out-
flowing from its border ranges and central volcanoes, it
is an agricultural district of a fertility proverbial among
wanderers on steppes and salt deserts. Mention has been
made already of a mountain Rim dividing Azerbaijan from
the Caspian Sea. A relief-model would show this to be
divided from the Armenian system, prolonged eastward
in the "Lesser Caucasus," only by the single depression
through which the Aras flows to join the Kur ; and physically it should be regarded as continuous with that system,
and therefore with the main spine of the structure of all
western Asia. South of the Aras, however, the complicated system of the "Lesser Caucasus," confused by the
gigantic eruptive forces which have upheaved Ararat and
Alagiuz, resolves itself into a simple ridge, and trends
south and south by east, throwing up for a long distance
no conspicuous peaks, and outlining very exactly the coast
of the Caspian Sea. Gradually depressed as it turns east

of south, it permits its wall to be forced by the great river of southern Azerbaijan, the Kizil Uzun, which has long been following in a broad gravelly bed the south-eastward slope of the tableland, pressing more and more on its eastern Rim.   At length, dammed by that swell of the land, already described as running up from the south along the north-western limit of the plateau of Irak, it is forced to turn abruptly north of east and seek an outlet ; and this found through the flattened chain on its left, it rushes down the steep declivity to the Caspian, as the Sefid Rud, changing both character and name.

The ridge, however, continues, and splits presently into two main chains, tied together just north of Teheran by the Kashang knot, and once more to part, as their course trends due east.   Thereafter, though the main division of this mountain system, now known as Elburz and grown more immense, into two parallel chains is maintained, till it is lost to our sight on the marches of the Farther East, the alignment is distorted and confused by an eruptive intrusion of such a sort that it has thrown up in the heart of the system, midway between the parallel spines, a colossal cone above 18,000 feet high.   This giant vent, known to all the world as Demavend, has long been quiescent, so long, in fact, that the most immemorial tradition of all, who live within sight of its cone, runs not to the contrary.   Of all the legends that regard Demavend, the latest and most obstinate ascribes continued or re-newed activity to its cone.   The most that can be estab-lished is the existence of hot springs and of certain small fissures on the flanks which emit steam.   Sven Hedin, who ascended to the summit in 1890, relates that he found the shallow crater coated with snow, and that neither during his ascent, nor in the four months that he lived within sight of the volcano, did he perceive the slightest sign of smoke.   Yet another mystery attaches to the mountain, namely, an unresolved doubt as to its precise height.   Estimates based on aneroids, hypsometers, and trigonometry vary by as much as 3000 feet, but 18,600, the Russian measurement, seems nearest the truth.

All that intervenes between the roots of this long wall and the Caspian Sea is the gift of the rivers which flow from the upper valleys ; and fenced from Persia and opening at either end into the other littoral districts on both hands of the Caspian, the coastal strip may be said to belong physically rather to Trans-Caucasia or Trans-Caspia. At its north-western end, in Talish, the short torrents, falling from the single narrow ridge which shuts off Azerbaijan, are able to create but little level ground below the mountain spurs, and the only thoroughfare lies along the sea-beach. The Sefid Rud, however, has built out a wide deltaic plain, fringed with marshy lagoons ; and by thus forming the rich lowland of Gilan, it has made and it mars Resht, port of all in the Nearer East most painful of attainment. Thereafter for a space, since no great rivers come down, the northern roots of Elburz are divided from the sea by only a narrow strip of marshy jungle. But abreast of Demavend the Lar, which, like the Shah Rud, a tributary of the Sefid, rises in the interval between the Elburz ridges and flows parallel to them for half its course, turns the flank of the volcano and comes down as the Haraz ; and this stream, helped by half-a-dozen others to the east of it, has spread abroad, about Amol, Barfrush, and Sari, the deep levels of Mazanderán, and choked the sea with sandhills and banks. The mountains close in again on the south-eastern angle of the Caspian, and when Astrabád is reached at the end of the coastal pass, the steppe of the Yomut Turkmans opens the way to the Farther East.

The contrast between this shore, over-watered and over-wooded but teeming with life, and the parched lands which stretch away from the other flank of Elburz, has struck every traveller, and even been held accountable for the tendency of the Persian mind towards a dualistic creed. The Plateau of Irak Ajemi is alive indeed only where springs, fed by the snows that lie in winter on the higher points of the relief, can counteract through the year the awful aridity which is caused impartially by the

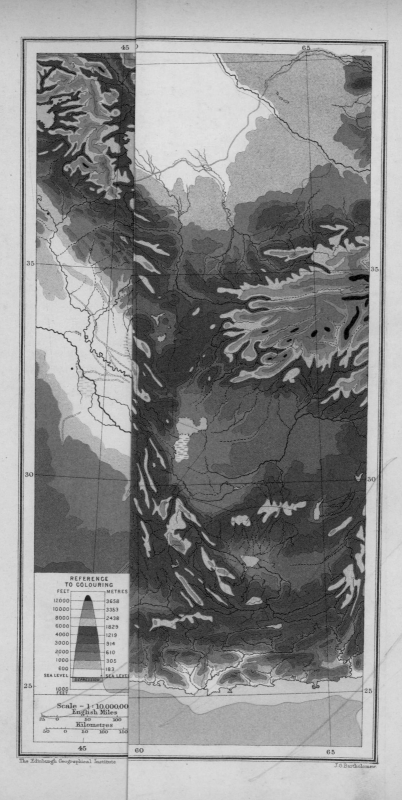

REFERENCE
TO COLOURING

FEET		METRES
12000		3658
10000		3353
8000		2438
6000		1829
4000		1219
3000		914
2000		610
1000		305
600		183
SEA LEVEL		SEA LEVEL
1000	DEPRESSION	
FEET		

Scale - 1 : 10,000,000
English Miles
25   0   50   100
Kilometres
50   0   50   100   150

The Edinburgh Geographical Institute

J.G.Bartholomew.

north-westers blowing down from the Turkman steppes, and the south-easters blowing up from the salt desert.

The descent from Azerbaijan to this lower step of the Plateau is, as we have seen, about 1000 feet ; but there is a continuous further fall of the land southward and eastward over Irak itself ; and all its greater streams (excepting only the Lar), which are not exhausted on their way by evaporation, infiltration, or irrigation, follow this slope into the great central salt hollows of the Kavirs, whose depths lie 2000 feet below the average level of north-western Irak, and not much more than 1000 feet above the level of the sea.

The first of these awful swamps, relics it would seem of an inland sea that vanished finally in the Pleiocene age, lies in the longitude of Teheran, and must be skirted by all who travel the great south road. This is the Dária-i-Nemek, or Lesser Kavir, which, though only an advanced post of the Greater, receives all of the waters of north-western Irak, draining by the channels of the Kara Su and Shurab, that have not been diverted, either to irrigate the land, or to form the new lake that blocks the old road from Teheran to Kum. Its heart, remarkable for the solidity of the ice-like sheet of pure sodium chloride that covers the most part of it, and may be ventured upon by well mounted and well guided travellers who would take the bee-line from Teheran to Kashan, was unknown to geographers before 1891.

It is only after passing Kashan that the traveller will see across hummocky sands to his left the edge of the Greater Kavir, which a low line of rounded hills, running north and south and linked by gravelly swells, divides from the Lesser. The Greater Kavir, which extends 150 miles southward from the foothills of Elburz at Semnan, and over 300 miles from east to west, is fed for the most part by drainage from the northern mountains. It differs somewhat from the Lesser, for its salt crust is hardly thicker than stout paper, and below lies desert sand transformed by saturation. The swamp is unqualified only after heavy rains, and for the most part of the year presents a swollen

and pock-marked cake of sour mud-crust round a few
slimy hollows, of which the largest and most impassable
lie near the western edge, between Semnan and Jandak.
The drier sands of the encircling plains merge insensibly
into this brown paste, and here and there advance far
into it ; and the level is further varied by a few lines
of hills of considerable elevation, among which the blue-
rock Gugird, or "Sulphur" range, lying near and parallel
to its northern edge, is the most remarkable. But
there are many others that support camel grass and
tamarisk scrub on their gravelly flanks, and yield springs
of brackish water to sparse palm groves and a few half-
nomad peasants, grouped about their roots. And by ad-
venturing from one to another of these sorry oases small
caravans may pass the waste diagonally from Semnan
to Tabbas ; from Nain to Anarek and Khur ; from Yezd
by Tabbas to Meshed ; and from Kerman by Naiband to
Tum. The last two routes, however (that from Yezd is
by far the most frequented, since it is on the most direct
line to Bunder Abbas), cross rather a chain of small
Kavirs to the south and east, than the Greater Kavir itself,
following an isthmus of sandy elevations, which swell out
of the central salt expanse in a north-easterly line, and are
disposed in parallel ridges over a breadth of some hundred
miles.

The last and most appalling of the Greater Kavirs is
not held to begin till these ridges cease. The terrible
Dasht-i-Lut, little known as to either its own area or its
immediate surroundings, intervenes between Kerman and
Seistán, and only one caravan route crosses its heart,
that from the feathery oasis of Bam, on the confines of
Persian Beluchistan, to Nasratabád ; but few merchants
ever venture themselves upon the shifting sands which
overlie its salt crust, or care to face its long waterless
stages and deadly airs. For Lut is one of the most
terrible reservoirs of heat on the earth, the source from
which the south-easters of the Persian summer draw their
destroying breath.

Narrowing to a gut south of Bam, between on the

one hand a line of quiescent volcanoes, Tuftan, Basman, and others, which range between 11,000 and 13,000 feet in height, and were probably in full activity before the Kavir ceased to be a sea, and on the other the last heights of the inner ranges of Farsistan, the salt sands sink to their lowest point beneath a long and shallow sheet of brine, the Milan-i-Jihun lake, whose area varies with the season; and expanding and rising again to a swell of shifting dunes, they fall at last in alternate naked ridge and hardly less naked furrow to the torrid shore of the Indian Ocean about Jask. South of the track which cuts across the horrid gut from Bam to Bampur, that is from the oases of Kerman to the oases of Persian Beluchistan, the waste has not been seen by European eyes, except in the immediate vicinity of the coast, whence the energetic officials of the Indian tele-graph, one of whose lines emerges from the sea at Jask and is carried thence above ground to British Beluchistan, can penetrate but a little way. The Beluchi coast is still what it was when Alexander's admiral discovered it, a tract, like the worst parts of the south shore of Arabia, so desolate that beast as well as man must get sustenance from the sea, and camels and sheep may be seen feeding out of the same basket of powdered fish as their master.

From this eastern frontier of the Nearer East we must look back over the structure of the southern half of the Region (Fig. 10). It would be noted on a relief model that the so-called "Plateau," to which we return, has little of a table-land about it at all; for hardly are the Kavirs left behind than hills start up, line behind line, in long parallels trending uniformly from south-east to north-west. Since the first seen of these ranges are the more distant one from another, the eastern plain intervals of Persia have more of a plateau than a valley character; and it is of these tracts, often desert and sometimes sheer marsh (as in the case of the hollow, east of Isfahan, where the most considerable of the Persian rivers that drain inland, the Zendeh, is lost) that the "Iranian Plateau" proper consists. The

tract, interposed between the margin of the Kavirs and
the first high parallel, is desert up to those points at the
foot of the northern or eastern hills, where the carefully
husbanded waters, ere lost in the deep sands or Kavirs,
can still irrigate the oases which support Teheran, Saweh,
Kum, Kashan, Natenz, Nain, Yezd, Kerman, and Bam,—
a widely spaced series of green islands, with lesser ones at
irregular intervals between them.   Most of these, were it

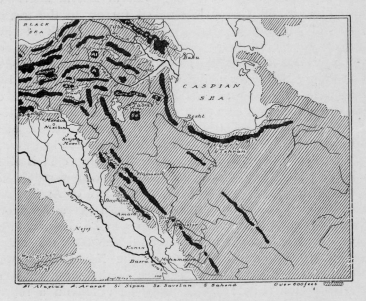

FIG. 10.—Western Iran, showing the general scheme of the
Mountain Ranges.

not for man, would be marsh or desert, and all the efforts
of the industrious Yezdis hardly prevail against the ceaseless attack of the sands on their town.

The range to the west of this line of oases may be
regarded as the Central Ridge of Persia.   Highest and
therefore longest retaining snow and consequent verdure
in the neighbourhood of Yezd and Kerman (where it shows
several peaks rising to between 11,000 and 13,000 feet) it
turns its abrupt face and smallest drainage to the west ;

and the tract below that slope is, as to its eastern part, an arid waste. The large winter volume of the Zendeh throws a salt tamarisk swamp, the Ghav Khane, far out into this desert; but not till the foot-hills of the next parallel are reached is there anything but a stony desolation. On the western edge of this tract lie the rich valleys of Hamadan, Daulatabad, Sultanabad, Isfahan, and Abadeh. Southward the general slope to the Persian Gulf begins to prevail. Instead of eastward, the long side of the ranges tends to fall more and more to south and west; and, by consequence, the eastern streams, affected already by the southing latitude and the neighbourhood of the Dasht-i-Lut, cease to be more than short winter torrents, flowing to small kavirs or steppes, desolate except in the monsoon season; and these bare tracts, after rounding the southern butt of the eastern range, eventually pass into the almost unpeopled Beluchi coast strip.

And this is about all of open plain land that can be claimed for the " Iranian Plateau," a name that has no modern local use. For all that we have just described is properly called Irak *Ajemi* to distinguish it from the lowlands of the Shatt-el-Arab, which are contained in Irak *Arabi*. In reality the " Plateau " is a region of parallel ridges and furrows, the last filled up to an average level of about 3000 feet above the sea; and with the hills of Faridán and Chahar Mahal, west of Isfahan, prolonged north to Silakhór and the solitary cone of Elwand, and south to the ranges of Niris, east of Shiraz, it ceases to be other than a broad prolongation of the axial system that we saw trending away to south-east from the Ararat group.

The general level rises rapidly as Isfahan is left behind to the west. A succession of ranges rising about 2000 feet above the valleys, which they almost enclose with interlocking spurs, have to be crossed or penetrated by the gorges of rivers still flowing east. Till on the farther side of the ribbed upland basin of Chahar Mahal the system rises abruptly into a long alignment of Alpine ranges, which, connected by ridges only less high than themselves, form a continuous wall and water parting, from Lar in the extreme south to Tandurek, west of Lake Urmi, in the extreme north. But this wall is not single. For much of its length it is faced, across an elevated trough seamed with gravelly ridges and ten to thirty miles wide, by a second wall of equally Alpine character, from whose farther flank the levels fall away in parallels of rapidly lessening ridges and ever lower valleys to the Tigris flats.

On leaving the ganglion of Tandurek this Spine, the crumpled edge of the central Plateau, does not develop all at once its double character. At first a single limestone ridge falls sharply eastward to the Urmi plain, but on the west is repeated by an infinity of very lofty parallels, through which the waters of the Greater Zab twist and turn back on themselves in painful effort to find an outlet down the south-westward slope to the Tigris. But hardly has the Lake of Urmi been left on the north than the main ridge changes to sandstone, and broadens out into a wide highland swell, the rolling home of the Persian Kurds, rich in flocks and grain, wherein rise the springs of large streams, the Lesser Zab, and the Diyála-Shirwan, which find their way through the western parallels to the Tigris with less pain than the northern Zab. The sandstone swell continues to the neighbourhood of Sinna, and thereabouts gives place to nummulitic rocks, which form a bolder Spine, the Zagros of ancient geographers ; and this runs down to the gap of Kermansháh, the western parallels being so far depressed that the main chain impresses the traveller from the Tigris with a conspicuous superiority. And it is only south of this gap, after about one-third of its course has been accomplished, that the system develops its double-crested character.

The main Spine, abrupt to the north-east but more easy to the south-west, continues east of Khoremabád and the head springs of the Diz river in Silakhor and Faridan to the bare rocks of Shuturún and the gravelly steeps of the Sefid chain and mighty Kuh-i-Rang, Mother of Waters. But it is faced by a western parallel as high as itself, which also runs into the great knot of the Kuh-i-Rang, where are born the three abundant streams of Persia, the Ab-i-Diz, the Zendeh, and the Karun. Once more opening out, the two giant walls enclose a second long upland basin ; but while the eastern admits of passage only over its high shoulders, the western is split by transverse rifts, original cracks of shrinkage, through which the many waters, united in the Karun, press towards the Persian Gulf.

South of the springs of the Bazuft river, the principal left bank affluent of the Upper Karun, the mountain system is little known, except where traversed by well-worn tracks from Shiraz to Bebehan and Bushire ; but it seems to maintain its dual formation, and the inward-bound traveller must cross by two *cols* at least, each about 7400 feet above the sea. Geographers have ascribed to several peaks in this region, notably the Kuh-i-Dinar, altitudes which are gravely discounted now by Colonel Sawyer's demonstration concerning the summits of the Bakhtiari belt, Shuturun, Kuh-i-Rang, Kuh-i-Ghezi, and the like, that the highest ranges nowhere exceed 13,000 feet. Beyond the Shiraz-Bushire road the mountain system has been explored only along a few Gulf trade-routes, that from Lingah by way of Lar to Darab, and those that radiate from Bunder Abbas to unite again at Yezd or Kerman ; but on all these roads it appears that some ten parallel ranges have to be surmounted, rising from the border chain of the Gulf, which averages about 5000 feet, to a ridge of waterparting of somewhat less than twice that altitude. The " Plateau " is finally attained at a mean elevation of about 5000 feet. But the system hereabouts is on a less gigantic scale than farther north ; and the intervening upland plains of Laristan, less seamed by interlacing spurs, form the wide grazing grounds of half the nomads of Persia. The decreased altitude of the main relief and the low latitude, cause snow to melt quickly, accounting for the fact that among all the streams of this region, mostly salt, there is no considerable body of water running to the sea ;

and indeed, after the parallel ridges have bent eastward to form the sandy swells of western Beluchistan, hardly any stream long survives the attacks of sand and evaporation.

The western slopes of the great Wall vary greatly. In the north they are rugged and abrupt, forming the savage home of the border Kurds and the fierce "Nestorian" Christians of Julamerk and Kochánes. Parallel chains of Alpine character fall directly to the Tigris and are even continued west of the river. But south of Rowandiz and the Jilu Dagh the ranges of nummulitic limestone become easier, though the higher peaks can keep their snows into August, and they shelter the charming valleys of the upper basins of the Lesser Zab and Diyála. Falling still lower to a gravelly upland in the Hamavand country, the ridges and valleys bear wheat, and allow easy passage by way of Khánikin on the trunk route from Baghdad to Kermanshahán. But immediately south of that track the slopes take a more rugged character again, corresponding to the great eastern wall at this point ; and the Kuh-i-Kebir, lying west of Pish Kuh, and other precipitous parallels shut off the hidden valleys of Pusht-i-Kuh, whose westernmost fence, composed of the sandstone of Jebel Hamrin, pushes its last spurs even across the Tigris itself, fixing a natural boundary between Assyria and Babylonia. Continuing to southward, the parallels become less abrupt, and rather rolling down-land than ridges ; and, encountering the great streams that escape from the Bakhtiari wall, they have their intervals filled up by the fair alluvial plains of Dizful, Shuster, Ram Hormuz (or "Ramuz"), Sultanabad, and Bebehan.

Thereafter the lower parallels are divided by but a little interval from the shallow waters of the Gulf. The streams are not large enough to form any considerable deltas, and the gravelly ground rises quickly from swampy coastal tracts to desolate boulder-strewn hills, bearing a few thorns and tufts of Indian grass. Stony plains, through which salt streams filter for most of the year in beds far too ample, fill the mountain intervals until a sufficient altitude is attained for snows to be collected

during a forty days' winter. In the south of the Persian
Plateau the line of permanent snow is about 14,000 feet,
an altitude to which hardly any peak attains, the only
possible claimants being members of the Shah and
Lalehzar groups, south-west of Kerman and Yezd.

All who attempt to describe the physical features of Persia as a
whole must fall back with thankfulness on Lord Curzon's comprehensive
volume, which exhausts the scattered evidence up to about 1890. The
principal advance since that book appeared has been made in our
knowledge of the northern Kavirs and of Laristan by Vaughan (*R. G. S.*,
Supp. 3, and *G. J.*, 1896) ; of Bakhtiari-land by Sawyer (*G. J.*, 1894) ; and
of northern Laristan by de Morgan (*Mission en Perse*, 1894). R. T.
Günther has made a study of Lake Urmi (*G. J.*, 1900) ; Captain Sykes
has told us much that was new about the province of Kerman, the
Dasht-i-Lut (*G. J.*, 1897–99), and the volcanic district in Persian Beluchistan ; and General Houtoum Schindler has given precision to our
knowledge of Irak (*R. G. S.*, special issue, 1897).

CHAPTER V

SOUTH-WESTERN PLAINS

FROM the foot of these slopes there stretches away westward for about three hundred miles, unbroken except by
the channels that two great rivers, which neither receive
from it nor give to it, have carved, a vast undulating plain,
everywhere ill-watered but not to be qualified as desert.
The northern left-bank affluents of the Tigris are hardly
able to push forward into this great waste any deltaic formations; for the silt has not opportunity to settle in their
steeply inclined beds ere finding itself in the strong
current of the main river. But the case is different with
the southern affluents, the Diyala-Shirwan, Kerkha, and
Diz-Karun; for these, together with two more southerly
independent streams, the Híndia and the Jerráhi, emerge
from the last passes of the mountain parallels almost at
the level of the high sea tide. Their slackened waters
begin to deposit at once, and for long have combined their
own alluvia with those of the greater western streams
in the creation of a huge deltaic tract, which runs inland
300 miles from the head of the Persian Gulf to an ancient
coastline south of Hit, and fills for all that length the space
between the last parallels of the Iranian Plateau and the
first swells of the Arabian upland, some hundred and fifty
miles to west.

The superficial area of this delta is about six times
greater than that of the Nile. It is, of course, growing
always. The coast at the mouth of the Shatt-el-Arab,
i.e. the estuary of the two main rivers, advances about
72 feet in a year or a mile and a half in a century, and
the mouths of the weaker streams have become, one
after the other, so greatly choked with silt that, failing

to penetrate the ever growing flats, they now turn their main currents towards the Shatt. The most ancient outflow of the Karun, the "Blind" channel, is now dry, and though a second channel still flows to the Gulf, its main waters, like those of the Jerrahi, have already lost independence; the Hindia cannot long preserve it; and the shifting uncertain outflows of these rivers have rendered the west of the lower Delta, from Amára to the sea, almost as hopeless a marsh as the long neglected floods of Euphrates have created on the east about Niffer and Nejef. When it is added that a huge swamp fills the apex of the angle between the two main streams it may be realised to what condition a tract, which was once the most productive in the world, has sunk in these latter days.

We turned from Euphrates and Tigris so soon as they had won their way to the open lowlands, the one south of Taurus, the other after clearing the last spurs of the Hakkiari hills. Thereafter the fate of the two is for awhile different. The Tigris, flowing on always within sight of high mountains on its left and receiving from them a continual tribute of large and swift streams, maintains the speed, which gained it its name of Dijla, or the "Arrow," and increases in volume all the way to the confluence. It cuts a deep straight-sided trench through the sloping plain; and never leaving within this a marginal strip uncovered for any length of time, it encourages no riparian cultivation, but flows on to Kurna, neglectful of its banks, and contributes much the larger volume of water to the common estuary of Euphrates.

The Frat, or Euphrates, on the other hand, when it leaves the Taurus, loses sight of mountains for ever, and receives no such full and perennial affluents as its fellow. The Belik and the Khabur alone bring more water than a torrent or an intermittent *wadi*. The lower Euphrates, therefore, decreases in volume as it flows south, and being dependent in the main on the snows and rains of a distant mountain region, it dwindles rapidly as summer advances, becoming even fordable in certain seasons as low as Birejik. In its lowest course the Frat escapes on both hands into marsh ; and when, the Shatra swamps passed, it reaches Kurna, now the sorriest site imaginable for Eden, it is become a stream much inferior to Tigris.

The common estuary, or Shatt-el-Arab, though not comparable to the rivers of the Farther East, rolls through two mouths a greater volume than the Nile ; and of these the larger admits ocean-going craft across its bar to the squalid riverine ports of Mohammera and Basra. Rather lower than half-way the Shatt receives the main flood of the Karun ; but some part of the latter's current still finds its way independently to the Gulf, as Euphrates used to do, ere human action began to tamper with the natural outflows. The present day Karun, as all the world now knows, is itself easily ascended by stern-wheel steamers of light draught for 100 meandering miles through grey flats to the sevenfold rock dam of Ahwaz. The upper reach again is navigable at all seasons to Bund-i-Kir : and thereafter the river offers two possible but not easy channels, of which the natural one is the least full ; and both lead to Shuster. The greatest of the Karun's tributaries, and the last to join the main stream, the Ab-i-Diz, can be used as a waterway to a point in sight of Dizful. But beyond these towns both main stream and tributary become mere tortuous stairs of rapids. The Karun falls 9000 feet in a 250 miles course from the Kuh-i-Rang to Shuster—points only 75 miles apart in an air-line. So painfully does the water that it gathers through half-a-dozen feeders from all the Bakhtiari basin, find escape through the western Iranian Wall.

The united waters of all these turbid streams thread their way through vast amphibious flats to a sea the shallowest and warmest in the world, but, in virtue of its extreme qualities, strangely productive. For the heated waters of the Gulf teem with fish above all others, and there the pearl oyster thrives most abundantly, and may be gathered on the shoals. We have looked already at its eastern shore, and noted a series of salt swamps or torrid sand-belts backed by bare and stony uplands. It remains to add to the indictment two counts, that the coast is most ill supplied with fresh water, most of its scanty streams being salt, and that it is almost destitute of natural harbours. Dilam, Bushire (Abu Shehr), Lingah, Bunder Abbas offer roadsteads far off shore (the depth two miles out from Bunder Abbas is only four fathoms) but no good shelter, and only the two last named enjoy any amenity of situation. There are islands, the blistered rocks of Tawíla or Kishm on which native Indian battalions were posted for half a century to overawe the Jowasmi pirates, and Ormuz, whose name conjures visions of the pearls and stuffs and spices that the first western conquerors of the Indies went so far to seek—glories that will never return to its crumbling fort and fishermen's huts. But by reason of heat and lack of water these islands are of small account to modern commerce ; and the Power that covets a port on the Persian side of the Gulf must choose one on the mainland, and will make but sorry gain at any point but the estuary of the Shatt.

The alluvial plain between Euphrates and Tigris swells in faint undulations of gravel and loam above a horizontal line drawn westward from Baghdad. For a short distance to northward the embankments of ancient canals and the furrows of ancient irrigation cuts may be seen, mouldering memorials of a dead civilisation, and then nothing but the monotonous waves of the " Desert," stretched east over Tigris to the roots of Jebel Hamrin and west across Euphrates beyond the range of human vision. Unrelieved in summer by anything but glistening salt pans, which collect the winter drainage of many Mesopotamian wadis, that are too feeble to cut their way to the great rivers, but in winter and early spring carpeted in all its hollows with flowers and thin herbage, the dusty waste rises insensibly to the latitude of Mosul, where a long hog-back, Jebel Sinjar, lies across it like a bar. This range runs down to the Tigris above Mosul, and is connected with the lower ridges of Jereibe, Abdul Aziz, and

Tektek which, by a north-westerly curve, join the Armenian highlands in the Karaja Dagh.   With Jebel Sinjar the scene changes to one of moderate verdure and fertility (though there are sands again to north), and the whole country is found to have been raised a step above the tracts to south of the hills.   Northern Mesopotamia is broad pasture land, for the most part of the year seamed by the upper waters of the Khabur and Belik basins, and graduated insensibly after a rise of nearly 1000 feet into the long vine-clad slopes of Tur Abdin and Karaja Dagh, which fence the low upland plains of Nísibin, Mardin, Diarbekr, and Urfa, on the skirts of Taurus.

Beside the slow rise of the land to northward, the student of a relief-model would note a gradual rise to westward also, crossing Euphrates ; and this at last brings up the average level to about 2500 feet on the rolling plateaux of eastern Syria, called generally the Hamad. The Hamad, however, like Mesopotamia, with which it is physically one, is crossed by a rounded ridge, running a little north of east from the Mediterranean watershed above Damascus to Euphrates ; and east of the river it appears again as a low swell defining on the west the valley of the lower Khabur, and at last crosses that stream to the Sinjar range.   North of this long ridge the Hamad, like Mesopotamia, is seen to be raised a step ; and the higher plateau, thus buttressed up, continues to rise slowly as a vast grassy down till it encounters obliquely the first offset of Taurus, a low range which trends from the Syrian coast watershed towards the Armenian highlands. By that range are limited the closed basin of Aleppo with its two salt pans and the valleys of Killis and Aintab, with the parallel vale of the Ak Su, whose waters at last find an outlet west of Marash through the frightful gorge by which the Jihun is admitted between Taurus and the Giaur Dagh (Amánus) (Fig. 11).   These valleys lie too close under the Tauric and Mediterranean walls to have any longer a desert or even a purely pastoral character.   They are monotonous agricultural upland tracts, seamed by outcrops of rocks, and to be reckoned rather to the rugged up-

heaval whose southernmost rampart bounds all their view
to the north, than to the softer southern plateau, whose
waters, where any there are, drain to the eastward.

The several parts of south-western Asia, on which our
survey has now entered, have the main features of their
physical formation so continuous and so completely in

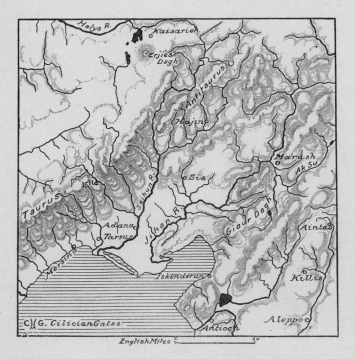

FIG. 11.—The Cilician Gates and the Basin of Adana.

common, that the whole oblong contained between the
lower Tauric ridges and the Arabian Sea will be best described as one. It is a featureless acclivity rising from
the east to a broad watershed, whose crest, culminating
to southward, is occupied at intervals along nearly all
its length by patches of volcanic erupted matter, called
" Harra " by the Arabs, wherever coated with corrugated

lavas ; but these are often fertile, the craters and cones overtopping abundant crops, as in the Hauran and Jaulan districts of trans-Jordanic Syria. This watershed has a short and abrupt western slope, wrinkled up into an almost continuous mountain " Fold," now single, now double, beyond which the land falls away abruptly to the sea with only such intervals of plain as the Jihun flats and the Phœnician strip, which its own rivers have made, or as the eastern coast of Sinai, and the long Arabian " Teháma," half up-heaved beach, half up-built reef of coral.

The long westward acclivity, which comprises two-thirds of this whole oblong, is varied, in its northern or Syrian section, by very shallow wadis, in whose gravel or loam-bottoms a little herbage survives the summer and the Bedawin may find water, and only one deeper depression collects a wider drainage, the Wadi Sirhan, whose broad channel trends south-eastward from Jebel Hauran, through the gypsums of the Hamad. Thereafter it opens out in mid desert to form the rich palm-pans of Jauf, the largest oasis of north Arabia, except Teima, ere its line is choked by the deep surface sands of the northern Arabian Nefud.

Here for the first time is seen utter desert, a broad reddish-yellow belt of perished sandstone overlying gravel. The action of a prevailing west wind has piled the deep sand into huge waves, the troughs between which, often some 200 feet deep, are scoured by the reverse eddy into horseshoe pits, where is sometimes exposed the basal gravel. These pits, called *fulj* by the Bedawins, probably owe their origin to the greater storms which at rare intervals pass over the Desert, carving its disintegrated surface into contours which last for centuries ; but thereafter the ordinary eddies and change of the wind suffice to keep the excavations clear for a long time. How far they shift their position or tend to fill again gradually with drift-sand is not yet known, nor is it certain to what extent they afford the Bedawins favourable spots for sinking wells and camping. The worst of the Nefud may be passed in some forty hours by a good camel ridden from Jauf to Teima, and in something more by one directed on Jobbeh. And, terrible as this Desert may be, it is so far from prohibiting all intercourse that it is not even a political boundary. Jauf has long been ruled not by the Power which is suzerain of the Hamad, but by the Emir of Hayil.

The main water-parting for the Syrian half of the oblong is, as we have seen, a continuation of the rocky

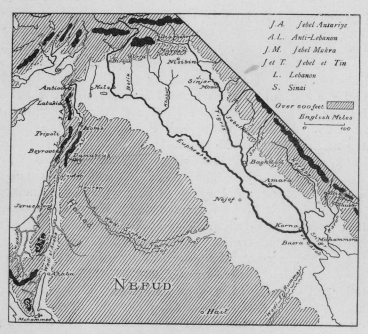

FIG. 12.—Syria, showing the general scheme of the Mountain Ranges.

but not lofty range which, leaving the Tauric system west of Béhesne, divides the plains of Marash and Aintab, and broadens out into a hollow swell, enclosing the basin of Aleppo. Thereafter the water-parting, split into a three-fold system, keeps a course due south; and when it has passed Homs, turns a point or two west of south and throws up on its western lip two mountainous ridges, the so-called "Anti-Lebanon," and after a low interval, Jebel-

E

es-Sheikh, or Hermon (Fig. 12). On its eastern lip lies
the rich self-contained basin of Sham, or Damascus, buttressed to east and south by the first of the Harras. This
lava track is nearly sixty miles broad by as many long,
not devoid of a red arable soil disposed among the craters
of Tulul in its northern half, but for the rest a fused and
blackened waste. Westward the swell of water-parting
rises presently into a hollow plateau, Jebel Hauran, which
together with the stony Lija and plains of Jaulan to north
and the fertile upper plateaux of Hauran and southern
Jaulan to west is as volcanic as any Harra but less grim.
South of the Hauran the swell changes its formation to
limestone, and so continues along the line taken by the
multiple track of pilgrims from Damascus to Mecca, and
by way of the mountains of Moab and Seir ; and not till
level with the head of the Red Sea does it reach in El
Hisma the second or Midianite Harra.

We remarked a low ridge running up the long
westward acclivity. The point at which this ridge
meets the longitudinal swell of water-parting coincides
with the latter's highest point, namely, the small plateau
from which Anti-Lebanon and Hermon rise. Thence
another low but distinct ridge, which, as we shall see,
forms an important secondary water-parting, trends away
on the western declivity. In short, the Syrian part of
the great oblong really slopes up from all sides to an
apex situated a little east of Baalbek, and would present
on a relief-model the aspect of a flattened and lop-sided
gable-roof, the regularity of whose apex was slightly
disturbed by certain excrescences, Anti-Lebanon and
Hermon. There is practically no drainage on the north-
eastern facet of this gable ; on the south-eastern those
"rivers of Damascus," that the angry Syrian vaunted
against Jordan, soon lose themselves in the hollow of
Sham, and are of account only in so far as they contribute to form the green expanse which seemed to the
blistered eyes of Mohammed, the desert camel-driver, to
be another Paradise.

The steep north-western and south-western slopes of

the gable, however, are broken, as we have already indicated, by a continuous mountain "Fold." Originating in the far north with the Giaur Dagh, anciently "Amanus," a high offshoot of the Tauric system which is thrown off in a direction slightly west of south, this "Fold" is carried on by an abrupt chain behind Alexandretta to the coastline, and at that point turns due south, and, taking a more down-like character, runs on as Jebel Ansaríyeh, till it rises to an Alpine height in the peaks of Lebanon. Thereafter it falls abruptly, and when it regains elevation is become more of a limestone plateau than a ridge—to wit, that bare rolling upland, relieved by low peaks and a series of small lacustrine basins, which is Palestine (Fig.13). Being continued farther south by the Jebel Makra and the other heights which line either hand of the Wadi el Arába, it constitutes the rugged coast range of Midian, and also, split by the "sea-river" of Ákaba, the peninsula of Sinai. To form the last,

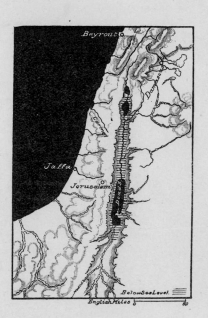

FIG. 13.—Palestine.

the "Fold" is first flattened into a triangular tableland of limestone some 4000 feet at its highest, draining towards its base by the great Wadi el Arish, and scarped at its southern edge in a vertical fall of 1000 to 2000 feet. This is the Desert of Tih, or the "Wandering." From the foot of the scarp rise again, step by step, masses of crystalline rock disposed like a notched arrowhead, point to south ; and these pile their bare steeps to form the peaks of Katerína, Musa, Umm Shomer, and Serbal, and fall abruptly to the Red Sea at Cape Mohammed.

The streams, which, issuing from the western face of the longitudinal water-parting, are directed north and south of west, find themselves unable to obey the dominant slope, and must coast along at the foot of the "Fold" this way and that till strong enough to break through its depressions. The whilom Orontes or Axios, now become in Arab mouths *Asi*, the "Rebel," wandered north till, blocked by the Tauric acclivity, it spread out into the lake of Antioch, and, combining its waters with the Kara Su, found means to break in a series of cataracts through the western "Fold," leaving the most of the lake to become fertile plain and reedy marsh. The Litáni, born also in the westerly ridge of the gable almost on the same level and not a mile away, finds itself drawn south along all the eastern flank of Lebanon to the depression at its southern butt ere it can obey the call of the dominant westerly slope, and escape to the sea between Saida and Sour as the Kasimíyeh. A second stream springs further south on the same slope, and flowing down the Beka as the Wadi-et-Tem, but little divided from the Litani, never succeeds in turning west to the sea, but has a singular fate under a new name, Nahr-el-Kebir, or Jordan. For after being joined by great springs from the southern butt of Jebel-es-Sheikh, the river falls into a huge rift of the earth's crust, and from pool to pool sinks to southward till arrested in the bottom of the pit, where at the last its waters, checked by evaporation at 1300 feet below sea-level, spread out into the bitterest lake in the world, more saline by two-fifths than even the sea of Urmi (Fig. 14). Beyond it the bottom of the Rift shelves quickly upward till sea-level is surpassed near the sea itself at the head of the Gulf of Akaba. This singular crevasse, the valley of El Ghor, receives considerable streams that flow south and west from the eastern watershed (the Menadíre and Zerka in chief) and, carrying their waters to its dead bottom, makes of Palestine the over-drained down that it is.

The coast, to which the western slope of the "Fold" declines gently, like all coasts which lie parallel to main structural lines, is without deep inlets, but has bays open to the prevailing westerly airs and surf. Since its rivers, if they flow from the sea face of the "Fold," can have but short courses, or, like the Nahr-el-Asi, are so much obstructed that they must deposit their silt before emerging from the mountains, deltaic formations are small; and the territories of Latakía, Trípoli, and Beirut owe more of their agricultural wealth to the lower slopes of the highlands than to alluvial coast tracts. Where the inland relief is less bold, as in Palestine, the littoral becomes more open ; but it grows also ever more arid, for reasons to be stated hereinafter, all the way to the dunes of El Arish, the alkaline marshes of the choked Pelusiac mouth of Nile, and the overheated sands and rocks of Sinai.

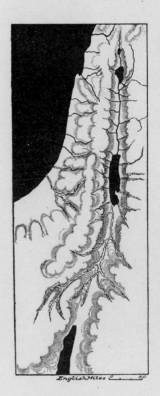

FIG. 14.—The Ghor.

The traveller who, leaving the Hamad, ascends by way of the northern Nefud desert to the southern part of the great oblong of south-western Asia, finds himself in what is for all practical purposes a huge island, and one that, except on its coasts and the main pilgrim tracks, is very ill known. We have said that the Nefud, or " Divider," is not wholly impassable. Indeed, both its flanks can be turned, west by the track from Maan to Medain Salih, east by Rumma, the great wadi of Central Arabia, which runs down to the Shatt-el-Arab at Basra, or even by a line some way farther inland which crosses the upper part of tributary wadis. The westernmost of these passages being the land-route of the Sunni pilgrims from Damascus, and the two eastern being affected by the Shiah pilgrims from Kerbelá and Nejef, wells have been dug and reservoirs constructed. But even so, Arabia is entered from the north only with so great difficulty and pain by man and beast, that present-day pilgrims have almost abandoned the land routes for the sea, and the central Plateau is become more an island than ever, in some communication with Egypt, India, and Persia, but hardly at all with north-western Asia or Europe.

In its main conformation the Arabian, as we have seen, continues the Syrian part of the Oblong, but, so far as may be learned from such hasty amateur surveys of the interior, as alone have been practicable, the long Syrian acclivity, ascending to a comparatively narrow Swell of water-parting, becomes south of the Nefud a much shorter and steeper slope, ended by a true Plateau of greater height than the most of the northern Swell, and of much greater breadth. There is thus, besides the north - westward gradient, rising across sevenfold sand ridges from the coast strip of the Persian Gulf, a steady slope up to southward from the Syrian Desert, across the Nefud, to the basaltic and granitic uplands of Jebel Shammar, whose general level is fully 4000 feet above the sea.

The short declivity from this Arabian Plateau to the western sea repeats the character of the Syrian maritime slope, in that it is interrupted by the same unbroken mountainous " Fold." This lifts itself as a continuous wall above the coast of the Red Sea from Midian to Aden ; and thereafter, bending first east and then north, goes on now single, now in duplicate, to outline also the other coasts of the Peninsula, dying away as it comes parallel with the head of the Persian Gulf.

This long tail of the western " Fold " goes far to isolate the central Plateau within the larger isolation of all Arabia ; and that isolation is completed by the almost unbroken ring of desert tracts, constituting one-third of the whole Peninsula, that lie within the mountain ring. The sands of the northern Nefud send down on the west a long tongue, which encircles the oasis of Teima, and reaches even to the lavas of Kheibar. On the opposite quarter, filling all the southern part of the inner Peninsula, lies a second and worse Nefud, the dunes of the Roba-el-Khali, sometimes known as the Red Desert, or Dahna, never yet crossed by a European. Indeed, it is not certain if even Bedawins can traverse it. Euting could not learn at Hayil in 1883 that any Kahtáni tribesmen knew its interior, and Halévy and Von Wrede found a superstitious terror of it on both sides of its south-western extension, El Ahkaf. But Van den Berg was told by Hadramut colonists in Java that it is possible to go from the Wadi Hadramut to Mascat in fifteen days, and in some uncertain time to Riad, but that there was no track and no commerce on either route. This awful Waste, of whose main expanse we have heard nothing but vague reports of shifting sands more bottomless than those of the northern Nefud, piled higher and more deeply pitted with *fulj's*, sends up a long tongue to north-east which reaches even to the Wadi er Rumma, and thereby is hardly divided from the eastward offshoots of the northern Nefud. Only on the south-west, therefore, where a short interval divides the Harra of Kheibar from the north-west edge of the southern Desert, is there a gap in the ring : and through this the Nejdward roads are conducted from Medina and Mecca making for the narrow Wadi Hanífah and Kasim, and the track from Yemen by Nejran and the two hundred miles of the Wadi Dauásir. But in what stint of water and rest the caravans must pass the western stages of these roads, may be gathered from the narratives of Doughty and Huber.

The nucleus of Arabia, enclosed within all this sand, is the pastoral tableland of Nejd (that term being taken to include all that lies between the northern and southern Deserts) which is hardly anywhere flat, but mostly

broken up into ranges of many hillocks and a few hills,
inclined abruptly from the plains. The chief ranges run
north and south, weathered to fantastic outlines by the
sand-laden winds and keen frosts of winter nights.
Being granitic, with patches of basalt, the Plateau, in
the territory of Hayil about Jebel Shammar, is a very
ill-watered steppe with few oases. But, changed to limestone in the south-east, it is of more varied and productive
surface in the hilly country of Arid and Jebel Towek,
where was cradled and grew the Wahábi power. While
in the angle between the two hard formations lies a sandstone hollow, receiving drainage from all sides, which is
the long and comparatively fertile valley of Kasim, a prize
long disputed by the hardier Arabs of the higher Nejd on
its either hand, Riad fighting against Hayil. In this palm-
studded bottom lie more villages than on all the rest of
the Plateau and the two most considerable townships,
Anéza and Boréda, both situated on the broad Wadi
er Rumma, that waterless stream whose course may be
traced for 1000 miles from the Harra of Kheibar.

Long tongues of the desert sand run into and even
across the tableland of Nejd, and it is nowhere better
than scantily supplied with water that must be digged
for, and conducted by underground passages. Nor
are even the richer oases green beyond the limit of
artificial irrigation. But, on the other hand, no spot in
Nejd is such utter waste that Bedawins may not camp
on it at some season, and find grazing for their camels
and a hidden water hole. And a very large part of the
whole is distinctively Oasis, tract, that is, where water
persists near the surface all the year, maintaining vegetation and permitting agriculture and some settled society.
But the word Oasis, in its common acceptation, further
connotes isolation, and in this respect also is properly
used of the fertile tracts of Nejd, for they are divided one
from another, or group from group, by intervals of sand.

The whole plateau is tilted up very gently a little west
of south, sending most of its scanty drainage to north-
east, and it culminates in a low semi-lunar limestone ridge,

which bends from north-east of Riad, where it is known as Towek, away far to the south-west, and probably at last joins the highlands of Yemen. And this hedge of all Nejd and of the Wadi Dauasir, whose water collects in a marshy lake, the Bahr Selima, is the theoretical eastern and southern water-parting of the Peninsula. But in effect probably no stream from the eastern or southern face of the ridge survives on the surface a day's journey ; and it seems as though the rains, which fall on the lime-stone formations of south-eastern Nejd, filter subterrane-ously to the Hadramut, and the Gulf coast, so abundant are the springs which well up in those districts, or flow to the sea some twenty feet below the Wadi beds.

A pilgrim or horse-dealer, going down from Nejd to the Gulf over Jebel Towek and some half-dozen sand-swells, will find at the eastern foot of the ridge the northerly tongue of the Dahna or Roba-el-Khali, and no water, till he shall reach the low tail of the coast range, to be crossed at a point not more than 1000 feet above sea-level. Once past the hills, he will enter after seven days a low deep oasis land of running streams and many springs, whereof a large number are hot and saline. This luxuriant strip of Hasa is divided again by an arid belt from a less favoured jungle tract shelving to a sluggish lagoon-like sea, chosen seeding-ground of the pearl oyster, from which rises the shoal island of Bahrein ; and both Hasa and the coastal tract of Katif are divided from the Shatt-el-Arab delta on the north by a broad belt of sand desert, which, ending in a rocky coast, makes of Koweit or Grane, distant about seventeen marches from the heart of Nejd, the most salubrious port of the Gulf. On the south the littoral tract passes presently into the more arid territory of Katr, divided rather by pebbly downs than hills from the Red Desert, and ceases altogether when confronted by a rocky ridge above 5000 feet high, which in tremendous precipice and crag projects from the " Fold " far into the Gulf as the dreaded Ras Musandim.
South of, and continuing this formidable barrier, the

coast range, become of greater elevation and double, falls back again from the shore, sending to the steaming plain of El Batna the abundant waters of its own palm-lined defiles, and even on its western side winning a considerable tract from the edge of the Red Desert. The inner range is the volcanic Jebel Akhdar, the "Green Mountain," which, feeding a line of oases, extending between it and the coast range from SE. to NW., makes the wealth of Oman. The coast range presently curves, embracing with dark serpentine spurs Maskat and its safe harbour, Key of the Gulf, which Great Britain, watching from India, keeps within reach of her hand.

After throwing out the rocks of Ras el Had the "Fold" turns west, and, dropping to some 4000 feet, becomes an arid belt of blistered rocks and sand-choked wadis, dividing from the desert dunes a coast as barren as that of the Mekran, across the Gulf. But ere half of southern Arabia has been traced, the coast relief is seen to rise again to 6000 feet in Dofar; and the seaward wadis, ceasing to be mere sand runs, make occasional patches of great fertility on the "Sahil" or coastal strip and among the foot-hills. And one great wadi in particular, whose waters originate at the back of the arid "Fold," in the elbow made by its northward bend, runs through a strip of alluvium, for more than a hundred miles parallel to the shore, till a depression lets it pass, already choked with sand, to the sea. This is the hidden Hadramut, which with tributary wadis makes a long oasis in the dreary aridity of south Arabia.

As the south-western corner of the Peninsula is approached, the coast-range rises still more in altitude, and catching the monsoon vapours on its seaward flank, sends a more copious drainage towards the shore. Here is "Happy Arabia" of ancient geographers. At first there is no more than a chain of green oases, set back between the roots of the hills, which approach the sea, and throw out into it at last jagged spurs of scorched plutonic rock about the harbour of Aden, one of the few protected ports found on the rectilinear Arabian coasts. But the " Fold," still rising, as it rounds to northward, and thickening somewhat, grows more blessed with waters and cool airs and fat soils ; and, like the Green Mountains of Oman, not only supports on its seaward slopes a region of luxuriant fertility, the "paradise" of the Yemen, but distils the monsoon landward to rescue from the Red Desert both the Hadramut valleys and the more northerly regions of Nejran, Jauf, and Dauasir, where once was "Sheba," when the running waters were husbanded behind mighty dams. But the newest of these great works is not later than the sixth century of our era, and all are broken now, and the waters filter away, allowing the sands to creep once more about the villages of the wretched Sherifs who represent the ancient kings.

"Happy Arabia" owes everything to the elevation of the south-western coastal range, whose highest summits, rather *plateaux* than peaks, attain east of Sana to 10,000 feet, and possibly more. And such is the plenitude of the rains that these mountains draw from the two monsoons, whereof indeed they serve to rob the rest of southern Arabia, that they send veritable rivers to be lost in the torrid strip of upheaved coral beach (Tehama) thirty to one hundred miles across, fringed by reefs and volcanic islands, which intervenes between the "Fold" and the Red Sea. But as the coastal range becomes once more depressed to some 7000 feet in the little known highland of Asir, and the humidity of the monsoon diminishes, all vegetation is confined to the higher ground. The "Tehama" dries under the burning breath of the Red Sea funnel, and the last of the mountain drainage filters away under the first stones of the level. In the Hejaz continuous fertility ceases. The Tehama (if the name be still used for the low coastal strip) stretches on, a rusty waste of salt clay on whose uppermost edge, among barren rocks and savannahs of coarse herbage, lies Mecca. The coastal hills, falling at Yambo to 4000 feet, can do no more than shelter in their shallow upper valleys rare oases, Tayif, the summer refuge of the

Meccans, Medina, whose greenery is of man's making, and the thick date groves of fever-stricken Ala. The waters of these favoured spots combine with drainage from the westward face of the Nejd Plateau and the Harras, here not entirely shut off by absorbent sands, to cut certain wadis longer and larger than any in Arabia, except Rumma. The waters filter below ground, and meeting in the Wadis Fátima and Hams, leak down to the Tehama, supplying wells and the possibility of life to Jidda and El Wij,—stifling "ports" that are no better than open roadsteads off a coast where land merges insensibly into water by way of sand spits and half emergent reefs.

With the double coast range of Midian, rising in Mowíla or Char to near 9000 feet, our survey of the relief of the Arabian "Island" returns round the head of the long Gulf of Akaba to the desert of Tih, linked by the intermittent chain of Seir to the Syrian "Fold." The lowest step of Tih, prolonged down the western coast of Sinai, is the limit of Asia.

No single book deals adequately with all S.W. Asia. For the E. lowlands most useful are Layard's *Nineveh* and *Early Adventures;* Ainsworth's *Euphrates Expedition* and *Karun;* Curzon's *Persia;* Blunt's *Bedawin Tribes;* Lord Warkworth's *Notes of a Diary*, &c. ; and Maunsell in *G. J.*, 1894.

For the Hamad, Blunt *op. cit.;* Oppenheim, *Reisen*, 2 vols. ; Humann and Puchstein, *Nord Syrien.*

For W. Syria, *Memoirs of the Pal. Expl. Fund;* Schumacher, *Across Jordan;* Doughty, *Arabia Deserta;* Palmer, *Sinai;* Ainsworth, *Jebel Ansariye.*

For Arabia there are two compendious works, Zehme's *Arabien* and Sprenger's *Alte Geographie Arabiens.* Zwemer's *Arabia* is incomplete and less useful than Tweedie's *Arabian Horse.* For Nejd, see Doughty ; Huber's *Journal*, and articles in *B. S. G.*, 1881, 1884, 1885 ; Euting's *Tagbuch*, &c. ; Blunt's *Nejd.* Pelly's short article in *R. G. S. Journal*, 1865, is a much safer authority than Palgrave. For the Fringe, Miles in *G. J.*, 1896, on Oman ; Hirsch, *Sud-Arabien;* Bent's *S. Arabia;* Van den Berg, *Hadhramut;* Hejaz, J. Snouck-Hurgronje, *Mekka.* I do not mention older and well tried authorities like Niebuhr and Burckhardt. Of Hasa, Yemen, Asir, and southern Nejd our knowledge has not been advanced during the past decade.

CHAPTER VI

EGYPT

To complete the Nearer East, however, we must glance at so much of the adjoining continent as is bathed by the Levant Sea. Structurally the north-western corner of Africa is as clearly distinguished from Asia as it is from south-eastern Europe, between which and itself there is fixed a profound sea gulf. It is true that the limestone ridge of Kántara, which it cost the makers of the Suez Canal much pain to pierce, links the Plateau of Tih to the desert hills north of Suez ; nor is it to be overlooked that the formations, the general aspect of the land, and the climatic conditions on the two hands of the Red Sea fissure are much alike, particularly to northward, where the porphyritic rocks of Sinai reappear in the coastal range of Africa. But a certain cardinal difference outweighs these conditions, namely, that the long slope west of the Red Sea falls not eastward but westward from the crest of a coastal range. What we have to survey is a single wide Plane tilted up eastward from a deep bottom, which is marked by a line of oases below sea-level, from whose other side swells up the great central mass of Africa. This Plane is bisected by the valley of a single mighty stream, which derives neither its origin nor any of its waters from it, but, itself an alien, has laid down a ribbon of alien soil and fenced the sea from the northern edge of the Plane with a large deltaic tract.

The southern limit of this Plane, marked by the beginning of a steady southward rise towards the highlands of Abyssinia and equatorial Africa, runs slightly north of west, from a point in the coast range about Sawákin, and crosses the Nile above Wadi Halfa to the southern ex-

tremity of the Greater Oasis.   South of this line, which is
nearly the northern limit of the equatorial rains, the plains
soon begin to be of the steppe character.   North of it,
except under the coastal range, and where coated with the
alluvia of the Nile, they are uncompromising desert.

Looked at from the Red Sea, the Plane presents a
steep edge, returning from the summit of the tilt.   The
land rises at once from the shore, showing steeply inclined
porphyritic strata, to a jagged crest of sedimentary rocks,
set some twenty miles back, and varying from 4000 to
6000 feet in elevation.   The short seaward slope is almost
entirely destitute not only of streams, but springs, from its
northern link with the Tih desert, down to the foot of the
Abyssinian slope, whose drainage keeps green the oasis of
Tokar; and the narrow littoral, composed mainly of recent
corals, must depend on cistern water.   Detritus and the
labours of the mollusc builders have made of this coast
a long even line without inlets, to be approached at most
points only through a maze of reefs.

From the crest of this naked parti-coloured ridge, interrupted by one low depression, Wadi Hamamát, the
land slopes away to the right brink of the Nile fissure,
and is hardly relieved by anything but the westward wadis,
half filled with pebbles and sand.   Slight horizontal swells,
whose butt ends raise the cliffs of the Nile trench at intervals to comparatively mountainous heights, make ribs to
the Plane.   No water survives above ground twenty-four
hours after the rare rain-storms that fall in this region,
except high up on the slope in fissures of the rock ; and
there are but very few wells in the depths of the wadis,
and still fewer palm-oases on the lower ground.   Those
that exist about the convents of Antony and Paul east of
Beni Suef, and at Gaita on the road from Keneh to Wadi
Hamamát, are very small, and hardly to be distinguished
from sheer desert.

From the opposite brink of the Nile fissure the same
dreary expanse of naked friable limestone resumes its interrupted downward slope, but less evenly.   For on the
north it is depressed immediately below sea-level in

a chain of basins, of which the central one, the Fayum, receives an off-flow of the Nile, while the others collect stagnant waters. Such are the nitrous swamps of Wadi Natrun on the one hand, and the marshy bottoms of Gharak and Wadi Rayan on the other. The main slope takes up again behind these basins, only to fall more steeply at the last below sea-level in the western chain of oases.

These last are irregular basins intersected by higher ridges, whereof some are so narrow or so little continuous as not to impair the unity of an oasis, some so broad as to divide one oasis from another. In the hollows under the eastern cliff water wells up and runs away to the centre, where is often a marshy lake ; and in such abundance does it issue that the lands cannot readily be drained, and are sour and malarious. Since these basins contain no alluvial deposits, they must be regarded rather as the bed of a dried up sea than a river, least of all of silt-laden Nile. But whence their gushing springs come is a mystery. Native opinion, and that of some geographers, supposes infiltration from the river of Egypt ; but it is hard to see why the Nile waters, if they may pass so freely though the surface strata, should not well up equally in the Fayum, which lies considerably lower than the level of the stream, but has no water bearing *strata* under it to a depth of near 700 feet. And it is more probable that the oasis springs are due to drainage which has come from south or west to this bottom of all Africa, either from Equatoria, or from the Sahara Plateau, which is held to be riddled underground by channels of running waters.

The southernmost oases, such as Selíma and Sheb, are not more than small patches on the face of the westward slope, where water can be got by digging, and the chain of considerable basins begins with Khargeh and Dakhel, which lie due west of Thebes, are hardly divided one from the other, while internally split up by bars of desert, and abound in water above all the oases. After a long interval of Swell the land sinks to the smaller basin

of Faráfra, and after a second but shorter interval to that
of Baharía. Thereafter the line of depression strikes
almost due west, and passes by a salt lake, Sittra, and the
palm grove of Bahrein to the deep saline hollow of Araj,
and wide plains of sparse *halfa* grass, and at the last comes
to Siwah, the "Oasis of Ammon," a shallow circle of
gardens and palm groves springing in a noisome alkaline
soil about a marshy lake. Thence a chain of similar
hollows continues westward through the Senussi country,
by way of Jarabúb and the deep salt hollow of Faredga ;
and it would seem that the sea once entered the whole line
of bottoms from some point on the Gulf of Sidra.

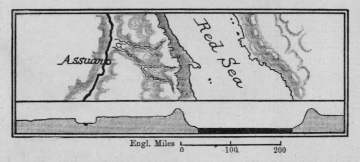

Engl. Miles

0   100.   200

FIG. 15.—Section through the Red Sea and the Nile Valley.

Such is the simple scheme of north-eastern Africa—
a Plane tilted up to east, bounded south by the acclivity
of Equatoria and north by the basin of the Levant Sea,
towards which it falls with abrupt face, high and scarped, in
the butt of Jebel Atáka by Suez, and low and monotonous
in the cliffs of Abukír, and the barren sandy shore to
west of Mariút (Fig. 15). But a foreign agency has to be
reckoned with, which does something to impair this simple
scheme, interrupting the Plane and thrusting back the sea
from its northward face. Arriving at the southern edge
of the Plane with its full volume, the Nile exacts passage
to the sea through a trough of its own making, and lined
with alluvia of its own spreading ; and, neither does it
receive aught, whether earth or water, from the land

which it bisects at mid-slope, nor does it give of its own to the deserts, but it flows to distant sea a mid-African stranger.

The energy gathered by the Nile in descending the long stair of the Second Cataract has caused it in the course of ages to cut through the limestone a trench so deep and steep that the waters do not escape from it even at high flood for some hundred miles; and thereafter the hard rocks, amongst which the river must swirl, have always so closely penned the stream, that it has had no opportunity to deposit its alluvia. But from the point of its escape from the granites at the First Cataract, the slackened stream has been able to spread its flood waters more widely; and beyond the sandstones of Silsileh it has scooped a broad valley, whose entire bottom it fills for the two months of the inundation, and for the remainder of the year leaves mostly open and coated with some 30 feet of alluvia; while the current is withdrawn to a shallow trench, now cut down the middle, now under this wall or that, but for the most part edging towards the east under the pressure of the prevailing westerly winds or of the earth's rotation.

This divided alluvial belt, which we know as Egypt, is never interrupted from Silsileh to the sea, a distance of 500 miles as the crow flies, but near 200 more if the curves of the river be followed (Fig. 16). In

FIG. 16. The River Nile.

F

one or two places, for example midway between Esne and
Erment, where harder limestones have been encountered
and a cataract used to be, it narrows to a gut, while at the
most open points the breadth is some thirty miles; but for
its whole length it averages some fifteen miles' breadth of
deltaic soils, strongly impregnated with carbonate of potash
and various salts, and rising slightly, like all deltas, to the
margins of the central trench, on which the first and most
dense alluvia are deposited by the rising flood. By these
deposits the whole plain is gradually being raised at the
rate of about six inches in a century ; but while the level
of the Lower Nile grows higher, the level of the upper
reaches tends to fall, as the rapids slowly but surely wear
away the cataract reefs. From either edge the calcareous
desert rises steeply and often precipitously, and only here
and there, is interposed a narrow and doubtful interval of
coarse *halfa* grass sprouting on detritus, slipped or blown
on to the mud — that

> " strip of herbage strown,
> That just divides the Desert from the Sown."

Some 400 miles below the cataracts the choked and
slackened stream shows its earliest disposition to split,
having long ago thrown off on the left a narrow channel,
the Bahr Yusuf, as the *fellahín* call it, believing it to be
the beneficent work of the Hebrew governor of their land.
All canalised as it now is, and, indeed, made to derive
not from the main river, but from the Ibrahimíeh cut, this
channel is undoubtedly of natural origin ; but whether it
always ran away into the deep Fayum bottom to be lost
in the Birket el Kerun is matter of dispute. As the case
stands now, the Bahr Yusuf breaks at Illahún through
the narrowest part of the limestone reef, which divides
the valley of Nile from the largest and most regularly
circular of the pans in the westward slope of the tilted
Plane ; and, flowing into this basin, splits into several
streams, which, owing to the steepness of the declivity,
tumble down shaggy miniature gorges, very unlike the
channels of the main valley. And these waters, drawn

off in all directions by a network of canals to feed the
north and south of the pan, reunite at last on the west
in a long brackish lake, whose surface, far below sea-level,
reflects the farther desert rising steeply to its former
height.

Signs of a second subsidiary channel appear fifty miles
lower down under the western cliff ; and possibly this
was originally a continuation of the Bahr Yusuf, ere the
Illahun reef was breached by the action of nature or
man. But it is now choked with sand and alluvium, and

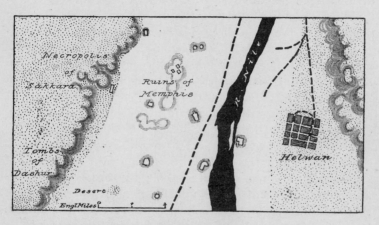

FIG. 17.—The Nile Valley immediately above Cairo.

the present division of the main stream does not take
place till both Memphis and Cairo have been passed, and
the Nile is flowing well within what, even after the latest
upheaval of Northern Africa, must have long continued to
be sea. From the present point of division, however, and
the salt water intervene above 100 miles of deltaic deposit,
spread fanwise between and beyond the two channels which
alone remain of seven mouths by which Nile once poured
its flood waters into the Mediterranean.

The general fall of the Nile Delta is only such as the
deposit, diminishing gradually along the course of the
streams, will occasion ; but it is sufficient to differentiate

the apex from the base, as firm land from marsh. The whole sea base, in fact, is occupied by a chain of choked and sour swamps, beginning east of the old Pelusiac mouth beyond the great ship canal that has been in part cut through them, continued by Lake Ménzaleh to Lake Burlos, and ended beyond the western Nile by the meres of Abukir and Mariut, the last become a sea-lagoon, thanks to the British besiegers of Alexandria in 1805. These marshes on east and centre filter through lagoons and sand dunes into a shallow sea; but on the west they are divided from the waves by an eastward trending spur of the limestone formation of the Plane, which has given a dry site and the possibility of a harbour to Alexandria.

The Delta swamps have become, it would seem, much more extensive since the Middle Ages, but rather from neglect than any irremediable action of Nile. Now that five of the old channels are permanently blocked, silt is deposited only about the Rosetta and Damietta mouths, and chiefly about the former, which emits the fuller stream; and various agencies combine to neutralise its increase— the damming of the waters inland and the diversion of so much of them on to the fields; the erosion by waves and marine currents on the Delta shore, now no longer sheltered in a bight, but flush with the rest of the southern Levantine coast; and finally a slow subsidence of the land, which has by now sunk the quays of ancient Alexandria well below sea level, and probably continues on all the coast-line. The Delta of Nile appears to be no longer growing, and the engineers can deal with its littoral marshes, without apprehension that, as they are drained on the north, they will advance equally to the south.

For the rest the Delta declines, for a reason already stated, not only north towards the sea, but slightly west and east away from the two Nile channels. Tracts exist both on its outskirts, at the base of the desert slopes, and midway between the two Niles, more wet and swampy than elsewhere, the coast-line excepted. And on certain other parts the winds blowing off the deserts tend to pile sand, causing yellow islands to stand up here and there out of the ploughed lands.   But it is needless to insist on these slight inequalities in so plain a surface, more especially since the whole Delta is nowadays subject to increasing control and modification by human action, which is capable in the long run of reducing to uniformity any and all of its minor irregularities.

The habitable part of the Nile Valley has been so thoroughly surveyed and "guide-booked" that nothing new is to be said of it geographically.   Milner's *England in Egypt*, 1892 ; Firck's *Ægypten*, 1894 ; successive State Papers by Lord Cromer, by Villiers Stuart in 1895 and by Sir E. Palmer in 1898 ; and Silva White's *Expansion of Egypt*, 1899, will keep the enquirer up to date as to reclamation of lands and other slight changes made in physical features.   But hardly any of the Desert fringes have been adequately described (*cf.* Schwein-furth in *P. M.*, January 1901, on the Farshut-kom Ombo desert edge). Off the beaten track, Murray's Guide is always best, *e.g.* the Oases.   The Fayum in Brown's *Moeris*, and Grenfell's opening chapter of *Fayum Towns*, &c.   Siwah, most recently revisited by S. White (*Sphinx to Oracle*); J. Bramley (*G. J.*, 1897) ; and Von Grünau (*Zeit. Ges. Erdk.*, Berlin, 1899).   No one has reached Jarabub.   For the Eastern Desert and Red Sea littoral, see E. L. Floyer (*N. Etbai*, 1893), and J. T. Bent (*S. Arabia*, 1900).

CHAPTER VII

STRUCTURE

THE cardinal lines of this relief, confused by subsidiary accidents, will stand out more clearly if the chief elements of the structure be made the subject of a very brief special consideration. It must, however, be understood that the geology of the greater part of these land-masses is known only superficially. Nothing like a serious survey has been made of the rocks of three-fourths of the Nearer East; and except in the south of the Greek peninsula, the Nile valley, and Palestine, there are no considerable areas in our region where a geological specialist could not break new ground.

The connection of structure with relief in the Balkan peninsula, however, has been generally determined by Austrian investigators. It appears that the peculiar division of Macedonia is due to the recent fracture of an archaic mass of rocks into a number of block systems, each of which has its enclosed basin. This archaic mass, continued from the Albanian Alp plateau, is represented by the existing Balkan mountain chains and their off-shoots, as far south as the Gulf of Volo on the one hand, and as the last foot hills of the Sredna Gora, above the Black Sea, on the other. The whole south-east of the peninsula, therefore, except the detached rocks on which Constantinople stands, is become a group of basins larger or smaller, elevated more or less, filled with Tertiary lacustrine deposits, and divided by interlocking ridges, through which in most cases a drainage outlet has been found. But certain existing pans, notably the very deep Ochrida and much shallower Presba, were lakes before the basins were formed. They fill part of a distinct 'rift, running down the western limit of the archaic mass, in which recent volcanic action may be studied in a series of *solfataras* north of Ochrida.

West and south of this central block the lateral pressure, exerted in the process of shrinking, has wrinkled up into a steep and broad fold a system composed mainly

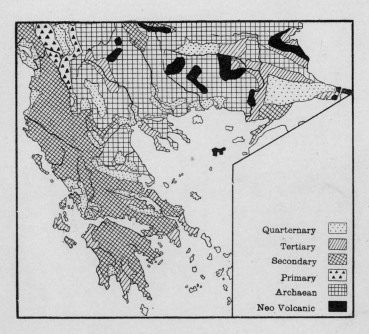

Quarternary
Tertiary
Secondary
Primary
Archaean
Neo Volcanic

FIG. 18.—Sketch of the geological structure of the Balkan Peninsula.

of Secondary rocks, which in the south, being of highly crystalline character, impart exceptionally bold outlines to the relief. These probably emerged comparatively late from the great middle sea, which seems to have flowed as late as Eocene times where the southern peninsulas of Europe and Western Asia are now. And on the south-west the same rocks are still slowly rising from that profound sea gulf, which compensates the abrupt incline of Crete. In the Taygetus range of Laconia earlier rocks have been protruded; but, with few other exceptions, all the land of Greece and the islands of the Ægean are one in their geologic composition.

A certain belt in the Ægean area, however, has a character apart. The continued action of volcanic forces, survivals of those which were responsible for the original metamorphosis of the Greek rocks, appears in and about four distinct *foci* situated in the north-west of the Morea, in the north of Bœotia, in the Gulf and inland vicinity of Smyrna, and in the southern-most Cyclades. A chain of vents, of which two groups wake from time to time to full activity, and two are quiescent, giving warning only by *solfataras* and hot springs, starts with the peninsula of Méthana and curves through the isles of Milos, Kímolos, Therásia, and Santorin to Nísyros, off the south-west coast of Asia Minor. Thus

Alluvium

FIG. 19.—The Alluvial Plains of Greece.

it outlines the northern limit of the great Cretan sea gulf. The harbour of Santorin, with its red contorted walls, rising sheer from a bottomless gulf and enclosing smoking islets and a steaming pumice-strewn sea, is among the grimmest reminders of the globe's internal fires ; and with the other outlets it offers ceaseless witness of a hidden peril, to which the earth crust of the Balkan Peninsula and isles is peculiarly exposed. For it has been calculated that there are on an annual average ninety-four earthquake days in all Greece, and a serious disaster happens at some point every nine months.

Subsequent denudation is, of course, responsible for the actual form which the whole Secondary belt now bears. The lie of the strata north and south has directed northward or southward all the infant rivers which have their source far within the mass; and these only break through at right angles to the sea, when much increased in volume. This is true of all the Albanian streams, from the Black Drin to the Aspropótamo, that are not merely coastal torrents. They cut steep valleys, evenly inclined, and unvaried by such basins as exist on the eastern side of the Spine; and the mass of silt, which their considerable volume (due to the heavy rainfall of the Adriatic slope) causes them to carry, is hardly deposited at all till the limit of the fold is reached. There it is spread out almost continuously in a low and marshy littoral. The richer territories of Greece, where not

FIG. 20.—Santorin.

desiccated Tertiary basins, enclosed in block systems, as is the case with Thessaly, Bœotia, and Arcadia, are little triangles of deltaic alluvia at the foot of seaward valleys of erosion, which have remained small in extent and sharply distinguished one from another through the hard enduring nature of the metamorphic mountain ribs.

The Rumelian plain, like the vale of Seres further west, is only a broader basin than the ordinary Macedonian type, a Tertiary floor within a horse-shoe of older masses. Its original limit on the south was not where it now is. The intrusive mass of plutonic rock, on which

Constantinople stands, has been split by a very recent and accidental fracture from the opposite shore, and the banks of the Dardanelles, which correspond in outline headland to bay and bay to headland, show sections of the same strata (Fig. 21). The earlier outlet of the Black Sea current may be traced trending south-west through

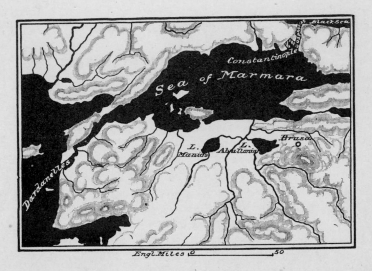

FIG. 21.—The Bosphorus and Dardanelles.

the Bithynian depression in which lie the lakes of Isnik, Abullónia, and Mánias.

Geologists seem to be agreed that all that part of Asia, which falls within our region, is as recent a continental apparition as the Greek peninsula and isles. The same sea covered Arabia and washed the roots of the Caucasus as flowed where Greece and immemorial Egypt were to be. Certainly the bed of the sea to south of the Anatolian peninsula has been elevated in unison with that of the Ægean. A deep sea gulf, continued from the south of Crete and lying some distance to south of the shoaling shore of Cyprus, sends an arm up northward between its eastern promontories and the opposite coast, to mark off the Anatolian from the Syrian upheaval.

Nevertheless, the land-masses of Western Asia have not as a whole the Balkan character, but are rather a group of wave-like upheavals, two of which, lying in the centre, *i.e.* the Syrian and Iranian, rise with a steeply-folded edge from the west, and fall with a long slope to east, and two to north and south, Asia Minor and Arabia, maintain, after the first rise from the west, a plateau character, and ultimately fall more abruptly down a short and crumpled slope, on which recent volcanic action is conspicuous.

In the case of Asia Minor it is notable that the axial swell of the plateau is marked along all its length by traces of volcanic activity in various periods. The recent craters and lava beds of the Kula district, the old *Katakekaumene*, flanked by an unusual wealth of hot springs in the Menderes valley, a notorious centre of seismic disturbance, are continued by the basaltic Kara Dagh and the trachytic cone of Hassan Dagh to the dead giant Erjies. And after a short interval appears that great group of cones unparalleled in our area, which rises from the Armenian highland, Ararat in the centre over-topping all, Alagiuz and the huge Savalan to north and north-east, Sahend and the igneous tract of Takht-i-Balkis to south-east, Sipan and Nimrud to south-west, overlooking the deep rift of Van.

We seem to stand here at the centre of a star-like upburst of the terrestrial crust, whereby the bowels of the earth have been made to emerge at points along four great cracks (Fig. 22). Westward run the volcanoes of Asia Minor and the Ægean isles to the smoking cones of Southern Europe ; northward, Alagiuz, Savalan, and the Eastern Caucasus connect with the Caspian oil-fields ; eastward, Demavend is reached through the Takht-i-Balkis ; and southward the chain of Syrian and Arabian Harras, reached through the Van volcanoes and the Karaja Dagh, leads to the igneous rocks of Perim and the active crater of Jebel-et-Tir.

How the rivers, falling south and north from the Anatolian axial swell, have to force their way through the crumpled northern and southern edges of the plateau, in some cases flowing for a long way westward before finding transit, has been already described. The rapidity of their final descent causes them both to cut very deep beds which over-drain the edges of the plateau, and also to carry down, without chance to deposit it, immense spoil of the powdery higher lands to the alluvial flats bordering the sea. Thus have been formed deltaic tracts out of all proportion to the water discharge of many of the streams, for example, the Kizil Irmak, the Gediz - Chai, the greater Menderes, and the Sihun - Jihun. A central undulating Tertiary basin, containing lakes, saline unless drained by *dudens* or subterranean outflows ; deep, rapidly falling valleys, hardly to be followed through the crumpled mountain fringes ; deltaic plains,

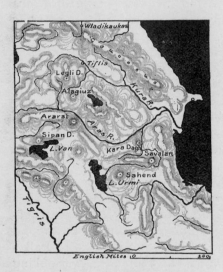

FIG. 22.—The Volcanic District round Ararat.

isolated from each other about the coast—such a common character has its structure given to the relief of Anatolia. There is, however, one broad distinction to be drawn within the peninsula. The crumpled edges are much bolder and more Alpine in character on the west and south-west than on the north or south-east, and this will probably be found to be the result of a difference in the folding of their structure. The former are comprised largely of Primary rocks : the latter of Secondary and Tertiary.

The volcanic convulsion already described is connected causally with the confusion of ridges that cross and re-cross the greatly elevated Armenian plateau. At this point the shrinkage process evidently happened to lighten in a special manner the subterranean pressure and so to permit the liquefaction of the rocks. Amidst all the confusion, however, the main lines of structure remain the same, and simplify their arrangement as the region marked by the volcanic chimneys is left behind. The effect of the greater pressure exerted in the north is still seen in the multiplicity of steep folds to west and south-west of Urmi, amid which sandstones outcrop in Mukri and Serdasht ; and perhaps again in the general elevation of the Azerbaijan shelf, set all about as it is with cones. About its midway point the main fold becomes nummulitic, and has split at intervals transversely (owing, perhaps, to the greater contracting capacity of its material) in those singular rifts which the Persians call *tengs*. Thereafter the fold resumes an even cretaceous character, with few marked depressions, until it fades away in the sands and gravels of the western Beluch steppe.

This is, however, as we have hinted, the crumpled edge of a plateau more in appearance than in reality, Western Persia is really made up of a series of mountain chains, running east of this axial ridge, and parallel to the wrinkles of the fold to west ; and the long furrows between these chains have come to be filled up with an excess of gravelly detritus, whose surface breaks up to sand wherever lying at a distance from the percolation of water from the hill slopes. The general level of the upheaval declines steadily to eastward from the axial line, and falls suddenly, beyond the high crystalline range of Yezd, some 2000 feet into a deep basin, the bottom of Western Asia. This is interposed between, on the one hand, the eastern prolongation of the Armenian convulsion, represented in chief by the recent upheaval of the enor-mous chimney Demavend, and on the other, a distinct up-burst of terrestrial fires through the vents Tuftan, Basman, and the lesser volcanoes of Northern Beluchistan. It is

the recently dried bed of a sea, coated with quaternary
sediment. The Elburz, which, except where recent
volcanic formations have intruded, is mainly made up of
Secondary rocks, has been its northern wall since at least
Eocene times. Into its hollow flow all Iranian rivers
(outside Azerbaijan, which is rather part of the Asia Minor
wave), but with such feeble and intermittent volume, that
they have served to score and carve the land far less than
the broader touch of wind and sand.

Corresponding to this Iranian wave of upheaval, and
separated from it by a broad furrow, is the Syrian
wave with a similar crumpled western edge. It once
fell by insensible gradations to the southern sea some
300 miles north of its present coast. For all the
Mesopotamian level south of Hit is a gulf-head filled with
recent deltaic alluvia, amid which one or two islands pro-
trude, such as the basaltic Jebel Zinam south of Basra.
Strange that the last formed land in the Nearer East
should have been chosen by the tradition of its peoples
as the first home of man !

The symmetry of the great Syrian earth-wave is
broken only by the intrusive volcanic formations of the
Harras and by that strange memorial of an earlier state
of the land, the long fissure of the Ghor. This, it is
supposed, ere the Meiocene upheaval of Western Asia and
Northern Africa took place, lay at the same elevation
as the surrounding lands. But when the land surface
crumpled up, a long "fault" was formed extending from
the Beka (or indeed even from Armenia) by way of the
Gulf of Akaba to the Red Sea, and in its profound bed
took refuge and was preserved a remnant of the earlier
fauna and flora, escaped from an uplifted and colder
world. And therefore there still survive in the Lake of
Galilee fishes proper to Lake Tanganyika, and in the
Jordan valley certain birds not otherwise found out of
India or Ceylon.

The Secondary formations, which show themselves
all over the south of Syria, except where interrupted by
the recent Harras, change abruptly in the north to Ter-

tiary, as in Mesopotamia ; and this change corresponds to a difference of level already mentioned. The upper shelves of the Hamad and Mesopotamia are geologically connected more closely with the Taurus to north of them than the deserts to south.

In its structural history the Syrian wave is one not only with the Iranian, but with Egypt, north of Silsileh, and with the greater part of the Sahara. The plateau of Tih links these continental masses of recent upheaval ; and that part of the Nile valley, which conventionally stands to us for what is most ancient, is a thing, comparatively speaking, of yesterday. Habitable Egypt proper is all deltaic and quaternary, the slowly rising alluvia having attained in the Delta proper a depth of many hundreds of feet. The great river slid off the original equatorial coast by the ladder of cataracts which declines from Hannek to Abusir, and in the dawn of time probably mingled at once with the sea. But when the Meiocene upheaval had caused this sea to fall back some 500 miles, the river after a short course through limestone forced its way above Assuan over and through intrusive ridges of hard rock, diorite and granite, towards an emerged bar of sandstone at Silsileh. And when the waters at length forced and wore down this softer rock, a last cataract was brought into being a hundred miles back, where the harder rocks dammed the stream, and from its foot a broad, unimpeded channel had to be cut by the flood waters through uniform limestones to the sea. Of this primeval southern extension of the East Mediterranean pool, the depressions to west of the Nile, the Fayum, Wady Rayan, and the chain of oases from Khargeh to Jarabub are perhaps the last inland memorials (Fig. 23).

Even the Primary rocks, which compose the west Red Sea chain, seem to have made their appearance about the same time as the formations of the northern desert, for they still bear, in spite of denudation, a crest of sedi-mentary rocks of the later period. This chain continues, from pre-carboniferous Sinai and the Dead Sea geysers, a line of volcanic manifestation, which defines on the east the great Asian-African rift, with its immediate border of upheaved beach and coral formation. On the west runs a parallel and even more distinct igneous limit. For begin-

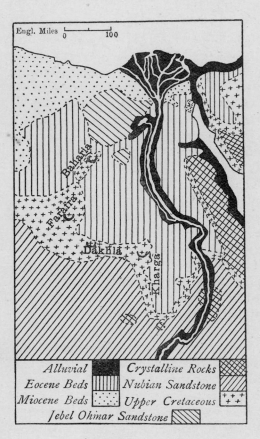

Engl. Miles 0 ——— 100

Alluvial   *Crystalline Rocks*
Eocene Beds   *Nubian Sandstone*
Miocene Beds   *Upper Cretaceous*
Jebel Ohinar Sandstone

Fig. 23.—Sketch of the geological structure of Egypt.

ning from the south we see a Red Sea island, Jebel-et-Tir, which still emits smoke and lavas. From Mecca northwards runs the chain of " Harras," great patches of black eruptive matter, upheaved partly on, partly behind, the crumpled " Fold," and in one case, the Harra of Kheibar, trenching on the Nejd plateau itself. These are continuous enough from Ala to form an inner wrinkle on the westward slope, which fringes with solemn black cliffs a desolate furrow interposed between itself and the rise of the plateau, and relieved by the small oases on the great Sunni pilgrim road. Doughty, who alone has wandered on the northern Harras and that of Kheibar, has described them as black shining platforms of broken lavas and basaltic blocks, relieved by but few cones, *volcanelli*,

and shallow craters.   The Hisma group, known as the
Harrat es Shefa, is elevated to some 5000 feet.   West of
this lie the lofty granites of Hadad and of Midian, the
latter bordering that part of the Rift which is represented
by the Gulf of Akaba.

This volcanic series is continued northwards, as we
have already seen, at short intervals by the Syrian Harra
and the craters of Hauran, Lija, and North Jaulan.   And
these again, perhaps, find a link through the extinct cone
of Kukab in the Khabur valley and the plutonic outcrops
of the Karaja Dagh, south and east of Diarbekr, with the
volcanoes of Van and the centre of the great eruptive star.

A distinct series of volcanic vents marks the south-
east and south of Arabia.   The Hasa oasis is the creation
of hot springs.   Ras Jebel and Jebel Akhdar, in Oman,
are reported, like the Maskat rocks, to be wholly of
recent igneous formation, and probably they contain
extinct craters.   South and west stretches the unknown ;
but Arab report speaks persistently of geysers and
volcanelli, if not of more considerable manifestations, at
Bir Borhut in the Eastern Hadramut.   It is not impossible that the Bedawin tales of yawning funnels and
moving quicksands, in which men perish if they adventure
themselves on the Dahna Desert, may be founded on real
volcanic phenomena.

The mass of the great peninsula, which is fringed
by these vents, is rather of wave than plateau form,
being, according to Doughty, uniformly composed of
limestones, sandstones, and igneous rocks, stratum below
stratum.   But the upheaval is highest in the north,
where two great patches of sandstone appear on the
surface, with a long strip of granite and basalt intruded
between.   The last makes that dry belt extending south-
west from Jebel Shammar to Mecca.   On the right hand
the broad sands of the higher Nefud decline.   On the left
is the fertile sand hollow of Kasim.   To south and east,
however, the strata resume their normal order.   High
Nejd shows a limestone region coated here and there,
especially on its eastward slope, with Tertiary gravels.

G

The slopes are long and even, for in Arabia, as in Persia and the Hamad, the broad touch of air and sand has determined the superficial aspect of the land more than the eroding influence of water. The courses of the greatest Wadis, Rumma and Dauasir, lie often in almost imperceptible depressions, and nothing creates any deltaic addition to the land except the insignificant storm-conduits that descend from the outer edge of the Fringe heights.

A certain number of recent special articles have been consulted— **Balkan Peninsula**, Cvijic and Oestreich ; chapters in books by Jiriček, Philippson, Clon Stephanos, Ehrenburg, Fouqué—mostly cited in note to Chapter I.   On the Ægean seismic region articles by C. Mitzopoulos on the earthquakes of Zante, Bœotia and the Menderes valley in *P. M.*, 1893, 1894, 1895, 1900 ; also F. Schaffer (*Mitth. Geog. Ges. Wien*, 1900).

Asia Minor.—The earlier travellers mostly had geological knowledge. In this J. Hamilton excelled.   Active investigations have been made recently by F. Schaffer, but only preliminary reports published (*P. M.*, 1900).

Persia.—A. F. Stahl in *P. M.*, *Erganz*, No. 120, and *P. M.* 1900, and H. Schindler cited above (note to Chapter IV.).

Mesopotamia and Syria.—No good recent special work.   Palestine and Sinai are of course well known under their geological aspect. Schumacher and Doughty are useful for Trans-Jordan.

Arabia.—For the interior I only know what can be gleaned from Doughty's map and appendix, from Pelly's article (*Proc. R. G. S.*, 1865), and from Huber.   For the Fringes, see the travellers cited above in note to Chapter V.

Egypt.—Article by H. G. Lyons in *Quart. Journ. Geol. Soc.*, 50, on the Western Desert, and by E. L. Floyer (cited above, Chapter VI.), on the Eastern.

CHAPTER VIII

CLIMATES

THE western Nearer East lies at a great distance from any ocean, and therefore exposed to the action of land airs and a high noon-day sun, little tempered by the influence of that element which best preserves an equable temperature. The hither part of the Region, falling in the oblique furrow between the Alpine systems of Europe and of Armenia, is traversed by the concentrated force of currents, originated to north and south. For the Russian steppes communicate directly with the Black Sea, while the African Sahara is not screened from the Syrtis by the high coast ranges of Algeria and Tunis. Greece and the Isles, therefore, which lie right in the track that contending influences from these nurseries of winds must follow, are in a very Cave of Æolus, and strong airs veering from north-east to north-west and south-west to south lash their shores for three-fifths of the year.

The cold current rushing over the easy north slope of the Balkan and through the Rumelian gap, gathers force as it nears the African vacuum. Local relief shelters the Adriatic coasts and, to some extent, western Macedonia, Thessaly, and Bœotia ; but Attica receives a full draught through the depression between its low hills, Pentelicus and Hymettus ; and the Isles, especially Crete, are scourged to such purpose that the higher vegetation in many districts will only grow in triangular patches to southward of sheltering rocks. The counter current blows off the Sahara with terrific energy for almost as many days annually as the steppe wind ; but the high relief of Crete breaks its force for the Ægean, and it is on the slopes of the White Mountains, Kedros, Psiloriti, and Lasithi, and the western coasts and Isles of Greece, that it expends the most of its storms and its rains. The burden of moisture, however, brought by the north winds to the Peninsula, is the greater, and the deposit of this on the highlands of Rumelia makes much rainy and inclement weather to prevail, as all who have lived in Constantinople know. Thereafter the Despoto group and the abrupt lateral offshoots of the vertical mountain Spines, one after another, lighten the wind of its load ; and the rainfall of Macedonia, Thessaly, and Bœotia diminishes southward in regular ratio, till little is left to Attica or the Cyclad isles but a hard cold current of more bracing and stimulating sort for a healthy human frame than is found anywhere else in the area of the Nearer East.

This wind, varying from north-east to north-west, according to the inclination given to it by the local Relief, blows from July to September on almost every day until the late afternoon, when, as in all sub-tropic countries, the overheated land begins to suck a current off the cooler sea,—that familiar *inbat* breeze which, after a short interval of stillness following midday, sets the caiques dancing in every Levantine harbour.

Violent winds from north, alternating with shorter lived airs from the other quarters, bring the snows of late winter, and make Ægean navigation full of perilous uncertainty in early spring ; but the south-west current prevails in the autumn and early winter months and supplies a sufficient moisture to the western coasts of Greece, the Ionian Isles and Albania, whose average rainfall is almost double that of Athens, and not much below the record of chilly Macedonia. These two great counter currents (for due easterly or westerly airs blow for not above thirty days in a normal year and then but lightly) are the formative causes of the Balkan climate. They cause the northern half of the Peninsula to be for the most part similar to Central Europe, a land of full streams, afforested mountains, deep rich plains, long springs and autumns and short summers, while the southern half is, as to its eastern part, a district of dusty aridity and many storms with much sensation of cold in winter, but of clear skies and a six months' period of tempered summer heat; but as to its western part, it is a relaxing region of soft opalescent lights and much and various vegetation.

A Relief so strongly accentuated as that of the Balkan Peninsula must introduce, however, infinite local modifications into the main conditions. We have seen already that it serves to unburden the air of its humidity in short space, as the north winds pass from lateral range to lateral range of the eastern coast. And similarly the main Spine itself acts as a decisive weather-parting. The zephyrs, which discharge rain on the Ionian Isles, bring their moisture no farther than Parnassus, and blow over eastern Greece as parching winds. The paramount influence of the northern current in chilling south-east Europe may be gauged by the wide contrast made by the vegetation and products of parts exposed to it with that of others to leeward of a high mountain barrier. The Marmora coast has the climate of the Crimea; the plains of Gumuljina and Seres, sheltered by the Rila-Despoto chain, remind the traveller of the Syrian coast strip. The Thessalian basin is intolerably hot, when Attica is merely warm. The valleys of Sparta and Messenia, not only fenced from the north by the high mass of central Morea, but exposed to the Sahara airs, which sweep round the west end of Crete, are balmy, when Athens, not a hundred miles distant, is enduring the rigours of mid-winter. The southern coast of Crete is to its northern, as Africa to the shores of the Black Sea.

The variety of the relief is so great that almost every gradation of climate from cold-temperate to sub-tropical is to be found within a very short radius from any centre in all parts of the Peninsula, and on certain of the larger islands such as Crete or Kefalonia. And this easy access to high lying land is of peculiar value in a region, which is fringed with deltaic deposits, and therefore with hot-beds of malaria. Nearly the whole length of the Albanian coast, the Ætolian valleys, Elis, Messenia, the Cretan Messará, the plains of Argos, Eleusis, Copais, and of the Salamvria, Vistritza, and Vardar mouths, and the Thracian shore from Seres to Yénijeh, are the worst of many malarious tracts, only less poisonous than certain others of Anatolia. No mountain, however, in this part of the Nearer East attains the limit of perpetual snow ; but numerous peaks ranging downwards from Liubotrn in the Shar, Musalla in the Rila chain, or the Thessalian Olympus, to the 7000 feet standard which is passed by summit after summit of the main Spine, from Peristeri to St. Elias in Taygetus, and by half-a-dozen crests of Crete, collect deep snows in winter and retain them to July. Mountains in southerly latitudes, which are above a certain height, make bounteous atonement of their snows for the difficulties they occasion to wayfarers and guardians of public security. Mountains below that standard are often little better than a curse, impeding intercourse while incapable of saving their rains for the spring ; and of this latter sort it must be allowed that the famous "chorus of hills," that stand about Athens, supplies notable examples.

The eastern shore and eastern islands of the Ægean are as much protected from the northerly air currents as the western shore is exposed ; and this difference is reflected in the contrasted character and history of the Asiatic and the European Greeks from the time of Cyrus to the present day. Open to westward, but screened from all other quarters by the high ribs of the Anatolian Plateau, the deep bays and long low valleys of western Asia Minor know neither frost nor snow, and wait for the *inbat* through long windless mornings. The heat of a Smyrna summer is hardly less tropical than that of the southern coasts and isles, more especially Rhodes, which are turned towards African airs ; and being both more moist and more still, it is the less easily to be supported.

With soft Lesbos left astern and the Dardanelles opening on the starboard bow, the traveller passes from the sub-tropics to the middle temperate zone, where fruit orchards and deciduous forest timber of Central Europe displace once for all the palm and aloe and tamarisk. The pitched and tiled roofs of the villages, peeping from umbrageous thickets, remind him that here is a land of cold rains and fresh nights. From the Dardanelles to Sinub the steppe winds blow unchecked on to the Asia Minor coast, keeping alive with their chill air and frequent rains a somewhat stunted vegetation. But eastward of Cape Injeh their first force begins to impinge on the north flank of the Greater Caucasus; and under the lee of that distant but enormous screen the deltaic plains of Bafra and Charshembe luxuriate in a more genial clime than prevails at the Sakaria mouth, tobacco becomes the great staple of agriculture, and the superb forests of Laristan have for undergrowth in all their clearings the yellow azalea and the rhododendron. Trebizond recalls a port of Sicily; Brusa, in a lower latitude, is a Balkan town.

The whole north coast of Asia Minor enjoys a copious rainfall. The west is more dependent on local showers, abundant enough in the later autumn; but the most of the south coast is robbed by the Tauric wall of its due share of moisture. Cyprus suffers especially. The few rain clouds that can escape from the Taurus are lightened by the abrupt northern chain of the island. The thin burdens of the south-west wind, discharged by Troodos and the high peaks to east, have but passing showers to spare for the deep Mesaoría, which is the agricultural district in chief. Add the efficacy of the northern screen in raising the summer temperature of Nicosía to a higher average than that of Cairo, and it will be readily understood why Cypriote " rivers " do not flow, and why this rich island has had to complain of fiery droughts more often than any other Levantine land, and to wage ceaseless war with the child, and in turn parent, of naked slopes, the locust.

The Central Plateau, however, can allege lack neither of rain nor chill airs. Its general high elevation and the little protection, afforded by its comparatively low northern rim, condemn the bulk of it to a long and rigorous winter, the winter indeed of the Russian steppes, with which in climate, flora, and fauna the Anatolian table-land is largely one. Snow lies continuously in its valleys for from two to four months, according to altitude, and even in the early months of summer a traveller had best be well provided against the cold, not only of nights but of occasional days. It has been the writer's experience on the west of the Plateau to ride, with fingers too chill to feel the bridle-rein, through afternoons which followed heavy storms both in June and in August. But for the most part the day heat is great in a summer which follows, and passes into, winter, with the briefest interludes of spring or autumn.

As the general elevation rises, climatic conditions grow, of course, more severe, and at the root of the Peninsula only the hollow plains of the middle Euphrates basin, about Malatia and Kharput, retain any appearance of the south. On the Sivas steppe snow falls in five months and lies for three, and corn ripens later than in England. Erzerum merits its condemnation as the "Siberia of Turkey" by a six months' winter whose mean tempera-ture is − 10° Centigrade ; and its valley, like all the larger plains of the central mountain mass about Bitlis, Mush, Malasgird, Van, and Bayazid, is often blocked with snow from early November to late March. Where the basins are so cold the rigours of the heights may be imagined. In the Merjan highlands of the Dersim the swiftest torrents are frost-bound three months ; and the blizzards, which sweep the higher passes on the section of the great Persian road that lies between Baiburt and Khoi, take an annual toll of many lives.

The distant screen of Caucasus can fend but little of the polar air from highlands almost as greatly elevated as itself ; but the much nearer ridges meeting in Tandurek keep out those warm south-eastern airs which endow high Azerbaijan with its long summer. Therefore, even when the vertical sun of July and August, cloudless except where vapours condense each morning on the Ararat snows, makes the clear mid-day heat in Armenia equal to that of northern Persia, the nights remain very cold. Both the vine and the tobacco plant can indeed be brought to a tardy maturity on the fecund soils of the deeper valleys ere the snows fall ; but, on the whole, high Armenia is a wind-swept land of wiry pastures and stunt sparse growths and scanty crops of coarser cereals thrusting their short straws through a cumber of stones.

Once the crowning ridges of the Armenian upheaval are surmounted and the descent to south, south-east, or east is begun, the mean temperature rises much more rapidly than the mere depression of the relief would warrant. The Hakkiari district of Kurdistan lying south-east of Van, on the lower parallels of the mountain system of the Iranian border, has a mean elevation above that of Van itself, but is far hotter ; and Julamerk, for instance, the centre of the " Nestorian " country, which lies over 5000 feet above the sea, is hardly habitable in midsummer. The plains about the Lake of Urmi, which are about 1000 feet below the level of the coasts of Van, stand to these as the Lombard plains to Sweden. The cause is obvious. Whether west or east of the Iranian border-chain, the polar influence yields predominance to the tropical. The first is shut off by the Armenian crown, by the Caucasus system, and by its continuation, the Elburz ; the second is admitted up those hot air funnels, the valleys of the two great Mesopotamian rivers, or comes from the south-eastern deserts and Indian Ocean by way of long furrows between the oblique ridges of Irak.

Azerbaijan, however, owes to its great mean elevation a four months' winter, and to the dryness of its atmosphere cool nights even in summer. The prevailing south-easterly airs of summer bring up an Indian heat without the Indian rains. But possessing a great number of points about and within its area, which touch or pass the limit of perpetual snow, Azerbaijan has perennial streams. The climate of its deeper depressions, as, for instance, the middle valley of the Aras, is sub-tropical, and except in the great lacustrine basin of Urmi, on the slopes of its volcanoes

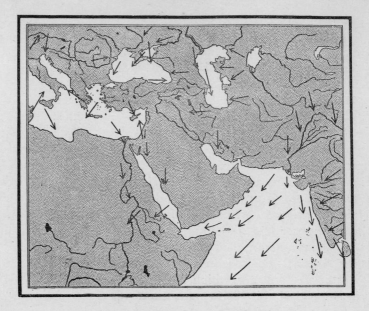

FIG. 24.—The winds in January.

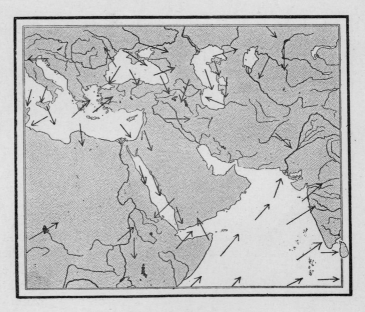

FIG. 24*a*.—The winds in July.

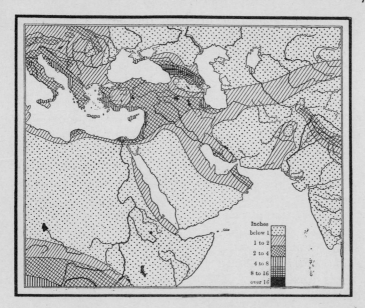

FIG. 25.—The average rainfall in January.

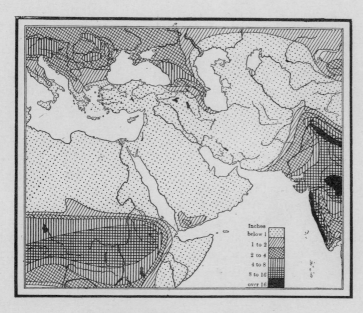

FIG. 25a.—The average rainfall in July.

and border chains, or in the immediate neighbourhood of its streams, Azerbaijan is a burnt up land.

The only region of Persia where vegetation can be said to be dense is the Caspian littoral, and there rather because of abundant waters than abnormal heats; for though the moist atmosphere preserves a far more equable temperature than prevails on the Iranian Plateau, it can boast but a little higher mean. But the prevailing northerly currents, which serve to temper its extreme heats, bring to its shore nearly all the Caspian vapours; and encountering the gigantic unbroken wall of the Elburz, these are at once condensed and sent back to their parent sea through Mazanderan and Gilan, which has a rainfall averaging 56 inches, or more than six times that of Teheran. Hence, while the mountains have densely afforested flanks, their northern roots are set in deep alluvia brought down by torrential floods, which spread hither and thither over the land and support a dense swamp-jungle down to the point at which the Caspian surf, choking all growth with its salts and sands, creates a chain of dead lagoons. When the waters and jungles fail, as the south-eastern corner of the Caspian is rounded, the cold asserts itself at once on the Yomut steppes. The sensation of oppression, recorded by travellers through Mazanderan, is evidently owed to humidity, their uneasiness being increased by these inevitable concomitants of marsh and jungle, malarious exhalations and insect pests, and by the absence of moving airs.

A small share only of the north wind's burden of vapours is deposited on the southern flank of the Elburz, and little indeed passes on to the plateau and deserts of Irak. The northerly currents which blow there come either from the Armenian highlands, or by way of the depression between the Tekke steppes and Khorasán, and, in either case, are dry airs, thanks to which general verdure is not seen from the southern roots of the Elburz up to the foothills of the Luristan water-parting. Between these distant points is spread a drab desolation, relieved by rare patches of oasis disposed along the lines of drainage from the higher peaks. Fortunately, what precipitation of moisture there is on the Iranian Plateau takes place almost wholly in winter, and thus the fall on its numerous heights is stored as snow against the summer. Else were Irak all as utter desert as the Dasht-i-Kavir. The prevailing wind of autumn banks up the sands of the central desert to the north; the wind of spring shifts the dunes to the south; and this is the single dreary change in the irremediable desolation. Even as it is, the largest stream of Irak, the Zendeh, does not survive in August as far as Isfahan; and the rest sink at midsummer below the boulders and sand of their beds ere they are clear of the hills that give them birth. The rainfall of Teheran is about that of Alexandria; the rainfall at Kerman is less than at Cairo. Greatly elevated, devoid of running streams or forests, and with a thin, clear atmosphere, the Iranian Plateau can only have an " excessive" climate; and being situated for the most part below the thirty-fifth parallel of latitude, its heat is long and its cold short. Kerman enjoys only about forty days of anything else than a tropic summer, and over the neighbouring Dasht-i-Lut passes the isothermic line of the world's highest August temperature.

The valleys of the western mountain system are, of course, more fortunate. In the south the fringe of the monsoons keeps alive the thin pastures of Laristan, and the gardens about the inundated tract of Niris, among which those of Shiraz have given to Persian poets their imagery, and to the western world a wholly false idea of Persian scenery. The great elevation of the Bakhtiari and Feili Lur country attracts to it a copious winter snowfall, which keeps its streams flowing deep and strong all the year, and its valleys green till near midsummer. But thereafter the herbage in the latter dries rapidly, and the rich winter-pastures of Ardal in the upper Karun basin will appear not less brown in August than the plains of Irak, when less elevated lands, lying a little to the northward, the Kurdish downs of Serdasht and Mukri, are still verdant. Some particular parching influence must be

looked for near to Bakhtiariland ; and it will be found in
the heat reservoir of the Persian Gulf.

In traversing the Nearer East, we first meet the
untempered influence of the tropics as we descend towards
that sea. Continued far inland by the low and broad
depression which divides the high relief of Syria from the
border ranges of Iran, the Gulf forms the widest and
longest avenue by which the breath of the south can
penetrate Asia. The heat of its own shores is a proverb.
The British in 1879, after fifty years' endeavour, had to
withdraw from the blistered island of Kishm native troops
born and bred in India ; and the gunboats, which Great
Britain keeps in these shallow and tepid waters to check
the Jowasmi pirates and protect the pearl fisheries, must
be of special heat-proof construction to render possible
the continued service of their crews. But hot as Lingah
and Bushire and even Maskat may be, they are somewhat
cooled by the north-west breeze, and must yield the
palm to the districts behind the north-east shore of the
Gulf. For from these all breath of the north is screened
by the Bakhtiari ridges, which, like huge fire-bricks, throw
back on the plains of Dizful and Shuster the southern
sun rays. The mean temperature of the latter town is
among the highest, if it is not actually the highest, in the
world. And were it not for the cooling waters flowing
from Luristan, all Khuzistan, fertile as it is, would be
abandoned to the half naked negrito and Arab tribes that
roam over the deltaic plains of the Hindiah, Jerrahi, and
Karun.

Torrid breaths of the Gulf are sucked far up the
valleys of Tigris and Euphrates, bringing to Mosul the
dreaded *sam* winds and a damp mildness in midwinter,
and to Der-el-Zor a terrific summer heat ; and even the
temperature of Diarbekr, 2000 feet up the slopes of the
Armenian mass, shows a very high annual mean. But
during the winter months the Gulf airs are met, and
largely repulsed, by the northern currents which, having
crossed the vast snow-fields of Armenia, strike downwards

on to the open plains, and in winter bring a rainfall
sufficient to clothe the gravelly steppe with a spring
herbage, and to attract to Mesopotamia and the Hamad
the largest groups of wandering Bedawins that roam the
Arab area. The thinness of this growth, however, and
the rapidity with which surface water filters through the
gravels and sands, keep these groups ever on the move.

These are broadly the climatic conditions of all the
eastern part of the Hamad, as well as of Mesopotamia,
modified, of course, to some extent by the greater or lesser
elevation of the divers tracts. There are no points in this
large area of sufficient altitude to retain snow for long,
though its fall is a common occurrence in the higher
Hauran, and is not unknown in the Jaulan as low as
Kuneitra during the rare prevalence of easterly winds.

The western Hamad, however, begins to feel a new
influence, and its air currents tend to take prevailing
westerly and easterly directions. This influence is that
of the Levant sea. The Syrian littoral presents a sharp
contrast to the arid central steppe ; and were it not for
the height and steepness of the " Fold " range, the benign
influence would make itself felt everywhere as far inland
as it penetrates in the northern trans-Jordanic districts, to
which its rains are admitted by the broad gap between the
Lebanon and the highlands of Judæa. But, unhappily,
from either hand of this strip of corn and vine land, the
wall trends unbroken north and south, and the steppe
runs far up its eastern slopes, rendered less arid in the far
north by the proximity of the Tauric ranges, and interrupted on the south by nothing but the fissure of the
Ghor, which has the atmosphere, as it has the fishes,
birds, insects, and plants of the lake-land of Central
Africa.

The littoral of Syria, from the mouth of the Nahr-el-
Asi to Carmel is the Garden of the Nearer East. Fed
with all those vapours brought by south-west winds off
the Levant sea which, sufficient for half a continent, are
caught and discharged for the benefit of the coast alone,
it nestles under its mountains, as fat and teeming now as

when it supported the luxurious cities of Phœnicia, or boasted in Antioch the capital of the East. Nothing but occasional blasts from the Karamanian Taurus chill the tobacco fields of Latakía and Tripoli and the orange and banana groves of Beirut, Saida, and Jaffa ; and every variety of temperate climate may be enjoyed on the successive slopes of the coast range among differing, but always luxuriant, vegetation.

But from Carmel southwards the conditions suffer gradual change for the worse. Jerusalem has only two-thirds of the rainfall of Beirut, while on the coast the decrease is even greater. For the Palestine littoral now fronts, not to the open Levant, but to a bight ; the lessening altitude and abruptness of the Relief no longer attract and discharge the vapours ; and the torrid influences of both the Libyan desert and the tropic Red Sea funnel begin to make themselves felt. Aridity increases from Carmel to Jaffa and Jaffa to Gaza till it reaches its worst in the African isthmus, where the desert of Tih is swept by an eternal westerly wind, which keeps the Libyan sands ever moving towards the Nefud ; and the end of this land in the Peninsula of Sinai may claim to be the most naked spot on all the nakedness of Arabia.

The sand belt of the northern Nefud, lying abreast of the lower and often interrupted range which joins Midian to the Moab system, is swept by the western current, and, were its upper soil of a different character, would not be desert. Even as it is, there is a certain rainfall which supports a wiry vegetation not only in the depths of its *fulj's,* but here and there on its surface ; and its rare hollows collect sufficient water to be oases of wonderful fertility, as the few travellers who have seen Teima attest. On the Plateau of Hayil, however, the northerly and southerly alternations of the winds which prevail in the Hamad reassert themselves. The polar current brings a hard keen air, long ago emptied of its humidity, to all Nejd, making the higher tracts and Harras very chill camping-grounds for the hardy Bedawins, and so greatly rarefying the air, that even in that low latitude summits of not more than 6000 to 7000 feet, such as exist in Jebel Tobek or Jebel Shammar, condense rare vapours in the form of snow, and retain it for many winter days. The counter influence of the south-west monsoon is less ener-vating in Nejd than are the airs from the Persian Gulf in Mesopotamia ; for the highlands of the south and south-west coasts empty the equatorial current of nearly all its moisture, and it blows soft and dry from the southern Desert. Central Arabia indeed as a whole, though torrid and terribly rainless, is far from "tropical." Even in its lowest depressions, such as the basin of Woshm, or the north-eastern end of Dauasir, the climate is easily sup-portable by those born under temperate skies, and the greater part of all the land is a nurse of hardy frames and active intelligences.

But if the climate of Nejd is uniform, that of the Arabian coasts presents great variety, according to their aspect or the elevation of their border ridges. Hasa, Katif, and Katr, though open to the parching airs of the Gulf and lying very low, have yet no barrier interposed between them and the north-westerly current from Meso-potamia ; but the littoral of Oman, screened by the prolongation of the "Fold" to Ras Musandim, swelters in a truly tropic heat. The Batna plain recalls to its Banians the Bombay littoral, and Maskat, baked in its oven of igneous rock, enjoys the evil distinction of being the most torrid spot on the Gulf shore.

The southern littoral of the Arabian Peninsula suffers from having at its extremities the high peaks of Jebel Akhdar and the Yemen, which draw off the monsoon vapours ; and, being sheltered from the north, it is terrifi-cally hot. But nevertheless it has a rainfall, and a fertile coast strip wherever the blowing sands of the Dahna are screened from the shore by sufficient barriers, and the slopes are not too steep. Dofar, backed by the Gara hills, has abundant waters and miles of a tropic vegetation in hidden hollows, as luxuriant as that of the Hadramut and Doan valleys where the north wind in winter can

H

thinly congeal pools ; and under Jebel Zahúra the coast
is only less fertile. But between these oases the cliffs
fall sheer to the sea, or the coast is a waste of blown sand
where fish is the only food for man or beast.

The west of the Peninsula forms one side of the second
of those long sea avenues by which concentrated equatorial
airs penetrate northwards, and there is little to choose
between the heat of Aden and the long Tehama, and that
of Maskat or Bunder Abbas. The narrowness and steepness of the trench turns all winds into its own direction.
The south-west monsoon rushes up it as a burning south-
easterly air all the summer months, and the north-easterly
currents off the Hamad, bending to north-westerly, keep
pace with the outward-bound steamers in late autumn
and winter, causing that stifling equilibrium which Red Sea
passengers know only too well. Flanked by over-heated
sands, both coasts of the Red Sea are among the hottest
places on earth, and as to their northern parts rank also
among the most rainless. No film of mist obscures the
naked porphyries of Sinai or the granitic Alps of Midian,
to which the north winds bring a measure of coolness and
the south winds a deadly heat, but neither one nor the
other more than a rare *seyl* of rain.

But the south-eastern coast is in very different case.
For it has the climate as well as the flora of opposite
Somali land, to which probably it was once joined by
an isthmus, that is now the shoal, dividing the abyss of the
Red Sea at Perim from the ocean depths beyond. Heavy
rain clouds ride up the Arabian coast on the current of
the summer monsoon, and are precipitated by the high
peaks of Yemen and Asir, till their last burdens melt
in the south of the Hejaz. The Tehama is rather the
worse than the better for an influence which converts
its dry heat to the steaming reek of Mokha and Hodeida.
But the highlands blossom exceedingly, and the terraced
coffee-gardens and the grassy plains and corn-lands and
orchards and gum-bearing groves of Yemen are a fragment
of the Abyssinian paradise, encircled by the sands and
crags of an alien Bedawin world.

The Nile valley is a funnel set contrary to the two sea avenues from the south. Its mouth opens nearly where the Red Sea funnel ends, and admits northerly climatic influences to the south. Leading far inland between vast areas of heated sands, the valley sucks an almost continuous draught of polar air towards the vacua of the African deserts ; and therefore the north wind blows up its stream all the summer long and for a great part of the winter, and indeed in the whole year stands to southerly airs in the ratio of six to one. The only serious interruption occurs in the spring, or rather early summer (for spring there hardly is in Egypt), when, equilibrium having been gradually established by the winter chill on the sands, there ensues an intermittent reaction against the normal current in the form of south-westerly sand-laden and highly electric airs, which Europeans know as the Khamsin—the winds of fifty days.

With such prevalence of keen northerly currents, and such vast reservoirs of saline dryness on either hand of it, the valley of Upper Egypt cannot but have a clear bright sky and an invigorating air. The small burden of vapours with which the north wind is charged, when it reaches the African coast, is precipitated before the current has ascended a hundred miles above the Delta ; and as the rarer southerly airs have to cross enormous arid tracts ere they attain even the second cataract of the Nile, they rarely have anything to discharge in Nubia or Upper Egypt. The extreme northern limit of the monsoon rains does not pass Berber ; and a heavy fall of even an hour's duration will not occur at Aswan once in three years. The rare storms, however, which are re-membered from generation to generation by the *fellahin*, set a mark on the land which almost justifies the rank of prodigy, to which the native elevates them ; for it is they that in an hour cut and carve the disintegrated pulverised surface of the land as no week of rain could do in our northern clime, making that familiar desert landscape of wide waterless channels, winding among

craggy waterless gorges, and fed by innumerable waterless runnels.

On the fringe of the tropics the sun shines powerfully
through the thin dry air, and hot windy days succeeding
to chill and quiet nights are the rule in Upper Egypt. A
climate this too defective in seasonal variety and of too
wide a daily range to impart as much energy as it does
temporary exhilaration to the human frame—a climate,
in fact, which combines with those obscure electric influences, that seem to reside in and in part to govern the
movement of desert sands, to keep nerves at a tension
which results in an early failure of vital force. Longevity
is rare in Egypt, and infant mortality is extraordinarily
high, and that not owing to zymotic disease ; and it has
been seriously questioned whether the ultimate effect on
weak constitutions of a sojourn in the Nile valley is
really anything but disastrous.

In the latitude of the Fayum light sprinklings of rain
pock-mark the desert every winter, and at Cairo the annual
fall can be measured by inches, which will be more than
doubled at Alexandria. But the heaviest year's rain is
hardly a third of the norm in London ; and the strong
sense of contrast which the Delta climate produces in a
traveller from Upper Egypt is due not so much to his
experience of rains (which still occur so seldom as hardly
to force themselves on attention) as to the thin cloud
masses which veil the sky through much of the winter,
and to the lower temperature induced by a higher latitude,
the neighbourhood of the sea, the incidence of untempered
northerly airs, and the remoteness of hot deserts. However produced, the change of air is patent, and causes the
Delta peasant to be a very different being from the *fellah*
of the Upper River, and the Alexandrian to regard himself as a European, who goes to "Egypt" when he takes
train to Cairo.

Of the western Oases it need only be said in conclu-
sion that, for divers reasons, they experience a hotter and
less healthy climate than the Nile valley. The concentrated and long continued northerly current of Egypt

gives place there more often to heated southerly and
south-westerly airs. The lusciousness of the Siwah dates
itself proclaims that the region, which bears them, is a
feverish swamp basking under sub-tropic sun ; for of
such sort are the most famous palm-gardens of the
East, the Muntefik country on the Shatt-el-Arab, for
example, and much of the Hasa Oasis. And, in fact, the
famous Oasis of Ammon is a foul soil, breeding disease,
and itself the main cause of the demoralisation which
reigns among its fanatic folk. Khargeh is little better ;
and take them for all in all, the Oases, like the Sudan, are
districts which Egypt would most willingly resign, were
not their possession by others a menace to her peace.

Of the climate of the Levant lands I have had some personal experience, extending over several years. For Greece proper, Clon Stephanos
(cited above), and Murray's Guide (Introduction), are especially useful.
Wilson's *Guide to Asia Minor* (Murray), Introduction, § 3, may be
referred to. It embodies not only the writer's experience, but has been
revised in the light of the longer experience of others. H. Schindler
(*E. Persian Irak*) has a useful section (25) on Meteorology, based on
long residence, and to some extent on observations taken at telegraph
stations controlled by the Indian Government (see his remarks). Similar
observations are taken at Baghdad. Maximum, minimum, and mean
temperatures are given for all provinces and even small sub-provinces of
the Ottoman Empire in Cuinet, but on what they are based I am ignorant.
Unfortunately, we seldom hear about the more important matters — wind
and cloud direction and humidity. In Palestine alone adequate observations are taken at several stations, Jerusalem, Jaffa, Beirut, Tiberias.
See the *Pal. Expl. Fund Quarterly Statements*, and a *résumé* of them
by Zumoffen in *B. S. G.* 1899.

For the Steppe and Desert regions we have only the travellers.
Best for Arabia are Huber's notes. Firck has a good section on
Egyptian climate (p. 78), but relies only on Lower Egypt observations.
In the Upper Valley winter observations have now been taken for some
years by the medical residents at Luxor and Aswan, but these have not
been published officially.

CHAPTER IX

HUMAN life is affected not so much by the direct influence
of these physical conditions, as indirectly by the superficial result of their action and reaction on each other, *i.e.*
by the Scenery.

The apex of our Region appears as a bare alluvial plain
laid down by its dividing stream, the White Drin, and
bounded by grassy slopes. After the contraction of the river
valley below the confluence of the Black Drin, a second
plain, this time deltaic, spreads its rank growths and deep
clays to the Skutari lake and the sea. To south, the nakedness of the rolling secondary ranges is modified by moist
influences of the Adriatic so soon as Shar no longer interposes a barrier ; and from any high point in the Mirdit
hills the eye travels over a prospect of dwarf oak woods,
interrupted by grassy glades. But the coastal strip is
treeless, rank, and marshy, and southward spreads back
inland, dividing the outflows of the large rivers, which
characterise Central Albania, till interrupted at last by the
Acroceraunian ridge. All travellers have remarked the
desolate aspect of the flats and undulations which they
must pass first in going up from Durazzo or Avlona
towards Monastir ; and the clays of the lower mountain
valleys are not relieved by any abundant growths except
those due to human culture. Even on the buttresses,
which the main Spine pushes westward (such as lofty
Tomar), there is not true forest ; the steepness of the
westward decline, the permeability of the calcareous
formations, and the heavy rainfall have combined to
denude ; and seen near at hand, the rounded heights
are as destitute of beauty of vegetation as of grandeur.

The upland basins of Dibra and Goritza, which open under the flank of the Spine on the higher waters of the Black Drin and Devol, alone smile.

Epirus is the more desirable in that the tangled formation of her mountains has blocked the valleys and made of them pans to hold lacustrine alluvia. Here in place of the scenery of North and Central Albania—one strait and bare river valley succeeding another— broad upland plains rich in plough-land and tufted with tree-clumps lie between recurring ridges more rocky than those to northward; and the coast, though not without lagoons above Butrinto and east of Prévesa, is for the most part abrupt and wholesome. Corfu, wooded to its low crest, green on the lower slopes, but hardly ever marsh, is an epitome of all the excellences of Epirus. On the other hand, however, let it be confessed that the Spine

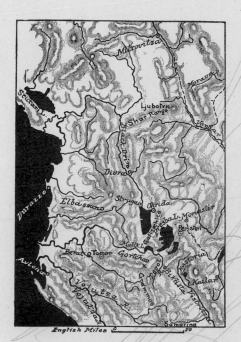

Fig. 26.—Albania.

presents to that province its most naked slopes, rarely bearing more than a low scrub. The rounded summits of Pindus rise desolately into the cloudy air, and the valleys interposed between the steep folds have none but the narrowest ribbon of alluvial floor.

In west-central Greece, south of the Arta Gulf, the lake margins of western Ætolia bowered in orchards, laid out in tobacco fields and terraced high up the slopes,

alone recall the basin of Janina.   For the rest the land
is steeply inclined, thinly covered and waterless, over-
drained by deep trenches in the limestones.   In the worst
districts, as that of Kravéri, there is no tilth because no
soil to till—nothing but
the ribs of the structure
showing everywhere on
the hillsides with loose
lying stone between ;
and the spurs fall sheer
to the sea, except where
such a small malarious
delta has come into
being, as at the mouth
of the Aspro.   Amenity
seems to have fled to
the Ionian isles, Kefa-
lonia and Zante, of
which the first has a
wealth of gentle slopes
about the base of its
peak such as the vine
and olive love, and the
other, low and soft, re-
ceives the prime of the
south-westerly rains into
a deeper bosom than is
found elsewhere on the
hither side of Greece.

FIG. 27.—The Ionian Islands.

The scenery of the
Morea and indeed of all
Greece varies according
as the several districts
open to west or east.
The structure of the
Peninsula admits of but few plains, but those that the
Adriatic influence can reach are moderately well clad.   Of
the number of these is that accumulated detritus of the
Arcadian hills which constitutes the Achæan shore of the

Gulf of Corinth, rescued from being a mere expanse of
stones by its aptness to the currant vine.   Such too are
the rolling plain of north Elis with its sparse oaks, and the
fat Messenian level, unique scene of extensive fruit culture
in Greece.   The central lacustrine pan is deep and bare,

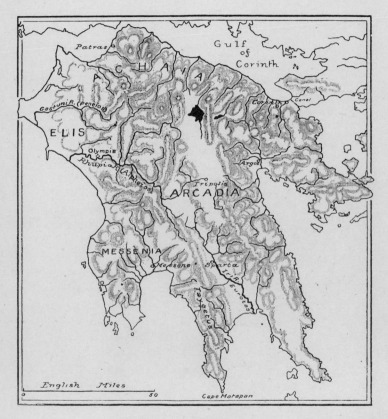

FIG. 28.—The Morea.

but the vale of Sparta is kept sufficiently green by the
snow storage of Taygetus.   The plain of Argos is stone
and dust where it is not marsh, and Attica is a meagre
province redeemed from utter barrenness by the presence
of a capital city.   The hills of the Morea, never far distant,

have their rare oases, most verdant on the gulfward slope of the north Arcadian group ; but even their westward faces, thanks to the prevailing steepness of incline and the limestone formation, present to the new-comer from Europe that view of stony scrub, rarely interrupted by short grass and still more rarely by stunted conifers, which he will see again on every west Ægean isle and west Ægean coast. The natural beauties of Greece are those of distance, beauties of outline on a large scale, beauties of white snows and grey rocks in juxtaposition to an ever present sea of deepest blue, beauties of opalescent lights cast by oblique rays shining through suspended dust raised by the daily winds.

Of the smaller isles adjacent to the Morea there is little more to be said than this —that except Cerigo, which has several little

FIG. 29.—The Environment of Attica.

plains, they are barren rocks, relieved only on the course of their torrents by green ribbons, which expand near the sea into tiny deltaic tracts. Trees of any size, growing without man's aid, are almost unknown ; the soil and its product are of the sparest ; and what wealth the isles have lies in their bones,—marbles, iron-ores, emery (Fig. 30).

Crete is large enough to be a little world in itself, compounded of mountain and plain, highland and lowland slopes. With its high relief arresting the burden of the sea breezes from south and west, and preserving snow far into the spring, it is a land that flows, at such times as man will suffer it to flow, with wine and oil. Little room as there is for coastal plains on a ribbon of land, attaining to such height, there is yet much easy gradient in the island in tracts both interposed, like the broad Messará, between the three main *massifs*, and also (since the headwaters of the streams almost all flow from basins that they have floored with lacustrine alluvia), shut within the mountains themselves. Man has done much to destroy the gifts of the south wind, but he cannot harm the carpet of flowery vegetation which comes up on the land, as the snows

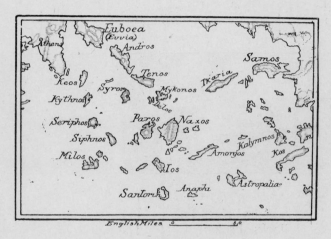

FIG. 30.—The Ægean Islands.

melt, and survives the year through in the higher valleys. A serrated and shaggy wall, rising from a wind-tormented, inhospitable sea, and interrupted by three main depressions, of which two are low ; little locked pans and long verdant valleys, hidden inland behind spurs ; spontaneous vegetation wherever the north wind is shut away—such is the impression left by Crete (Fig. 31).

On much smaller scale but not otherwise wholly dissimilar is the long isle of Eubœa, which succeeds to Andros, northernmost of the Cyclads and by a little the least rugged. There again fair undulating tracts, fed by rains,

forestalled ere they attain the mainland, lie behind the
abrupt coastal hills and invite culture of vines and fruit
trees.   In which culture the opposite mainland is in a fair
way to become a triumphant rival ; for the hollow basin
of northern Bœotia, once a mere, is now a chequer of
rich alluvial plots, through which the melted snows of
Parnassus, Oxia, and Oeta are filtered artificially, and
drained away by subterranean ducts to the sea.

Thereafter the buttresses of the central mountain system
leave room for only the small deltaic plains of Atalanta and
Lamía, till, Othrys passed, the undulating Thessalian basin
opens wide within a ring fence of snow-streaked hills.
Too wide indeed for its population ; and neither are its

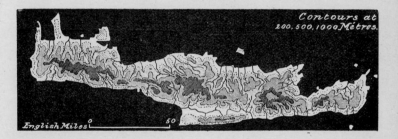

FIG. 31.—Crete.

higher hillocks broken by the plough nor its bottom
marshes drained ; but cultivation follows the easiest lines,
making brown and green the environment of half a score
little towns, whose dull aspect is relieved by the slender
perpendiculars of minarets, and that also of many villages,
but leaving much to bear only a dusty wild herbage.   But
though the plain is singularly unrelieved by trees, the
less accessible of the surrounding slopes, under the
influence of the northerly winter rains, are comparatively
well wooded, the eastward slope of Pindus, especially,
being better clad than that which is exposed to the
Adriatic airs.

Where beyond the cloud-arresting swell of Olympus
the moist influence of the north wind is more keenly felt,

all the Macedonian slope of the Spine and the eastward
tending lateral ridges are shaggy with much and varied
wild growth ; the plains are softer and the streams more
full.   Moreover, since the latter, owing to the conformation
of the relief, have mostly been dammed back at various
points, lakes or level lacustrine plains on the upper courses,
straight and steeply inclined valleys succeeding them, and
finally marshy deltaic flats, are the rule for the river valleys,
exemplified equally by those of the Vistritza, the Kara Su,
and the main Vardar.   And in a land where for various

FIG. 32.—Bœotia.

reasons artificial drainage on a large scale is not to be
looked for, it will follow that the upland plains are far more
productive than the coastal—that of Monastir than that of
Salonica.

All the high and broken region to east of the Vardar
is still what it was in antiquity, grass on the summits,
abundant forests below, small basins opening one above
the other on the course of the two main streams, the
Struma and Mesta—a region of shepherding and very
primitive village life, making marked contrast to the
deltaic strip under the southern butts of the vertical

ribs, which slowly advances towards Thasos.   For this
with its full southern aspect, abundant waters, and spoil
of the lofty hills behind, encourages a much higher
culture and, except where needing drainage, is one
long garden, displaying far up the last slopes of the
background the tobacco plant, lover of hillsides which
overlook marsh and sea.   The Rumelian plains forcibly
recall Thessaly.   The same ring fence of hills ; the same
fat soils but intermittent culture ; the same monotony of
expanse relieved not by trees but by lines of scrubby
hillocks ; the same marsh in the bottoms ; the same slack
rivers winding along clayey beds far too ample for their
summer floods.   And again as in Thessaly the smiling
southern coast offers facility of access, though few good
harbours, and space for many shore settlements, while
the eastern is abrupt, shaggy, and inhospitable, and
compels trade to flow out to south and south-east, where
Constantinople and its suburbs cover sixteen miles of the
hillocks which bound the great plain.   But the fence to
east and south is far less formidable than that compounded
of Ossa, Pelion, and Othrys, while the northern wall is
higher along its whole length, and being duplicated, shelters
in its interval a series of luxuriant arable vales.

Seen from the north-west the mountains of Asia Minor
stand back behind a broad tract of gentle undulations ; but
east of the Sakaria estuary or south of the Dardanelles the
ribs of the central mass, whether their flanks or butts be
presented, arrest attention at once, rising well clad with
forest out of a zone of cultivation.   The Black Sea coast
shows only rare and small triangles of lowland, backed
by tier on tier of long undulating crests touched with
passing snows, till the silver *sierra* of the Pontic Alps
rises in the eastern sky.   But if there is little snow, there
is much growth both of evergreens and deciduous forest
trees coming down to the sea, wherever populous centres
have not cleared the ground for cultivation ; and more
than anywhere else in all our region the aspect is of a
south European shore where nature neither oppresses

man with too rank a luxuriance, as on the south Caspian coast, nor lets him starve among the scanty scrub of the Ægean rocks.

Approached by way of the western isles this Anatolian Peninsula, as we have already explained, shows deeper insets of plain and in all respects a softer face. About the quiet sea of the long bays, closed by island break-waters, and sheltered landward by the continental mass, continuous cultivation climbs steeply up every main valley and tributary gulley. Sparse but persistent forest-growth clothes the hills to their summits, interrupted only by frequent clearings, green or brown, about high climbing villages. But the crests are sharply defined, and running out into bold capes define each bay-head as a paradise apart, sufficient for its own settlement, but hardly so ready to communicate with the next to north or south, as with the oversea western world, to which all the easy sea lanes tend.

The southern shore, however, is of more savage colour, —bristling flanks of mountains, snow-capped two-thirds of the year and falling in precipitous or most abrupt incline to a heaving sea. The Lycian hills are both too steep and too greatly exposed to torrid influences to bear dense forest, and their sparse conifers and evergreen undergrowth would soon succumb altogether were population to return in force to these coasts. In the two considerable plain strips, the Pamphylian and East Cilician, which attract urban settlements and nomadic graziers, the absence of tree-growths is general, and hot and swampy levels are only relieved by planted gardens or plots of sub-tropic cultures, rice, cotton, tobacco, and maize. But in the high intervals of the ribs, especially the broad valleys behind the Lycian coastal wall, there is both forest and grass and the usual upland cultivation ; and it is the nearness of such retreats to the hot lowlands on the west and south of the Peninsula which tempts the peasants to change domicile according to season, and keeps in Anatolian life, for all its exposure to western influences, so many features of semi-nomadism.

And not only is there contrast with the coastal plains

but also with the central Steppe. For compared to any
of its seaward slopes the crown of the Anatolian plateau
is a nakedness. There are few contrasts more striking
than that presented to a traveller looking first backward
and then forward from the crown of the Zigána pass
on the road from Trebizond to Erzerum. Behind him
lie waving crests of woods and grassy fern-fringed glades,
through which he has climbed, deep pastures and long
planted valleys ascending from the sea. Before is no
prospect but of naked and rounded ridges varied by outcropping rocks or patches of dingy snow. And though
there are luxuriant strips in unseen hollows and occasion-
ally a grassy pine region, like the broad upper valley of
the Yeshil river, and orchards and gardens about all the
larger settlements, his general impression will only be
strengthened the farther he goes inland, till it is confirmed
for ever by the rolling monotony of the Sivas and Axylon
steppes. The gypsum soil of the central plateau, its
permeable limestones, and the impact of polar winds, too
fierce and chill for struggling saplings, combine to make
its conditions little favourable to forest growth ; and goat
and man certainly have not humoured the feeble and
reluctant energy of nature.

Yet in this matter too much blame may easily be
laid on the human agencies of destruction by those
whose lot is cast in lands where even long centuries of
neglect and extravagance can do little to discourage
growth. Disafforesting, as has been pointed out by many,
is at the first as essential a condition of progress as
the draining of marshes. All pioneers wishing to establish settlements must cut away trees ; and none but a
very highly organised social system will introduce rule
and measure into this necessary destruction. Encouraged
beyond a certain point, the agencies, which militate everywhere against vegetable growths, acquire more and more
effectiveness ; rainfall diminishes, and the chill winds and
destroying animals penetrate to the heart of the woods.
And thus it comes about that, where soil is not kind, a
peasantry will suffer far more for small acts of neglect

and waste than for much greater crimes committed on more kindly soils. How easy it is in such a land as Anatolia for even the most enlightened administration to lose trees, and how arduous to restore them, may be learned from the experience of the Cyprus Forest Department on the western ridges of the Troodos range, and the Salaminian dunes.

The central plains, however, are not desert but steppe. Dusty and spotted with coarse growths, crossed by rounded swells of schist, their aspect is dreary enough ; but still they are neither waterless nor unproductive, where there are hands to till. Sluggish streams wind to the swampy lake, often lost for a time in marshes on their way ; and everywhere there is much grazing ground. And if the south-western corner, which is fast filling with re-fugee colonists from

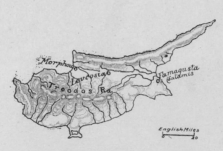

FIG. 33.—Cyprus.

Europe, ever receives irrigation, as has been proposed, from the Beysheher Lake, it will be as rich as any region of Asia Minor.

The isles to west and south-west have a relative, but hardly an absolute, individuality. Lesbos, Chios, Samos and Cos are not naturally different from the near mainland coasts. Nikaria, Patmos, and certain of the smaller rocks differ from the Cyclades only in being more barren. Nisyros is a steaming crater, but of a much less fearful sort than Santorin, and the broad elevated surface of Rhodes repeats on a lesser scale the thickly forested south-western Taurus. Cyprus, however, in virtue of the greater scale of its features, stands apart —a broad island about equally divided between mountain and plain, the last very ill watered, and some part of the first, especially the lower south-eastern hills, very

I

ill clad.   Long slopes to the west and south coasts, well
suited to the vine, olive, and charub, but not of deep
enough soil for other cultures except in the narrow valley
bottoms ; tracts of stony pasture on the spines of the
spurs ; a belt of carefully tended forest, mostly pine on
the main ridge, climbing almost over the rounded summits ; a steeper fall of green buttresses to east and north ;
a huge undulating plain declining eastward from the
mountain roots, deep and rich when watered ; a spiky
wall carried out far into the sea to north-east, which
rises abruptly out of the plain and falls as abruptly northward, stony and scarred, to the Karamanian strait—such
is the view that the eagle sees sailing high over Mount
Troodos (Fig. 33).

As the central mass of Asia Minor rises towards its
Armenian crown, it grows greener but not less naked of
large growths.   For some days' journey in any direction
from Sivas a forest tree is a rarity sought from far and
wide by shepherds at noon ; but grass grows abundantly
in all hollows, and the rolling lower hills retain, after
three months' snow, their tufted heathery growths far
into summer.   But the higher summits keep white caps
so long, that where anything springs on the rock it is a
short herbage ; and presently the elevation of both peaks
and valleys becomes so great in an air so dry, that
between the long frosts of winter and the short flaming
summers, there is little opportunity for any luxuriance of
herbage.   The heart of Armenia is at best a wild broken
land far from any sea, and approached only by painful
paths often snow-bound.   The higher levels are fit for little
but pasturage ; only the lowest, such as the valleys of the
two arms of Euphrates, the littoral of Van, and the
hollows of the buttress chains to north and south of the
crown, owe to the shelter of the highlands, to the unveiled
sun of their latitude and to abundant waters, a vegetation
almost luxuriant.

The prospect from the icy cone of Ararat, as described
by the few who have seen it, is very different to west and

east. Facing the setting sun the climber looks over a sea of snow-streaked billows cut by a long seam, the valley of the Murad, and can imagine in their hidden troughs only small and isolated plains. But turning towards the other face, he will see the spurs fall into more level lands, on the left into the broad Aras valley, and on the right beyond a rough hill tract, into the expanse of Azerbaijan, broken by two intrusive masses not flattened even by the great height from which they are seen, Sahend and Savalan (Fig. 34).

To Persian eyes, little accustomed to running waters but such as are artificially conducted below ground, any land, where vegetation is not confined to oases, passes for an earthly paradise. And indeed by comparison with the most of the Iranian Plateau, the deep loams of Sulduz or the park-like downs of Mukri are fair enough to look upon. But in respect of these and many other "paradises" in literature, let it be said that the promotion of verdant spots to the highest honour by dwellers or travellers in burnt and half desert lands is as much to be discounted, as descriptions of hill scenery, penned by those who have long been used to flats. The garden of Eden, the plain of Sharon, the grove of Colonus, the oasis of Damascus, the vale of Shiraz—how much have not these to thank the nakedness of the lands about them for the grace they have found in the eyes of Babylonian poets, of Isaiah, of Sophocles, of Mohammed, and of Hafiz ?

In sober fact, the alluvial lands west and south of the bitter sheet of Urmi are fat and well-developed with irrigation runnels, the flanks of Sahend and Savalan and all the border hills shelter perennially green valleys, and nowhere is the plateau desert, hardly ever is it even steppe. But no traveller from western Europe, who has fared along the great road from Tabriz to Teheran, has described the general surface of Azerbaijan as either beautiful or obviously abounding in fertility. It is an undulating down, arable for the most part, and never lacking a little water, but clad with but thin and prickly herbage even in spring, and parched and dusty in summer.

To our thinking, indeed, which always associates Eden with a tropical luxuriance, the Caspian littoral would the sooner have suggested Paradise. But a Persian poet must have, even in heaven, something like the keen saline air and the openness of his own plateaux ; and this deep deltaic land of Gilan, with its heavy malarious air and clouds of mosquitos, pleases him as little as the rude and muddy forests of Talish, or the tangled jungles and

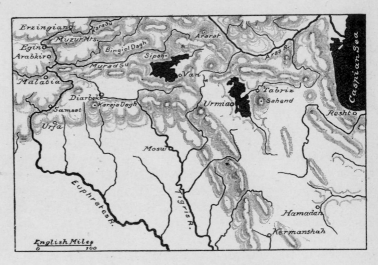

FIG. 34.—Kurdistan and Azerbaijan.

choked lagoons of Mazanderan. Had he been, what no Persian poet is, a mountaineer, he had found a better Eden in the healthy luxuriance of the upper forest belt on the northern slope of Elburz, or in that English landscape of hedge-rows and deep lanes and mossy walls, which cheers the jaded Teheráni in his summer retreat on the southern slopes of the same chain, or in the intra-mural valley of the Lar. As it is, however, the Persian bard must choose between the monotonous plough lands of Azerbaijan, the stony pastures of Nishapur, or the unambitious gardens and vine plots of Shiraz, if he would paint a refuge from the blistered desolation of the plateau of Irak.

For there exists hardly in the world a country of more sterile aspect than central Persia. Great glaring plains of dust and stones and salt efflorescence, divided by bare black hills from which all snow quickly vanishes ; squalid villages and towns cumbered with the unsightly ruins that are the fruit of the Eastern preference for a new dwelling over an old repaired ; no grandeur but of emptiness and silence ; destruction and decay of things inanimate and animate alike ;—these and their like are the impressions that never fail in the records of travellers through Irak, north to south or west to east.

At their best, these plains, equally naked whether gravel, salt or sand, take on a somewhat rusty vegetation along the course of the more perennial streams, as in the oasis of the Zendeh above Isfahan, or where springs emerge at the foot of high mountains near Kerman. Hidden away in the plateau ranges are such little green valleys as smile about Taft, above Yezd, or in the Kuhrud hills ; and on these Europeans dilate in terms which bear unconscious witness to the horror of the rest of the land. Even the much sung vale of Shiraz and the plain of the Bund Emir, which travellers, who have ridden over the plateau, see with something of the rapture òf Sadi, strike the visitor, who has come straight up from the sea in spring, as arid tracts enough, whose sparse vines show hardly more signs of life than bundles of sticks.

At their worst the plains are *kavir*, awful tracts, already described, where salt overlies mud, or sand overlies salt, equally formidable if the surface shift with every wind, or be a frozen mineral sea, or a caked bog of ochrous slime. A knot of melancholy palms, a group of half subterranean huts, a nomad tent or two, a line of hillocks looming mountainous and detached in the shivering heat—this is all the relief in five hundred miles by two hundred. And this most scientific frontier of the Nearer East is carried to the southern sea by the grey gravelly ridge and furrow of western Beluchistan, here varied by lavas, there by shifting sands, there again by tumbled boulders, but everywhere, except for a few palm islands that depend on feeble outflows from the volcanic hills, a howling waste.

The appreciations, to which explorers of the wild mountain buttresses on the west of the plateau have given expression, vary according to the season of their respective visits. In spring and early summer the Kurdish down country, Pusht-i-Kuh and the Bakhtiari valleys, are soft loams and lush meadow-lands, stretching from the margins of full rivers to mid slope of the ridges. But though the rivers never run dry, the latitude is too low for hills, even of 13,000 feet, to keep their snows beyond June, and the sun in that clear atmosphere soon burns up the vegetation of the valleys. The traveller therefore who explores in late summer and autumn sees a very arid surface. The long Bakhtiari mountain crests appear bald and monotonous, when snow-caps no longer supply a scale of relative height ; and the most of the slopes are wofully denuded of trees, a consequence inevitable in a region of great climatic variation wherein roam numerous goat-herding semi-nomads, ignorant of mineral fuel. The least disafforested districts seem to be the northern, Serdasht, and Pusht-i-Kuh, tufted like an English park. The nakedest is Laristan, where the surmounting of each gravelly ridge opens a monotonous prospect of bare undulations divided by the stony beds of scanty saline streams.

Similarly, while the northern valleys of the western parallel ranges from Hakkiari to Sherizór are green with fruit orchards and almost continuous cultivation, the country fringing the Persian Gulf is of a very lean aspect ; and between these districts lies one of mean fertility, well tilled on its upper plains, grey and arid, except in spring-time, on the lower levels, and deep marsh on the lowest. This is that hot region of Khuzistan running down between Hawízeh and Fellahíeh into the amphibious Delta, where old and new outflows of rivers, survivals of ancient canal-beds and newer irrigation basins make a malarious labyrinth of meandering waters and reedy swamps, which, continued into the apex of Mesopotamia, forms a fringe to the south-west Asian steppe.

The full yellow flood of the Shatt-el-Arab, outlined by a continuous right-bank border of date palms, which continues a hundred miles up the Euphrates, is the true boundary. East of this, up to the latitude of Baghdad, lies an alluvial plain, as to two parts lapsed to swamp, and as to one part laid out in rice and maize fields, date gardens, and tobacco plots. But to west and to north all is steppe relieved by the narrow riband of alternate cultivation and jungle which follows for five hundred miles the trough of the sandy Euphrates, but in no way benefited by the fuller and more decisive stream of Tigris. For sheer waste runs up to either brink of the latter's channel from Mosul almost to Baghdad, and except Tekrit there is not for many days' journey a settlement on the banks of more consideration than a group of huts sometimes peopled by half-settled Arabs. The palm gardens that surround and divide the yellow houses of Baghdad have been created with diverted waters ; and on a modest scale old canalisation has been re-used thereabouts on the right bank and at Kut-el-Amára ; but uninvited the Tigris will do nothing for cultivation.

Upper Mesopotamia has been described in spring-time as more like a Wiltshire down than a desert ; but in autumn it is hardly to be distinguished by any name but the most opprobrious. Similarly the Hamad is not unqualified desert. Were it not for outcropping limestone and gypsum on its lower eastward slopes, it would all afford grazing ground in the spring of the year; and it has a line of true, though rather saline, oases succeeding one another below the midway swell from the " Paradise " of Damascus, through Tudmor to Der. But the term steppe applies strictly only to regions of open rolling country with sufficient rainfall to render them arable, were it worth while, or were there inhabitants enough ; and accordingly such non-arable surfaces as those of Mesopotamia and the Hamad are often called a desert for want of some better term, which does not include in the same category rolling downs, on the one hand, clad in spring with short flowering herbage and aromatic tufts, whereon a frugal pastoral people can support themselves if they have room to move from one hollow to another, and on the other hand such wastes forsaken of men, as the Dasht-i-Lut, the northern and southern Arabian sand-belts and the impassable dunes that lie six days' march to west of the Greater Oasis of Libya.

In all this wide expanse north of Jebel Shammar, and south of the low range Has-Sinjar, there is not only no mountain but nothing worthy to be called hill; and nothing relieves the grey monotony on either hand of Euphrates except the shaggy fringes of its left bank tributaries, Khabur and Belik, until from the crown of the western water-parting the eye looks over the lavas of the Harra to Jebel Hauran or Hermon, or across the Rift to the more distant coastal ridges.

The basins of the northern Fringe are preceded by a belt of pasture more persistent than the desert herbage. And the basins themselves, disposed in a shallow crescent from Mardin to Aleppo, are, but for the rocky ridges which divide or back them, hardly less uniform in aspect than the pasture belt. Only round the villages and towns does any foliage appear, but wherever there is neither outcropping rock nor marsh, cultivation supersedes grazing.

The nakedness of the inland ridges and plains of north Syria makes striking contrast to the increasing verdure in the hollows of the seaward slope. First, we find on the crown of the water-parting, the "Paradise" of Damascus, overlooked by somewhat forbidding flanks of Hermon and Anti-Lebanon; and to south broad tilth of the Hauran declining to rich volcanic fields in the Jaulan and park-like slopes of El Belka. Still greener beyond Anti-Lebanon lie the Rift, El Beka or "Cœle-Syria," and all the long valley of the Nahr-el-Asi even to its elbow in the black alluvia of the Antioch plain. But greenest are the lower seaward slopes and the coastal strips sheltered below the walls of Lebanon and grassy Jebel Ansariyeh. Every beauty of Levantine foliage is seen in the district of

Beirut—wild forest graduated from pines and firs to planes and chestnuts on the higher levels, and orchards and mulberry gardens on the lower, dividing rich ploughlands.

But the limestone uplands of Palestine are hardly less naked than Jebel Hauran, and even the coast plains seem not capable of such wealth as those to north.   Indeed, it is not conceivable that to any eyes, but those of wanderers in the deserts of Tih and Seir, Palestine could have seemed a land comparable to its northern neighbour.   That it is susceptible of far more cultivation than has been its lot for many centuries past, the imported Jews are already demonstrating.   But the conditions making for aridity—excessive drainage into the sunken Rift to east, parching breaths from the Red Sea and surrounding deserts, defect of sea vapours—must have been always the same as now ; and Solomon had apparently no more timber of Palestine, wherewithal to cover the first Temple, than the Sionists will find when they come to roof the last.

The awful aridity of Sinai has been already emphasised. Whether it be the dunes of the northern sand belt, or the smooth gravels of the Tih upland and the raised beach of Tor, or where the roses and purples of majestic granites are seamed with porphyry dykes, it is the same desert.   And, hardly interrupted by the desolate mountains of Midian, whose most favoured hollows and coastal strip seem to be as waterless, year in and year out, as the Sinaitic wadis, or by the corrugated lava crags of the "black shining platforms" of the Hisma Harra, sterility resumes sway in the Nefud.   All parts of this formidable sand-belt, however, are not quite alike.   Leaving out of account the rare hollows, deep enough to collect water and maintain large date groves (those of Teima and Jauf are considerable), one finds much of the Nefud which, though waterless, bears the "desert flora" in early spring and serves for the browsing of camels and even horses.   Only the midway belt is continuous deep sand, worked up into shifting dunes ; and it is the labour of camel and man in this belt, added to the impossibility of filling water skins for a day to north or a day to south that constitutes the danger of the passage. The corresponding Red "Dahna" Desert, or Roba-el-Khali, "abode of emptiness," in the south of the Great Peninsula is another Nefud, deeper and without alleviations, to judge by the absence of any local knowledge of it even among natives. Von Wrede, who saw a tongue of it from a hill above the Hadramut valley lying like a sea on the horizon, heard vaguely of "moving sands," deep pits and saline oases of wild palms. It is doubtful if even the Bedawins know what is in the inner heart of that fearful waste ; but on the east it is probably less formidable than they represent, for names located there suggest the existence of wells, and the passage from the Hadramut to Maskat seems to be sometimes effected, as well as the direct journey from Maskat to Riad.

The habitable interval between these deserts is to north a high granitic shelf, where vegetation can only be kept alive at the foot of the ridges ; then a succession of sandy hollows, which, collecting from a large area, have ground water enough to maintain almost continuous tracts of thin grass, date groves and maize ; and to south a calcareous highland region, in whose rocky glens are sheltered ribbons of date palm and maize. The whole is shut in west and east by a desert rim, whose surface is rather gravel and dust than sand ; and desert tongues not only divide the three main belts, but also subdivide these into this oasis and that. On the rolling wastes water lurks under the gravel in hollows known to the Bedawin, and there is an intermittent thin herbage, enough to keep their camels and flocks alive, but not enough, except in late winter and spring, to keep these in milk ; and for their own food supply the human wanderers must depend on the central oases, or the outlying date groves of Teima, Ala, Kheibar, and the Wadi Dauasir, where their sheikhs own or share irrigated plots.

Outside the desert ring the Fringes of the Peninsula vary in fertility according to the relief of the border mountains and their exposure to the south-west monsoon. The Hasa, or "low swamp," is an exceptional and isolated oasis, due to an upburst of hot springs ; and, with unfailing water supply in an atmosphere of the hottest, its luxuriance is tropical. But spotty wastes surround it, and all the rest of the north-westerly shore of the Gulf is a sorry tract of dusty gravels, often fenced from the sea, as in Katif, by sour and slimy flats. Beyond Katr the coast grows bold and rocky. At the issue of the torrent beds little detached alluvial tracts front to the sea ; and it is probable that in the recesses of the unexplored hills are many such palm-lined wadis as are known in Jebel Akhdar behind Maskat.

In sharp contrast both to the plains to northward and the iron crags of the Pirate Coast, the Batna plain of northern Oman, with a fringe of palm groves a hundred and fifty miles long, opens as the mouth of the Gulf is cleared. Hardly more luxuriant but more continuously fertile than the Hasa, it stands to lowland as Yemen to highland Arabia—exotic tracts both, the one a strayed fragment of India, as the other is of Abyssinia. The palm-lined wadi beds of Jebel Akhdar and the thinner herbage of its farther slope continue verdure north-westward to the edge of the great desert ; but south-westward from Maskat there is little to be seen but blistered rock, sand-choked wadi, and stony beach on all the frontage towards the Indian Ocean. The irrigated littoral of Dofar and the hollows among the roots of its high coastal range, the long inland ribbon of the Hadramut, and the very scanty oases of the British Protectorate at the south-western angle, are the only exceptions to the continuous prevalence of desert conditions, against which the torrid coast villages, which live by trading with Aden and the Somali shore, can only oppose brackish wells.

Nor would the more level Red Sea shore be better off were it not for the fact that a higher and broader system of hills extends behind. For not only do those cause moisture to leak into the stony flats of the Tehama, but they maintain a large agricultural population, whose needs have called considerable ports into existence ; and these, by grace of wells, create a series of mean oases on the rusty stony tracts which run back from the coral reefs to the roots of the hills.

As the fertility of the coastal range grows less, so does that of the Tehama, and north of Jidda not above half-a-dozen spots on the shore-levels are worthy the name Oasis.

The upper levels of the Yemen, as we have said above, are the exotic garden of highland Arabia. These broad uplands, whose air is warmed and refined by the influence of the great desert, but cooled at nightfall by the general elevation, whose higher ridges keep out the sands but attract the burden of both monsoons, have aroused the

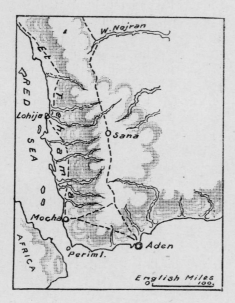

FIG. 35.—Aden and Yemen.

enthusiasm of the few Europeans who have penetrated to them. The broad though treeless tilth and grassy meadows of the plateaux with their rippling streams, the elaborate terracing of the sandy loam to make coffee gardens on the hillsides, the stretches of plantation and orchard about trim villages and clean substantial towns, must strike strangely on the eyes of the Kahtani tribesmen from Nejran and Dauasir. Indeed, the Yemen is a physical anomaly on the Arabian plateau, which has imbued its inhabitants with the anomalous character expressed in all their history (Fig. 35). East of the main range the aspect changes. The Jauf about Mareb was seen by Halévy to be a sandy region, with stunted tamarisk vegetation but no surface water, offering evidence of happier days in the shape of massive ruins and refuse of gold-washings.

The lower hills of El Asir are reported grassy but not

rich in vegetation; and from Mecca northward the Hejaz presents stony slopes, tufted with dusty aromatic scrub, and only at very rare intervals relieved by palm bottoms. A line of these extends northward to Tebuk under the eastern flank of the Harras, growing ever more lean and scanty; and on the heights of Midian, beyond the deep gap of Wadi Hams, the zone of vegetation that must depend on more than a thin dew or rare storm waters, not to be looked for once in a year, is left finally behind.

The land which rises steeply from the opposite coral - cumbered coast of the Red Sea is all desert. The land which declines gradually on the further side of the oases at the bottom of the northeast African plane is desert too, but for the single ribbon of the Nile valley. But even as this tract is not a uniform level expanse neither is it wholly sandy or utterly without vegetation. Two agencies ceaselessly

FIG. 36.—Mecca and Medina.

modify the aspect of a sub-tropic desert, rare rain storms, which, owing to the scorched disintegration of its surface, seam and score it as a rain five times greater in abundance and duration will not seam and score a northern land, and the sand-laden winds, that cut away and pile up in dunes the perished faces of rock, leaving the strangest outlines of cliff and hill. There is much variety of landscape, therefore, in such deserts as are not mere

dried salt swamps, or composed of the softest materials.
The Egyptian wastes are of limestone formation from
the sea to Silsileh near the first cataract, where a bar of
sandstone occurs followed by granitic intrusions ; and
thereafter limestone resumes (Fig. 37). Accordingly,
except between Silsileh and Aswan, the traveller will
expect to find in the desert all varieties of contour, hill
and cliff, valley and gorge, beds of streams and of tributary
rivulets ; yet neither verdure nor water, but a skeleton of

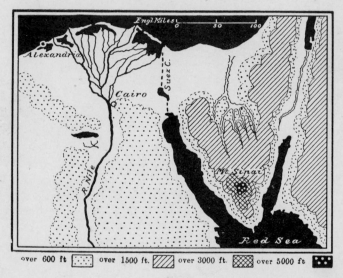

over 600 ft [...] over 1500 ft. ▨ over 3000 ft. ▨ over 5000 ft ▨

FIG. 37.—Sinai and the Nile Delta.

earth, such a landscape as may be imagined in the moon.
Furthermore, as limestone varies much in hardness and
there are often intrusions of conglomerate and other formations, he will observe that the texture of the surface varies
greatly, being in some stretches stony, in others sandy
or dusty, in others again smooth, pebbly, and hard as a
macadamised road. Of which likeness is the most of the
swell between the Nile and the oases, and beyond them
again for six days' journey to the sands. And here and
there in the hollows and wadis will be even such tussocky

vegetation as camels love, drawing its life from a hidden humidity, which becomes more and more apparent as the bottom of the plane approaches.

Owing to its elevation the eastern desert of Egypt is more greatly accidented than the western ; the wadis are larger and more deeply eroded, and rugged spurs run far down the slope. But for all that, the Red Sea mountains can hardly maintain any permanent vegetation against the parching atmospheric conditions prevailing to east and west ; and the scanty Bedawins appear to know but very few water-pools hidden in caves of the lower strata. Aromatic scrub and an occasional thorn is all that can be expected in the wadi bottoms, and the palm clumps are of the rarest and the most miserable (Fig. 38).

FIG. 38.—The Desert between Kosseir and the Nile.

The prospect of the valley of the lower Nile affects one who comes out of this waste to the brink of the trough at a precipitous point, with the strongest emotion that contrast can occasion. Perhaps no living thing has been seen outside the caravan and no green blade for many hours' march, and lo ! sheer below, defined as sharply as with a graver, this verdure without limit to north or south, this panorama of man's handiwork and his myriad settlements. There is not much variety in the long level below the Cataracts. Small clumps of palms mark the villages, and now and again, but rarely, lengthen or widen out into larger plantations. What other trees there are, sycamores, tamarisks, or thorns, stand for the most part singly near the desert edge. The squat mud cabins, dominated often by the white " Italianate " house of a *sheikh*, are raised a little on their own débris. The long line of a curving dyke, carrying beside a canal a cultivation road or a railway, cuts the horizon. The angles of white sails or a smoky funnel indicate the river ; the chimney of a sugar factory is a landmark for miles. The rest is one flat stretch of varying hues, brown, green, red or yellow, according to the season, or is for two months a burnished sheet of inundation, now wider, now narrower, now defined by high cliffs, now melting into an easy gradient of desert, now more to east, anon more to west of the central stream. And the Delta is at first only the same view expanded, with larger and more numerous human settlements, more waterways and general evidence of civilised man's labour in roads, railways, bridges, pumping stations, long alignments of trees.

Serious change in the landscape occurs only far south and far north. Above Silsileh the green belt narrows to a thread. Golden ruin of the sandstone slides on the west almost to the margin of Nile, and low cliffs rise steeply to east with little interval of plain ; and presently, with the intrusion of plutonic rocks, the scenery loses all amenity and the river flows with obstructed current between beetling crags which only recede to admit the naked waste within a few yards of the stream. Far northward again the deep lands grow ever more salt and sodden, till reedy marsh supervenes and passes insensibly into permanent inundation ; and shallow and slimy meres with few intervals stretch all the length of the Delta base, washing their wavelets on the low sand hills and bars of stony beach, which scarcely keep out the discoloured sea.

The western desert of Egypt is as the eastern in general aspect. Where not rock or pebbles, its surface is rather dust than sand. But inasmuch as it has one distinguishing feature of much importance, namely, the presence of isolated pans, abundantly—too abundantly—supplied with water, it can boast far more vegetation. There is no richer or better wooded province of Egypt than the oasis of the Fayum, which can boast the only true lake in the country, and a certain unstudied wildness of landscape, refreshing after the formal canals and basins of the main valley. Wadi Rayan is an unproductive saline swamp. But the western pans at the base of the plane, wherever the too copious yield of their great springs can be drained away, stand thick with date-groves and crops for fodder and food. But the larger part of their sodden alkaline soils, it must be admitted, bear nothing but sour growths ; and while sufficient to support a considerable agricultural population, the Greater and Lesser Oases are so manifestly less blessed than the Nile valley or the Fayum, that no desert poet has ever put them into the long list of Mussulman Edens.

The foregoing chapter is naturally more a record of personal impressions than other chapters, and it will be well to state how far I speak at first hand. I have seen most of the Hellenic peninsula, with typical islands, including Crete. Also something of lower Macedonia, and Eastern Thrace, but not any part of Albania nor west-central Greece, nor upper and eastern Macedonia. Of Asia Minor I have seen all coasts, and have traversed the interior of the peninsula on four zigzag lines, which have shown me the general character of the land up to Euphrates, with the exception of the N.W. corner. I have crossed north Syria, and been more or less in all parts of Egypt. For the rest, I have used books already enumerated, and certain more pictorial works, *e.g.* for **Albania and Macedonia and Islands,** Lear's *Journal,* Bérard's *La Macedoine,* Tozer's *Highlands of Turkey,* and the latter's *Islands of the Ægean.* For **High Armenia,** Bryce's *Transcaucasia and Armenia,* Lord Percy's *Highlands of Asiatic Turkey.* For the **Persian border,** Mrs. Bishop's *Journeys in Persia, &c.* For **Persia,** Browne's *Year Among the Persians,* and Miss Sykes's *Through Persia on a Side Saddle,* both dealing with little-known Kerman. For the **Gulf Coast,** Stiffe's articles in *G. J.* are useful. In **Arabia** all travellers have had to subordinate scientific to superficial observation. Doughty is *facile princeps ;* but the older travellers, *e.g.* Niebuhr and Burckhardt, could paint pictures, and so could Palgrave and Burton, if less convincingly.

SECOND PART

CHAPTER X

DISTRIBUTION OF MAN

THE physical conditions are means to an end which is human life. Our proper study, therefore, from this point is Man; but it will not be within our province to present a finished picture of the actual organisation of his society. Geographical conditions constitute only one, if a powerful, determinant of an ultimate result, to which many other elements, racial, religious, political, even individual, contribute their influences. Certain of these influences may be indebted for their remotest origin to physical conditions; but the attempt to trace them thereto would be an idle speculation. We live too late in time to be able to resolve the problems of human society, in any but the rudest regions of the globe, wholly in terms of geography.

Since the land-route to the rugged western belts of the Balkan Peninsula lies through the more desirable eastern country, it is natural that the inhabitants of the former should represent races of older standing in the land than those that now people the most part of the eastern tracts. The western and south-western highlands are the last natural refuge into which emigrants from that gathering place of myriad peoples, the central continental plains, have pressed the remnant of their predecessors. And as the pressure continued and the land proved inadequate to support a growing population, a certain proportion of it, where natural conditions favoured, was forced on to the sea, and by way of the new element has found a wider expansion, and has even returned to the same eastern lands it had left.

The difficulty of the access to northern Albania, whether from the inner land or from the harbourless and marshy coast, has led to its being packed with the oldest remnants of this population, driven up by the pressure exerted from the east upon the centre of the belt.   Philologists have agreed that the north Albanian language, which the Ghegs speak in its greatest purity, is an offshoot of the Indo-European family of tongues, independent of, and prior to, the development of the Greek and Latin schism. The long skull, osseous physiognomy, and dark type which, south of the Skumbi, come to be mixed with other types, exist pure in the north country.   In all likelihood the Ghegs are the sole undiluted remnant of an aboriginal population which once had a far wider range, but has lost all but the northern hills.   In these it dwells in preference to the marshy and malarious coasts.   But the Rockmen (*Skipetar*) affect, rather than the rocks, the open uplands, wherever these exist in their territory ; and the denser population of North Albania is to be found in the wide basin of the White Drin north of Prisrend, and where the Black Drin valley expands to enclose the plain of Dibra. Next to these rank the rolling oak-studded downs of the Mirdit and Dukájina countries ; but the levels south of the Skutari lake, and about the issue of the Skumbi, are left in the main to sparse settlements of later comers. On the whole, urban settlements play less part in north Albania than anywhere else in the Nearer East.   The villages about the castles of feudal chiefs are the centres of life, not the insignificant towns, for the most part given up to the alien garrisons, and to Jews, Italians, and Greeks.

South of the Skumbi river the prevailing type changes. Here is no longer any sanctuary of a pure race.   The variety of Toskh skull-forms, and the confusion of dark and fair physiognomies, show the traveller that he is in presence of an aboriginal Albanian stock greatly contaminated by oddments of immigrant races, of which a large element is evidently Slavonic, and has been drawn from beyond the eastern ridge.   The settlement in the mountains of one of these groups of former plain dwellers (not in this case Slavs), since it falls within historic memory, may be dwelt upon for a moment as typifying the way in which the south Albanian population has been built up at one time or another.

The mountaineers of Grammos and Pindus, ranging from near Goritza even to the Ágrapha district of Ætolia and the lateral chain of Œta, distinguish themselves in common as Vlachs or Wallachs from the Toskhs, with whom, however, they admit at least a cousinship. Witness the attempt made a few years ago by a Rumanian Wallach to incite all the "Skipetar" to weld themselves into one nationality with his own people. Though racially solid and of similar type and character, the Vlachs of the north are distinguished from the Vlachs of the south by their particular designation, their speech, and to some extent their religious and political sympathies. The Massaret or Ruman Vlachs of Grammos speak a Latin idiom, and have always had tendencies towards pan-Latinism; the "Lame" (Koutzo) Vlachs of the Pindus speak Greek, and are now, at any rate, all Orthodox and Hellenist. The truth is, that the two sections are of one stock, but have had different histories. The one appeared in the hills some time before the eleventh century; the other was still spread over the Thessalian plain, part of which was known as Anovlachia, as late, at any rate, as the middle of the twelfth century, when Benjamin of Tudela found even Lamia a Vlach town. There can be no doubt that both sections of the mountain Vlachs represent whilom dwellers of the plain, the one set pressed up from Macedonia, where a remnant still survives west of Berœa, the other at a later period from Thessaly, by the influx of Slav and Turk.

The easier communication with the east by the *cols* of Grammos and Zygos has evidently been taken advantage of by such immigrants in great force; and of these the majority, attracted by the long low valleys of the centre, and the upland basins of the south, of the Albanian Belt, have resumed their habits of plainsmen. The denser population south of the Skumbi is no longer to be found on the hills. The seaward openings of the river gorges are studded with the villages of the mixed population, and the littoral plains, wherever they are not swamp (as about Avlona), are no longer avoided. Town life begins on a considerable scale with Berat and is thoroughly developed southward of Argyrókastro, as may be expected among a population which, in most respects, is more Greek than Albanian. Where the mountainous tracts are still held by a considerable population, as in the range of Khímara (Acroceraunos), there appears to be a surviving remnant of aborigines who, rather than be blended with the immigrant element of the plains, have sought a defensible asylum.

The various elements in the population of the south of the Hellenic Peninsula and isles are distributed in the main according to the circumstances and periods of their coming to their present habitats; for they have been introduced at many epochs. A surviving strain of old Hellenic blood, itself drawn from various sources and largely contaminated even in antiquity by an imported population of servile origin, has been mixed with the blood of Slav immigrants, whose speech survives in a tenth of the Romaic place-names; with the blood of communities of Epirote Toskhs, who though settled in the south since 1770, still retain their language and a certain racial distinctiveness; with the blood of Turks and Anatolian intruders, who took Greek girls to their harem for near three hundred years; with the blood of Italians, who have left their faith in the Ionian and certain Cyclad Isles; and finally with the blood of the Vlachs, whose wanderings have been described. But while the short skull of the European " Hellene" is a degree farther removed than even that of the Asiatic from the type of his long-skulled predecessors, and every variety of facial angle accosts the eye in Greece, the Hellenic type of civilisation, preserved by the agency of the Orthodox Church, has assimilated by its superiority all others, and given to Slav and Toskh, to Vlach and half-breed, Italian or Turk, community of tradition and hope, language and creed, and one character as a nation.

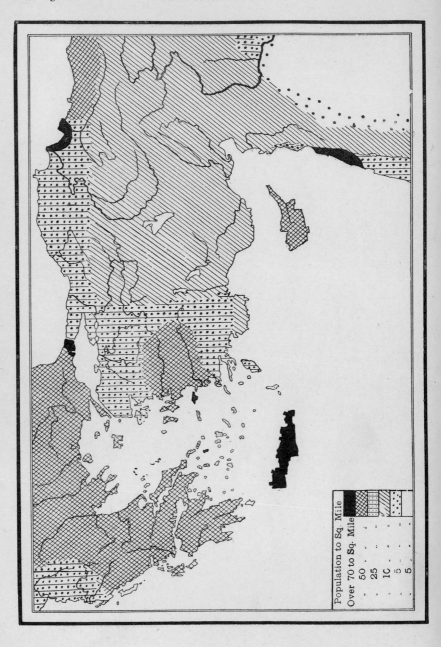

Population to Sq. Mile

Over 70 to Sq. Mile
  „ 50 . „
  „ 25 . „
  „ 1C . „
  „   5 . „

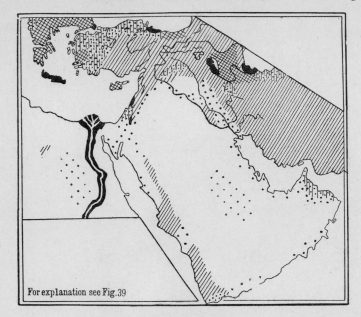

For explanation see Fig.39

FIG. 39a.—Arabia.

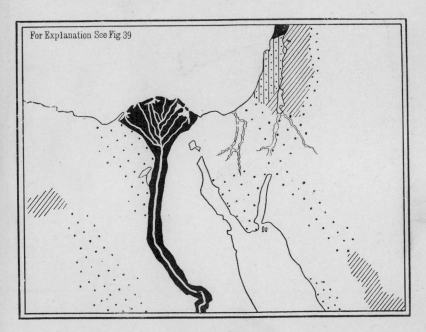

For Explanation See Fig. 39

FIG. 39b.—Egypt.

The coast dwellers, whether on the mainland or in islands, are for the most part the oldest inhabitants, who may claim now to represent the true Hellenic stock, whatever purity that may ever have had. The sea has been their refuge and defence. Into the inland plains have been collected the north country elements, which, for many centuries after the fall of the Western Empire of Rome, came south to possess the desolate land. The hills are held by newer stocks, Vlach and Toskh, except in certain localities where the high ground, rather than the sea, has offered safety to such old communities as the Mainotes, or the blonde Sphakian families of Crete.

All the easier communications being by sea, it might be expected that the density of population would be greatest on the coasts. But certain districts, notably the Morea and some larger islands, among them Crete and Cyprus, show evidence of a shrinking of population away from the shore. There at this day the urban centres of life remain for the most part withdrawn from the neighbourhood of an element, which a hundred years ago suggested not commerce but corsairs to the Greek mind. But that evil association is only part of the explanation : the malaria of Levantine deltas must take its share of blame. On the whole, neither sea nor land trade has been of a kind in Greece to create large towns, and the population, little over fifty to the square mile, is distributed very evenly over the more level parts of the land. Nor are the hills by any means deserted ; and everywhere village life has revived greatly of late years since public security has been better assured.

More densely populated than the rest are the narrow Achaian littoral with the Isle of Zante, the broad Messenian plain, Crete, Syros, and Attica—in the last case thanks to the presence of a capital city. But none of these districts can be compared with the most thickly inhabited parts of the Nearer East, namely the Nile Valley and the Phœnician littoral.

The three basin districts which make up the second vertical Belt of the Peninsula, Bœotia, Thessaly, and

western Macedonia, show a common characteristic of distribution which distinguishes them from the first Belt,—
namely, that the population is almost entirely confined to
the lowest plains. What human life there is in the hills,
is that of a very few and sparse settlements and of a larger
proportion of unsettled wanderers. This fact would imply
at first sight that the aboriginal people of the plains had
never been disturbed and driven into the less desirable
lands. But, on the contrary, it is known that in all three
plain districts the mass of the inhabitants is of comparatively recent introduction. Bœotia, with Eubœa, is
largely in the hands of Toskh Albanians ; Thessaly in those
of Vlachs and Anatolians, introduced from Konia about
the tenth century ; and Macedonia, north of the Vistritza,
in those of a blend of Slav with Bulgar mixed further with
Vlach and Anatolian elements. The truth, therefore, seems
rather to be that the disturbance of the aborigines in the
early centuries of our era was of a most drastic sort, and
that both the basins and surrounding hills must have been
greatly depopulated ere the immigrants appeared. It is
only in the valley of the Vistritza that any large remnant
of a Hellenic population appears to survive.

The re-peopling of the basins has been fairly complete
except in the case of Thessaly ; and that exception must
be due to the character of the principal imported element.
Whereas Toskhs agreed readily enough in Bœotia with
the relics of the older population, and the Slavs established
a *modus vivendi* with the Greek and Latin elements in
Macedonia, the Turko-Anatolians of Thessaly were probably antagonistic always to the earlier folk, as later they
proved to be to the Vlachs.

Again, the northern part of this middle Belt differs
from the western Belt in virtue of the racial contrast
which subsists between the inland and the shore folk, and
holds for nearly all the north and east of the Ægean area.
Whereas neither in Albania nor in Greece proper can such
a distinction be drawn, in Macedonia, Eastern Rumelia,
and Western Anatolia the elements, which predominate
in the upper country, are not the same as those on the

coasts. Western Macedonia, as we have seen, is pre-
eminently Slav. A population, partly Christian, partly
Moslem, but wholly Greek by origin on the Vistritza,
interrupted by a Turkish wedge near Dzuma, makes, with
Moslem Turks near Monastir and Moslem Albanians at
Goritza, the main exception. Eastern Macedonia and
the western hills of Eastern Rumelia are in part the
present home of a settled population which is probably
one of the indigenous survivals of the Peninsula ; for in
its fineness of facial type, its jealous exclusiveness, and
its tendency to diminish, it presents all the leading characteristics of a very old race. This is that folk which
distinguishes itself as Pomaks, and has been variously
conjectured to be of Bulgar and of Greek origin. Its
speech is a Slavonic dialect infused with many Turki
elements ; and it seems that it must represent one of two
nationalities, either a branch of the original Bulgar immigration, or a remnant of earlier " Thracian " hillmen
who were never Hellenised, and accepted Islam when the
stronger Slavonic and Greek elements resisted it.

The plain of Eastern Rumelia, however, is in some
sense an exception to our rule, in so far as it is still held
by Greeks. The circumstances are peculiar. All this
district is directly affected by the great city at its south-
eastern corner, and predominance of this or that race in
Constantinople has generally been followed by predominance of the same race in the plains to the north-west.
Under the Byzantine Empire these tracts were largely
Hellenised, except where settled by Armenian "Paulicians."
On the first introduction, however, of Turkish dominion
into Europe, the Maritza valley was garrisoned with
Turki colonies ; and gradually these were reinforced in
the upper plain both by new importations and by the
conversion of the less thoroughly Hellenised communities,
till the north became predominantly Moslem, as the
enormous preponderance of Turkish place-names there
sufficiently attests. As the Turki colonists tended to die
out for want of recruits, the Greeks regained some ground
in succeeding centuries, but the most of the vacant space

was filled not by them but by a new and more vigorous element from the north, the Bulgar. The pressure from the north and the movement to the south still goes on. The Greek element steadily declines in Bulgarian Eastern Rumelia, that is, the upper plain, until at present it does not represent on an average 20 per cent. of the whole, and that mainly settled in the towns ; while it gradually grows in the lower plain of Adrianople and in the capital itself. The coasts, however, from Olympus to Burgas are Greek, with only such accidental exceptions as are supplied by Jewish Salonica, the Moslem settlements in the plain of Seres, and the Turkish and cosmopolitan elements in Constantinople.

Taken as a whole, the population of Macedonia and Eastern Rumelia is most dense in the higher plains, such as that of Monastir in the former province, and those of Philippopolis and Kasanlik in the latter. Of the coasts, all the western side of the Gulf of Salonica, much of the Chalcidic Trident, and the sea line from the Struma mouth to Dedeagach are too marshy and malarious for continuous settlement : but on the other hand, inland lies a thickly populated Belt, which is resumed on the Marmora shore. Most thinly peopled are the mountainous districts between the Vardar and the Rumelian plains, the southern part of those plains, and the hilly *hinterland* of the Black Sea coast. The passage of great routes of communication has encouraged urban life in the Vardar valley and the Rumelian plain ; but much of the eastern half of the central mountainous Belt has no settlements more permanent than the booths of Yuruk or gipsy shepherds ; while, of the neighbour isles, only Thasos and Lemnos are inhabited by more than a sprinkling of humanity.

In the west Asian Peninsula it is broadly true that population diminishes regularly as one penetrates inland, until from a maximum of some seventy to the square mile in the Menderes Valley it falls to a *minimum* of nine in the highlands of Armenia. But to be more exact, while certain coastal districts are thickly inhabited, others are not better filled than the central basin of the Plateau. Very populous are the larger western isles, especially Samos, and the mainland shores from the mouth of the lesser Menderes to that of the Sakaria, and from the delta of the Kizil Irmak with some interruptions to the eastern limit of the province of Trebizond. But the south-western, and much of the southern, coast line is almost deserted ; and where the Pamphylian and east Cilician littorals make exception to the rule, the inhabitants are comparatively recent settlers.

The distribution on the Plateau is uneven. The hill and valley country of the west is fairly full, and the northern hilly Belt continues the well-inhabited region far to the north-east. But the central basin and the south-eastern down districts are very sparsely settled, the paucity of population on the south coast spreading inland. Pressure of nomadic peoples, added to former fear of the corsairs in the Levant, is probably responsible for this distribution. The vacuum, which resulted from the whole-sale depopulation of the Peninsula in the long struggle between the Byzantine Emperors and successive waves of Islamitic invasion, drew to itself the surplus wandering populations of the Central Asian steppes ; and while the earlier settled folk of Aryan type were pushed up to west and north, the incomers "nomadised" the south-east, establishing a state of unrest which is only slowly simmering down into sporadic settlement at the present day.

The proportionate local distribution of the Plateau population between urban and village settlements is a further and lasting result of these processes of depopulation and repopulation. All the settled elements having been driven to the northward and westward, the modern towns lie almost entirely in those regions, and indeed are of a number and size altogether disproportionate to the villages,—a fact which speaks to a long period of insecurity, during which peaceable folk were disposed to herd within garrisoned walls upon main lines of communication. In the south-eastern plains an effort has been made by the Ottoman administration to induce a more stationary order of things by the introduction of

such refugees from settled agricultural peoples, as, being
Moslems, seek from time to time asylum under the Crescent:
but the south-eastern hills are still hardly inhabited, except
by groups wholly or half nomadic.

As the land rises to its crown in Armenia and Central
Kurdistan, the prevailing insecurity of life, of which the
arduous nature of the Relief and the neighbourhood of
political frontiers are equal first causes, has brought it about
that the plains are more generally deserted of man than
the hills. Here the war of the immigrant and aboriginal
elements has not been, in the first instance, for the possession of the lower lands, but of the higher, which encircle
and command them. Though the Kurds were introduced
two centuries ago to settle the plains of the upper Euphrates
basin, it is not there that they now have their homes, but
in the dividing hills; while the older and numerically
inferior Armenian folk are the dwellers in the lower levels.
Since, however, the great elevation of the ridges makes
them an almost impossible place of abode in the winter
season, the hill tribes, or "Áshirets," descend periodically
on the lower lands, and by partially "nomadising" them,
reduce further their desirability for settled inhabitation.

It is only on the outskirts of the mountain mass,
south-west and east, where open country, spreading away
from the foothills, inspires confidence, that the lower
slopes support a large and settled population. Notably
on the east of the highland region, Azerbaijan, open, fairly
well watered, and of warm but not torrid climate, is so
much better adapted than all neighbouring tracts to produce cereals, that it has fallen inevitably into the hands of
the strong and patient Turki race which, alone among all
the races of the Caspian region, adapts itself to a slow and
steady agricultural life. Where the land will make a more
varied and rapid return, as on the western and southern
strand of the Urmi lake, other races less enduring and more
ambitious than the Turki enter into competition,—the Kurd,
the Armenian, the Semitic "Nestorian" from southern
Mesopotamia, and the Aryan half-breed, who ranges over
Central Persia. But on the dreary disafforested downs,

which stretch away to the roots of the Caspian coastal range, the patient Turki Boer ploughs, undisturbed by nomadism or the intrusion of any migrants. The greatest density of this population (which, as a whole, averages more to the square mile than any other folk dwelling far inland in that part of Asia with which we are concerned) is found in the west and south of the Urmi basin. The low and pestilential trough of the Aras and the broken Kara Dagh country immediately to its south are not better inhabited than the western highlands ; but the rolling Kurdish upland of the south and the hilly Afshar country at the head of the streams, which drain eastward to the central Persian hollow, are scenes of frequent and active village life.

The Caspian littoral is a region which, except in central Gilan, is apparently tending to revert to its original state of nature from failure of population. Only a numerous and active peasantry can cope with its superabundance of water and consequent rankness of vegetation ; and once the physical forces begin to prevail over those of man the relapse is rapid. Of old there was constant recruitment of the early Mazanderani stock, both from invading Turki peoples and from those whom invasions had pushed off the Iranian Plateau. But now, with the cessation of Central Asian movements and the decay of the Plateau population, the gaps made in the human line by the influences of an enervating and malarious climate are no longer filled ; and those influences themselves grow more deadly as their work is less impeded. A very scanty race of shepherds and beach-combers is to be found on the teeming shore of Talish ; while the clearings in Mazanderan, as they grow less in number and size, are frequented more by nomadic elements descended from the lower Elburz, than by their own clear-skinned and bright-eyed Medic farmers. But, as has been said at first, Gilan must be emphatically excepted. The rich delta of the Sefid Rud, under the stimulating influence of foreign enterprise, is at this moment the most progressive and prosperous province of Persia.

A similar failure to cope with different but not less disastrous effects of natural forces is conspicuous on the

Plateau of Iran. There the enemy is no longer moisture and vegetation, but excessive evaporation and salts and sands. Persia has been growing drier in the historic age ; for the Kavirs were once lakes, and the Yezdis have not always had to fight sand drifts for dear life. But evaporation has now prevailed against the central waters, and there is not sufficient precipitation in Iran to keep one-tenth of her plain area under cultivation. Desiccation was followed by steady decline in the numbers and vigour of the inhabitants, and in turn their decay has lessened the hands which might have delayed desiccation.

The inevitable result on distribution has been the collecting of the settled Plateau folk into groups in such oases as are fed by the outflow of mountain snows, and the nomadisation of all the rest of the land that is not sheer sand, swamp, or surface of salt. And since climatic influences in another way, which will presently be explained, dispose the Persians to urban life, it is not surprising that village society is less characteristic of the central Iranian region than of any other in the Nearer East except the Syrian Desert. To find the usual proportion of rural to urban settled communities, the traveller must make for the western foothill Belt, wherein the districts of Hamadan and Silakhor prolong the bucolic life of Mukri and Azerbaijan to Chahar Mahal and the Niris plain. It is as little informing, therefore, in Persia as in Arabia to learn that over the whole of the realm the average of humanity is only about ten to the square mile. On a population-chart immense districts, for example the whole broad central Belt from the Elburz foothills to the Indian Ocean, and indeed all that lies east of a line drawn from Kasvin to Shiraz, with the exception of two chains of isolated oases, ought to be left blank as having no settled, and often no unsettled, inhabitants whatever. And, as in the case of Egypt, the text-books should state what is the proportion of humanity to the acreage, that can fairly be reckoned inhabited at all.

Anything like continuous population begins with the first rise of the western mountains ; and all that western hill system contradicts the ordinary rule by being better inhabited than the plains out of which it rises. Owing to the peculiar conditions obtaining in the lowlands, we do not look in the Persian highlands, as elsewhere in the Nearer East, for a population of distinct racial type. Broadly speaking, the constituent elements of the mountain folk in Persian Kurdistan, Luristan, Bakhtiari-land, and Laristan are the same as those apparent in the plain folk distributed over the area between the Aras and the Beluch country. All alike seem to be mongrel races. Ajemis of north Irak, Tajiks of the east country, even Haikáni Armenians, transplanted from Azerbaijan to Isfahan and Chahar Mahal, are all as much half-bred Aryan and Mongol as the nomad " Íliats " who wander here and there, seeking pasture in Irak and Fars. This last floating population, a scarcely used staple for Persian armies, is to be found wherever there is grazing and drinkable water outside the oases immediately surrounding towns ; and it is most pure and numerous not in the north but the extreme south, from the rolling uplands of Laristan up to the plains of Niris. The effect of the physical conditions on the plains is to assimilate representatives of all these blends ; and only the almost ineradicable instinct of nomadism acts as a serious rival. To take one typical example. Of the four main divisions of the exclusive Bakhtiari one claims to be Afshar Turkman, and another is hardly less certainly of Turkish origin. A third is said to have come into the mountains from the eastern lowlands within this century ; and the fourth is chiefly of Semitic type. But all are equally Bakhtiari.

Such is the inextricable relation which the mountaineers of the Iranian Border hold to Iran. And probably no clearer distinction could have been drawn two thousand years ago between the same mountaineers and the plain folk of the lowlands for a long distance to west of them. In later ages, however, different natural conditions acting on another and a purer race have completely altered the social order on the western hand.

The key to the distribution of population over all the
south-western section of the Nearer East is to be sought
in the influence of its central region on the Semitic stock.
We find here a vast steppe, the physical conditions of
which can hardly be modified by human action, endowed
with a singularly bracing climate, and containing in its
high southern part large tracts of thin oasis. These and
the surrounding steppe have bred for many ages a
vigorous and increasing race, the surplus of which, unable to extend or develop further the oasis area, is
driven at recurrent intervals on to the steppe, and has
gradually overrun the whole of it to its uttermost limits.
Indeed, the greatest northward migration, that of the
Shammar Bedawins, took place within very recent historical times. A thin population, therefore, is distributed
very evenly, but very uncertainly, over the whole of the
vast central steppe from the Tigris to the first slopes of
the hilly system which, running south from the Taurus,
outlines the western coasts even to the Yemen ; and from
the first spring of the Armenian highlands in northern
Mesopotamia to the Arabian Ocean.

The only considerable *nuclei* of settlement formed by
this population are on the lowest reaches of the Mesopotamian rivers, and on the highest ground in the south
of the steppe region. Of the former the Euphrates valley
has the most settlements, there being a series of villages
and small towns scattered sparsely from Der to Hit,
resumed with Hillah and the holy Shiah cities to the
west of the stream, and of late years continued to the
Shatt estuary by new urban centres created among the
Muntefik date-growers. The Tigris bank can show no
considerable nucleus of population between Mosul and
Baghdad, and hardly any worth mention below ; but in
Baghdad itself it can boast the one great city of south-
west Asia.

Among the oases of Central Arabia that of Kasim
alone has a considerable urban and village organisation,
and its largest town, Boreda, though, according to the
highest estimate of any traveller, it possesses a bare 20,000

L

inhabitants, is the "metropolis of oasis Arabia." The rest of the fertile tracts have their one urban settlement such as Hayil, Riad, or Hootah, or their one large village, but little lies outside its walls except clusters of huts and palm gardens. About each oasis, and in a circle round the whole group, range the steppe folk, observing certain limits of tribal territory, and depending on the oases for food-stuffs in the summer and autumn seasons. But except that these nomads appear to be more numerous in the west and south-west of the Plateau than in other quarters, nothing can be said profitably about the distribution of a population, of which certain tribes are known to wander in a twelvemonth five hundred miles from point to point.

Offshoots of this same population have forced their way in differing numbers and to varying distances into all the Fringes of the south-west Asian Steppe and far into north-east Africa, driven partly by pressure from behind, partly by the imperious necessity, under which all desert folk lie, of coming into relation with a fertile area. And bringing with them the acquired habits of steppe life, these nomad tribes have succeeded in sterilising on the inner edges of the Fringes much of what once was fertile, and rendering it undesirable for such of its earlier settled folk as may not have been forcibly driven out by the first invasion. There is accordingly found now on the outer edge of each Fringe, east, north, west, and south alike, a huddling *congeries* of similar refugee elements, and these are mainly of Iranian type whether in Khuzistan or Jebel Sinjar, in Jebel Ansariyeh, Yemen, or the oases of Oman and Hasa, albeit the groups are divided one from another and all from all by wedges of Semitism. The influence of Iranian ideas survives not only among such isolated communities as the Sabæans and Yézidis of Lower and Upper Mesopotamia, but among the Ansariyeh, Maronites, and Metuáli of the Lebanon, the Hauran Druses, and even the Carmathian Arabs on the very skirts of the focus of orthodoxy in Islam.

The density of this Fringe population depends on

fertility ; and where there is ready access from other regions than Iran or the Semitic Steppe, it is not composed wholly of such refugees and their pursuers. On the east there is great fertility and no easy access from elsewhere, and therefore the numerous and thriving population about the middle courses of the great westward flowing streams, from the Jerrahi to the Greater Zab, is not recruited from without the Iranian and Semitic areas. On the northern edge of Mesopotamia and Syria, on the other hand, both nature is less favourable and the momentum of Semitic invasion is spent ; and accordingly a folk, largely drawn from the Armenian area, is sparsely distributed over the lowland basins which extend from Mardin to Aleppo and Marash. But in the more fertile parts of the western Fringe, where the Mediterranean is both a source of climatic conditions, unknown farther east, and of racial elements of which we have now for some time lost sight, both the density and the variety of the population is greatest in all the south-western Asiatic area. The basin of Antioch, the Asi valley, the lower slopes of Lebanon, and especially the wider coastal plains from Latakia to Haifa, excel the best filled districts of the Ægean region, and yield pride of place only to the Nile valley. And even the Giaur Dagh, the Jebel Ansariyeh, and the Palestinian highlands, this side and that of Jordan, have more inhabitants than the average of plain regions in the Nearer East.

Thereafter for more than a thousand miles the Desert has swamped the western Fringe, and there is no settled life either on the Tehama or the coast hills except in very rare oases, of which the chief are about the Holy Cities of Islam and the port towns that these have called into being. No advantage of physical surroundings or position has made Mecca and Jidda the large urban settlements that they are, but the accident of the Moslem pilgrimage. By that they live, and on its decay they will shrink again to the villages they once were. It is not till Yemen is reached that a considerable fixed population is encountered, and then only on the upland plateau, which divides a littoral uninhabited, save where ports must exist for the upper country, and the high range, behind which stretch the great southern sands. Here unusually favourable physical conditions have called into existence an organisation of town and village communities not matched elsewhere in the Arabian Peninsula. But east of Aden, which is an accident in Arabia, and, so far as it has any local relation, is rather an African than an Asian town, the Desert resumes sway, and its scanty people of nomads is only interrupted by the half-settled folk who inhabit a succession of large villages or small towns, none having above 5000 inhabitants, down the middle length of the Wadi Hadramut, and by little settlements of coast traders in torrid ports and cultivators of the thin coastal oasis tracts. The gorges of Jebel Akhdar, behind Maskat, shelter numerous small villages ; but the mass of the Omani population, outside the ports of Maskat and Muttra, is gathered into the hundred settlements of the northern coastal plain of the Batna, and the ultramontane region of Dáhira, which fades west and north into the Great Desert.

The chain of settlements occupying successive coves on the mountainous Pirate Coast, the villages set about the considerable urban centres, Hofhuf and Mubarriz, in the oasis of Hasa, and the port towns of Katif and Koweit, with the populous pearl fishing community of the Bahrein Island, are all that remain to be considered in the East Arabian Fringe. Katr is given up to a scanty population of intractable Bedawins and beach-combers, former robbers of the pearl boats ; and with the exception of the two ports just mentioned, the low and steaming coast is practically tenantless up to the amphibious flats of the Shatt-el-Arab.

The waste, which overflows into Africa by way of the north Sinaitic plateau of Tih, has about it less of the steppe and more of the true desert character than any region to east, except the northern Nefud and the southern Dahna of Arabia. And since there are no Bedawins, where there is never at any time pasture, the south Sinaitic

Peninsula is uninhabited except in its lower wadis, and the tract between the Red Sea and the Nile trough has even fewer nomads. The western Red Sea coast line is deserted except where two or three small ports are kept in existence by artificial encouragement for the sake of cross communication with the Nile, and probably not five hundred families, all told, roam the " Arabian Desert " between the coral shore and a line drawn a day's march from the edge of the Nilotic cultivation.

The western or Libyan Desert, however, though not in itself less arid, is in its southern part so soon relieved by large oases that even its waterless tracts are somewhat better peopled ; and if the Oases be reckoned to its credit, it may be said to support a considerable tribal and half nomadic society. The northern part, however, where the distance between the Nile and the Oasis pans lengthens out to several days' journey, is very empty ; and the numerous population of Siwah, its largest oasis, when reached, is found to be of a more fixed, because more isolated, sort than in the southern pans. Towards the north-east, where the Mediterranean clouds precipitate moisture in spring, there is a more truly nomadic steppe folk, migrating between the Delta fringe and the uplands behind Derna, but it is numerically very weak.

In striking contrast to so thin a sprinkling over tracts so enormous, appears the pullulating life of the lower Nilotic trough. Egypt, with desert areas included, has a population averaging little over 12 to the square mile. If the cultivated land be reckoned alone without deserts the average soars to nearly 600. Above the Cataracts this life clings in a single series of widely spaced villages to the waterway itself, and after expanding about the last fall of the stream into a considerable group of settlements, again contracts to a thin line, keeping in the main to the right bank, till the valley opens to south of the sandstone bar of Silsileh. But from that pass to the sea, hardly a village but has half-a-dozen others in sight, and towns occur at all the points where roads debouch from the Oases or the Red Sea. The distribution of population is about equal on both banks as far down as Akhmim ; but thence to the parting of the streams by far the greater part of the Nile peasantry is located on the west of the valley ; and often the east or "Arabian" bank, even where cultivated, is not inhabited except by half-settled Bedawins. Cairo, however, goes far to restore the Arabian bank to equality with its half million souls, the largest city aggregate in Africa, and largest also in all our Region, the total of the four quarters of Constantinople alone excepted.

The density is maintained over a broad belt of land in the central Delta expanding from the apex to within fifty miles of the sea. And indeed the average has increased of late years in this tract with the extraordinary growth of the urban centres of the cotton-growing industry. The base of the triangle, however, clogged as it is with half reclaimed swamps, supports a very meagre population outside the three port towns of Alexandria, Damietta, and Port Said. The large area of "Lake" Menzaleh is void but for an amphibious fisher-folk, and much of the rest of the coastal tract between the Damietta arm and Rosetta is given up almost entirely to small groups of tenting Bedawins. Nor until a generation ago were the sides of the triangle in much better case over most of their length. Since, as we have seen, they lie lower than the central Delta belt, their lands receive a natural drainage which renders them sour, and in two cases, the Mariut region and the Wadi Tumilát, the natural disadvantage has been aggravated by the fault of man. Shunned by the *fellahin*, these tracts, where is much salt pasture and the possibility of raising weedy cereals, have offered for many years a doubtful asylum to the wandering surplus of Arabia ; and by far the largest part of the Bedawins, who are reckoned as Egyptian, hang upon these flanks of the Delta, sure indicators of bad land. The washing and draining of these tracts, which has been making good progress of late years, has exercised, however, a settling influence on the migrants, and a large proportion, that was nomad a generation ago, is to be reckoned now to the fixed population. Another generation will probably see the flanks of the Deltaic

triangle, and perhaps even its base, cultivated down to the
edge of high desert or sea beach, and a population settled
east, west, and north as dense as fills to-day the districts
of Tantah or Mansúrah.

The statistical tables given in Bickford Smith's *Greece under King
George* (1893), are about the only available material for Hellas. Crete has
just taken its first census. For European Turkey I could obtain almost
no decent *data* at all ; the tables drawn up by rival nationalities in Macedonia are intended to create facts. For the provinces of Asiatic Turkey
we have Cuinet's statistics, and his *data*, being official, are perhaps more
to be depended on in this matter than in some others ; but much of the
official reckoning is done by averaging the inmates of a house or members of a family. Arabian figures are mere approximations, and Persian
little better. On the distribution of the Armenians, see translation in
P. M., 1896, of Selenoy's article in *Sapiski* of Caucasian sect. of Imp.
Russian Geog. Society. For Egypt the general results of the census of
1897 are in White's book, cited above. Upon racial types in Greece Dr.
Clon Stephanos has helped me. He has measured some thousands of
soldiers from all districts, and compiled a valuable racial chart. The
best short notes on all the races up to Persia are Wilson's in Murray's
Guide. The Persian types have been elaborately dissected by F. Hous-
saye in an appendix to Dieulafoy's *Acropole de Suse*, but this must be
checked by both Reclus and Curzon. Doughty is the most informing on
Arab types, but one must take the common measure of all the travellers
both in Arabia and Syria. An instructive article on the Egyptian
fellahin appeared in *Bull. Soc. Khed.* (1900), by Piot Bey.

CHAPTER XI

THE social body in a Debatable Land is hardly to be reduced to any final scheme of groups. As each criterion of community is applied, the units will re-assort themselves in the kaleidoscope. But the idealistic tendency of the people of this Region, coupled with the backward state of their civilisation and with their continued fluidity, gives to Religious Creed a grouping value far exceeding that exercised by political ideas, by racial or national identities, or even by common speech. It may be said broadly that, wherever true community of tradition and hope is now found in the Nearer East, it rests on a basis of community of creed; and that the several groups express their sense of their own unity and distinction from others in terms of religion. Both the nature and the location of religious beliefs, however, are notoriously conditioned by geographical facts. If, therefore, we inquire to what degree the creeds held in the several districts of the Nearer East are so conditioned, we shall have dealt with what for all practical purposes is the part played by geography in determining the grouping of the population.

The value of creed in this matter is, as might be expected, more conspicuous in the centre of the Nearer East, which is the focus of Idealism, than on its western side; for there the influence of Europe, where the political basis of community is paramount, tends to supersede and confuse the religious basis. At the same time, the nationalities of the Balkan Peninsula, actually nascent, owe their unity to creed in the first instance, and where, as in Macedonia, not yet crystallised, they take Church as their touchstone. Albania, so far, at least, as the northern districts are concerned, may be dismissed from this question, as snakes from the description of Ireland. For reasons already indicated in which the broken and isolated nature of the land plays a chief part, creed, like every other influence, is inoperative to group tribes either one with another, or with larger external unities. The Arnaut can be a Catholic without sympathy for any Latin race, a Moslem and hate the Turk, an Orthodox Christian and ignore all national ideals. The most peaceable of the race, the farmers of the Skumbi plain, are so far from being committed to any group that they hold equally with circumcision and baptism, and observe the fast as much in Lent as in Ramadan.

Thus devoid of any inner focus of attraction the clans, which lie in geographical contact with alien unions of any vitality, ought to tend to lose their individuality in these. And indeed if the Serb were not the least effective of Slavs, and the Macedonian Bulgar had had time to realise and assert his national unity, there would be more local absorption of Ghegs and northern Toskhs than there is. The southern Toskhs have succumbed so readily to the influence of the group that has been formed to south of them, that it is no longer easy to draw any northwestern limit to Hellenism. Argyrokastro is the first essentially Greek town; but the southward-bound traveller will have made acquaintance already with the Hellenic unity not only at many points on the coast, but inland as far north as Elbassan.

This Hellenic group, although nowadays held together more by a political idea than by anything else, supplies in reality a striking instance of our main thesis. For it owes its existence to a Church, which proved more persistent than race, and its actual cohesion and boundaries are alike determined by a great geographical fact—the sea. Modern Hellenism, like ancient, rarely penetrates farther than the sea-breeze. All the subsidiary Peninsula depending from the main Balkan land; all the Ægean coasts and isles, including Crete and Cyprus, and excepting only the rich tract between the Struma and Mesta mouths ; most of the

western and southern shores of the Black Sea ; a great
part of the other Anatolian littorals, and many points on
the Syrian and Egyptian coasts—this is the domain of
the Greek. But note his limit. When the sympathies
of Europe established modern Hellenic nationality in
independence, it stood alone in south-eastern Europe
possessing a civilisation of the higher type and free to
promote its expansion ; and for a time its absorptive power
upon contiguous peoples less well endowed promised to
become independent of sea-communication. For it had
assimilated Albanian-speaking Toskhs in Greece, and introduced Greek to the Toskhs in Epirus. Koutzo-Vlachs
of Pindus had become as Hellenic as the Moreotes,
and Christian communities of inland Anatolia and of
part of Macedonia and Rumelia were fast learning their
part in the union. But the same forces which had brought
Hellenism to a new birth acted equally on other peoples
of the Nearer East. The Danubian Slavs drew together,
and met the Greek with an ideal and a Church as vigorous
as his own ; while Europe stood aloof, content to see
fair play, and no longer caring to fight for a sentiment
of classicism, or for the rights of man, or even for the
Cross.

In the equilibrium of opposing forces geographical conditions are deciding the issue. Nature certainly proposed
(however man may dispose of her) that the inhabitants of
the string of Macedonian basins, from the Vardar head to the
Vistritza, should form one group. And here, as in Rumelia,
she has made it so much easier for the northern peoples to
come south, than for the southern peoples to go north,
that, unless there be very strong reasons, not physical, to
the contrary, the folk of the doubtful lands must eventually
group with their northern neighbours, if they be not
strong enough to retain independence.

This geographical necessity has asserted itself deci-
sively since the last Greco-Turkish war. All that Bulgar-
speaking Christian peasantry of central and southern
Macedonia, whose puzzled allegiance was long courted
by four rival claimants, has gone far to make up its mind,

declaring itself to be at least not Greek. Pan-Hellenism has
not succeeded in transcending its natural geographical area
any more than the pan-Latinism, which was once preached
to the Berœa Vlachs. The bulk of the Macedonians show
unmistakably that their religious sympathies are with the
Slav churches to the north. For the battle has been
fought over episcopal sees, and the stages of victory have
been marked by the granting of *berats* to the Bulgarian
Exarch in spite of the Œcumenical Patriarch. The rival
Slav appeal, the Serb, never adequately backed by its own
Propaganda, has been well-nigh strangled by the violence
of the Prisrend and Dibra Ghegs ; and, as things are
now, the Bulgar group is expanding over Macedonia
without fear of any rival, except, perhaps, Austria, waiting patiently in Novi Bazar.

Eastern Rumelia is in much the same case as Macedonia. The long northern slope of the Balkans permits
the Danubian people to pass easily over the crest and
descend on the Maritza plains ; and the Greek is falling
back before them, as a race, based on the sea, always
falls back before a race of about equal strength with a
convenient base on land. As the Bulgar group pushes
southward on the west and the east, the position of the
small independent sub-group of Pomaks, whose existence
has been fostered by the highland nature of eastern Macedonia, will become untenable. It is already shrinking,
and must eventually, together with the scattered colonies
of Asiatic Islam in Macedonia, Thrace, Thessaly, and Crete,
be fused with a Christian group, or take refuge over sea
with that strong Moslem unity which calls itself " Turk."

The distinction and distribution of this great group, of
prime political importance in the Nearer East, appears to
be determined indirectly by geographical conditions ; for
it is confined within a clearly marked area, if its artificial
European colonies be left out of account. The "Turk"
group—if that name be understood as members of the
group themselves understand it, to express a community
not dependent on race—is found all over the Peninsula of

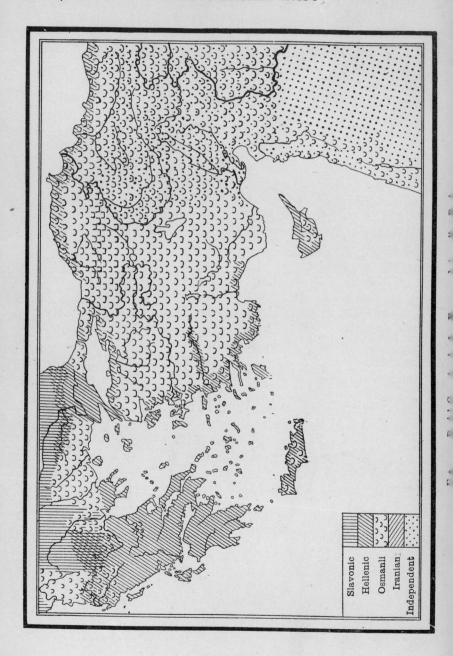

Slavonic
Hellenic
Osmanli
Iranian
Independent

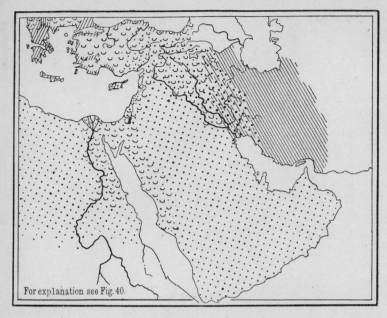

FIG. 40*a*.—Arabia.

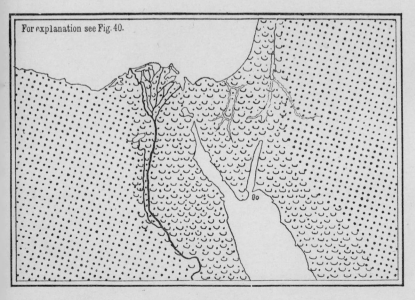

FIG. 40*b*.—Egypt.

Asia Minor, but beyond it does not include an indigenous folk. The name, so used, implies complete accord in tradition and hope with the Osmanli, as distinct from the Iranian, Turks. But seven-tenths of the units in the group have no Turkish blood, and their cohesion is due to the fact that the character of the Islamitic creed, held by the Osmanli conquerors, proved congenial to the great mass of the conquered in this particular region.

The broad distinction of Moslem society into Sunni and Shiah recognises within Islam inconsistent attitudes towards the Supreme God. But really there are among Moslems three attitudes observed towards Him, not two. The maintainers of the first are unintellectually content with an overlord, having no essential relation to themselves, to whose will, as communicated, they make complete surrender in hope of reward here and hereafter. The maintainers of the third attitude postulate an essential relation of Allah to themselves ; and seeking such relation through Incarnations and Immanences, they range over a scale which can descend to the grossest naturalism, or soar beyond refined Sufiism to the most spiritual doctrine of the Son made Flesh. Between the two are holders of the second attitude. Feeling the necessity for some intelligible relation between themselves and a Supreme Being who dwells apart, these vaguely assume spiritual affiliation to an Allah, Father of Man.

It will be noticed at once that Shiism, in its various forms, expresses the third attitude, and designates one great group, the Iranian. But Sunnism must cover under one name two groups, distinct at heart, and brought into a measure of superficial accord by the easy though often only apparent surrender of the more indifferent to the sterner attitude. It is strange irony that Arabia of all Moslem lands should be the one most characterised by such a compromise. Not the Arab but the Turk has had to save western Islam from being dissipated long ago in indifferentism and general relapse to those congenial " heathen " beliefs, which were old before Mohammed appeared in Mecca.

That these three attitudes towards the Supreme Being, which assort broadly all the rest of the folk of the Nearer East into three main groups, should characterise the distinct geographical areas, that, in fact, they do, is due in large part to the physical conditions prevailing in certain tracts, which for various reasons have been radiating centres of influence. We shall have occasion to show in the sequel how the circumstances of the Persian Plateau cause a folk of keen intellect to lead the stimulating life of towns under conditions more favourable to thought than to action. Such will inevitably apply every test of reason to religious creed. On the other hand, the meagre conditions of the Arabian steppe-desert and Oases dissipate the society, and fail to excite or nourish its intellectual powers. The Arab's religious sense, therefore, like everything else about him, is weak, and his attitude towards the supernatural follows the line of least resistance. As the natural patriarchal relation governs all his earthly society, so it inevitably governs his conception of the Divine.

Remains the influence on the Turk of a northern origin among snows. Half Highlander, half child of the monotonous cold plain, he wants imagination and ebullition of sentiment, but abounds in reverence and obedience. For him it is sufficient that an external Lord has communicated his will by a prophet, be he Mohammed or Ali, and he asks for no relation more intimate or more essential. Within these great groups the Turk, the Arab, and the Iranian, many sub-groups, some of them Christian but not for that outside the classification, must, of course, be reckoned with.

I. Finding congenial the natures of the sturdy farmers of the chill and open uplands of Anatolia, the Osmanli Turk has succeeded in completely assimilating the great mass of the indigenous Plateau folk ; and these, now forming one group with him even to the roots of the Armenian Alps, rapidly digest in their turn all incomers, who are of like northern origin, such as the most part of the Yuruks, the Turkmans, and the Caucasian refugees. But a leaven of Iranism, due to earlier and closer contact with the east, keeps apart the majority of Kurds and Armenians, and also the miscellaneous " Kizil-bash," a term once of great honour in Persia, now come to be applied as a reproach by Sunnis to various comparatively newly-come Moslem communities apparently marked by tendencies to Animism, which are scattered over Eastern Asia Minor. Such are the Kurdish tribes of the Haimané, north of the Axylon, and several of those of the Euphrates valley. Such are also certain peoples of undoubted Turki blood, the Afshar of the Anti-Taurus valleys, some of the Yuruks, and small isolated peasant sub-groups, resident mainly in the valley of the Kalkid Irmak, said to have been transported from Azerbaijan during the Persian campaign of the Ottoman Sultans Selim I. and Bayazid II.

Those Armenians of the Plateau, who have resisted absorption into the Turkish group (for many Moslem communities in Eastern Asia Minor are of Armenian origin), owe their independence of the main local group to the fact that the tradition of an original mountain home, not so long ago abandoned, was still potent when the Osmanli influence was at its strongest. Iranism and Christianity are eastern and western developments of one common effort to solve the problem of the relation of Seen to Unseen, which is the problem of all religion ; and that, which absolutely divorces an Armenian from a " Turk," often finds in a Kurd something more compatible.

Infinitely scattered as the Armenian sub-group now is, it is no longer in danger of local absorption. The Turk is far less of a religious force than he once was : the centre of Armenian gravity is now fixed on a Christian soil ; and the profession of most Armenians wherever settled has come to be greatly " westernised." But so long as this sub-group is distributed over too vast an area, where in every administrative province, but the Russian governorate of Erivan, and every great town but three, it is in a conspicuous minority, and so long as its Iranian instinct leads it to seek diverse solutions of the intellectual religious

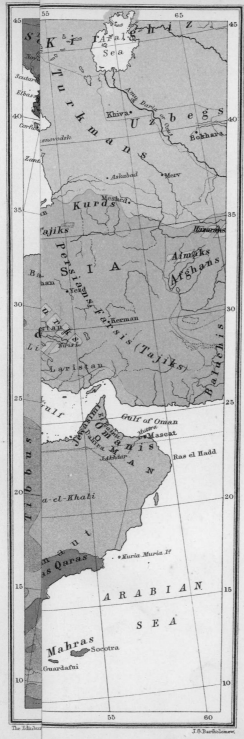

problem, and to cultivate exclusive sectarianism, Gregorian, Catholic, and Protestant, it can itself exercise little or no absorptive power ; and such gradual change as is being effected on Anatolian grouping at the present time by any Christian influence is due rather to the slow spread of the single-minded Greek from the western shores, who is reviving old Orthodox communities of the Plateau that had well-nigh forgotten their faith.

The more partial and imperfect Iranism of the Kurdish sub-group, however, needs to be reinforced by strong separatist influence of physical conditions to escape contamination by Sunnism, dominant to north and west ; and indeed many Kurds, notably those of the south-west, have come of late years to group with the Turk. In their wild stronghold of Merjan Dagh, the " Kizil-bash " Dersimlis show much apprehension of Turkish religious influence, and like the Arabs of Hasa will pay the Sultan's taxes more willingly than allow their children to attend his schools. And now that the isolation even of central Kurdistan has been so largely broken down by the Ottoman administrative subdivision of the Bitlis, Van, and Hakkiari districts, there is little doubt that the Turkish group, if left free to exercise its faculty of assimilation through common military service, will go far, in a generation, to transform the already weakened Iranism of the Kurds into a Sunnism of its own type. How strong such influence may prove, if unrestrained, may be estimated by the difficulty found in certain districts in inducing Armenians, forcibly converted during the late troubles, to return to their pristine creed, when the path of recantation was once more made open and safe.

The Kurds, however, of the inner Iranian Border ranges should be more subject to the influential group that lies to east of them. But so strong is the physical contrast between the western ranges and the eastern plains, that, while the Turki peoples of Azerbaijan fall readily into one group with the Plateau folk of Irak and Fars and the people of the Caspian littoral, the Kurds for a long distance south of Lake Urmi are wholly Sunni in sym-

pathy, and only slightly Iranian in character. From the
Zagros onwards the Ali-Illahi Kurds, the Lurs of Pish-Kuh
and Pusht-i-Kuh, the Bakhtiaris of the upper basins of
the Diz river and the Karun, and the Mamasenni Lurs
to south of them, are distinctly of Shiah colour, though
little better than Animists ; but they are so differentiated
in tradition and hope that they must be reckoned so many
sub-groups of the greater group. Thanks to the broken
and arduous nature of their mountains, their organisation
is much like that of the north Albanians. The Bakhtiaris,
whose valleys, shut off from the rest of the world, are in
easy communication with one another, form the most solid
community among the hillmen, but even in their case there
is little in common between those to north and those to
south of the Kuh-i-Rang. While, except in Pusht-i-Kuh,
the Lurs are merely clansmen, and the Zagros Kurds have
scarcely more unity.

II. A land, so sharply divided as the Persian Plateau
between large self-sufficing Oases and immense tracts of
steppe-desert, is bound to show within its broad unity a
distinction (almost amounting to a division into sub-groups)
between the nomadic and the settled folk. In Persia,
where urban life is highly developed, while rural life is
led under physical conditions which make it of the most
primitive sort, there exists far more estrangement between
the wandering and the settled folk than in Arabia. Further,
the separation of one oasis tract from another has always
exercised a disintegrating effect. The Ajemis of northern
Irak, whatever their racial origin, must be distinguished
from the Farsis of Isfahan and Shiraz, and those from the
men of Yezd and Kerman ; and this influence of infinite
subdivision is probably in part responsible for the variety
of solutions which the keen Persian intellect has pro-
pounded for the religious problem.

To say, that with the exception of small communi-
ties of fire-worshippers, most numerous at Yezd, and of
Armenian Christians at Julfa of Isfahan and in Chahar
Mahal, the population of Persia, except on the extreme

west, is all Moslem, and distinguished from the Sunni by
a disagreement as to Apostolic Succession, is to convey a
very inadequate idea of the subtlety of Iranian faith, owed
largely to geographical influence on the Iranian mind.
When the least intellectual of creeds was imposed by the
Arabs on the most intellectual of eastern lands, it found
the most of the field occupied since time immemorial
by two philosophies of religion which still contend for
mastery among the more civilised nations. The essential
relation which Man desires with the Divine, was sought
by postulating either the Incarnation of God or His
Immanence in Creation. The Semitic creed of surrender
to an external omnipotent God, whose will is revealed by
prophets, proved, however, from its very simplicity more
capable of adaptation to both these philosophies than
might have been supposed. Pantheistic or Quietist mysti-
cism is a Semitic almost as much as an Aryan symptom ;
while belief in divinely inspired flesh has tended not only
in the Nearer East to pass into a belief in incarnate
God. The personality of Ali served to make reconcilia-
tion possible. Congenial to the Persians by his character,
adopted by the native dynasty, champion against the
Semite, and dying for Iran in the flower of youth, the
martyr of Kufa appealed to popular superstition as the
grim Meccan Founder would never have appealed. And
therefore the Moslem faith of the Persian masses at this
day is based not so much on Mohammed as Ali, not on
the radical incompatibility of man and God, insisted on
by the Koran, but on a deep-rooted sentiment of their
essential identity. This the Ali-Illahis, at one end of
the intellectual scale, satisfy by a materialistic creed of
perpetual Incarnation, the Sufis at the other end by the
doctrine that all creation, from Ali to the beetle, is not
less divine than the reflection of man's face in a mirror
is human. At both ends of the scale there must be
that surrender of Individuality which Islam implies and
Quietism approves, and if there be still any discrepancy
between individual creed and that officially required of
the community by the Semitising Seyids, the *ketman*, or

concealment of belief, a trick of the intellect congenial to the Persian race, easily reconciles practice.

While, however, the two philosophies are brought thus into some sort of accord by Shiah Islam, the distinct tendencies, which they imply, remain in the Persian nature, and despite outward conformity and inward juggling, pull underground one against another, and all against the missionary influence which the Arabian centre never ceases to press on the heretical half of the Moslem world. Intellectual Persian town life is, accordingly, an ever active laboratory of creed manufacture, varying and combining elements of instinctive belief: and the semi-secret sects thus originated are a constant source of disturbance of communal unity, apt to identify themselves, or be identified by others, with social ideals that, like Babism at the present day, may easily be brought into opposition to the established political order. Thus the unity of the Iranian group is much less well assured than that of the Turk.

The Iranian tendency must at one time have dominated a much larger area than now. For the broad wedge of Semitism which has been driven into south-western Asia from south to north, finds itself still fringed by isolated survivals not in sympathy with itself. Such are, on the eastern side, the Sabæan "star-worshippers" in lower Babylonia, the Sarliis and Chabuks of Mosul, element-worshippers, and the more numerous Yezidis, of whom more anon. All these appear to show markedly the characteristics of superior race in decay. So strong is the Iranian influence on the western border of its native plateau, that it has absorbed even the Arab tribes, who have been attracted to the easy lowlands of Khuzistan ; and these, becoming Shiah, have set up a barrier between themselves and the mass of their kin, although often, as in the case of the Beni Lam, theirs is the purest blood of Nejd.

The same influence is found to predominate also on the western coast of the Gulf. Very few of the Arabs of Hasa or Katr are in accord with their Sunni masters, but remain at heart Carmathians (*i.e.* followers of Karmut, a Naturalist of the earlier Sabæan type, affected by Persian ideas, who appeared in the third century of the Hejra). While among the Jowasmi of the Pirate Coast and the Omanis prevail other expressions of the Iranian tendency, now Naturalist, now Incarnationist, now, at lowest, no better than Animist.

From Ras el Had, therefore, to the Kerkha, it is necessary to detach the Arabs, who are found in the Arabian and Mesopotamian Fringe, from the central Semitic group. But these do not for that form altogether a single unity with the Iranian group, but remain so many small sub-groups, isolated one from another by deserts, as on the Arabian littoral, or by marsh and rivers in the Tigris basin. For so various are the expressions of which Iranism is capable, that it cannot induce cohesion in the face of even weak physical barriers.

In the plains, north of the Kerkha, the sympathies of the Shammar Bedawins have not yet been contaminated by the neighbourhood of even such extreme Incarnationists as the Ali-Illahi Kurds of the Zagros. But Iranism reasserts itself so soon as the hill country, beginning to close upon the Tigris valley, sets bounds to the tide of Semitism. It is in Jebel Sinjar and the lower mountainous tract north and north-east of Mosul that the Yezidis make a small sub-group, of mingled Incarnationist and Naturalist colour, which holds itself rigidly apart from both Turk and Arab – so rigidly that at very frequent intervals it has called upon itself the persecuting energy of the Ottoman administration, which, like the Roman of the Empire, can tolerate anything better than a secret society. Similar tendencies to those of the Yezidis distinguish local Christian groups, the Syrians of the Mardin district and the "Nestorians" and "Chaldean" refugees from the lower valley, now partly scattered on the hills between Julamerk and the frontier of Persia, but in larger part settled on the fat lands to west of Lake Urmi. For the present these small sub-groups are wholly divided from one another and from their neighbours in tradition and

hope ; but will they be always so ? They have been exposed for but a very few generations to the influence of
a Moslem organisation that takes itself seriously, and much
of their aloofness from the great groups on either hand
of them is due to political conditions which will be modified when the frontier between Turkey and Persia is finally
fixed.

The northern Fringe of Mesopotamia and Syria is in the
hands of settled Armenians and half nomadic Kurds, and
in the doubtful pasture-lands, north of Jebel Sinjar, there
is no hard and fast boundary between the northern sub-
groups and the Arab wedge.   Iranism, however, reappears
in the western or Mediterranean Fringe, and has combined
its intellectual influence with that of Semitism to give to
this region the importance that it has had in the history
of religion.

The survival in this Fringe to our own day of so much
that is not of the Semitic group is due, of course, to the
highland character of the locality ; but the future continu-
ance of these sub-groups as groups apart is likely to be
owed rather to the measure of support which they will
derive from the western sea.   Already the integrity of the
northernmost sub-group, the Ansariyeh, is being seriously
affected by the missionising energy of the Ottoman authorities, who for some years have lost no opportunity of
forcing at least the usages of orthodox Sunnism on the four
occult sects that form a loose unity of varying creed but
common secrecy in the little-trodden hills north of Jebel
Libnan.   Between hammer and anvil, between the fanatical Sunni farmers of the Asi valley, and the rich Sunni
population of the north Phœnician coast strip, the Ansariyeh are in perilous case.

The Christian Maronites of the Lebanon find present
salvation in the arduous character of their mountain home,
and in their immediate contact with Beirut ; but the same
progress of civilisation, which has placed them in so favourable a position, will probably end by merging Maronite individuality in the more catholic union of Christians of the
west.   The two Shiah sub-groups of the same mountains,

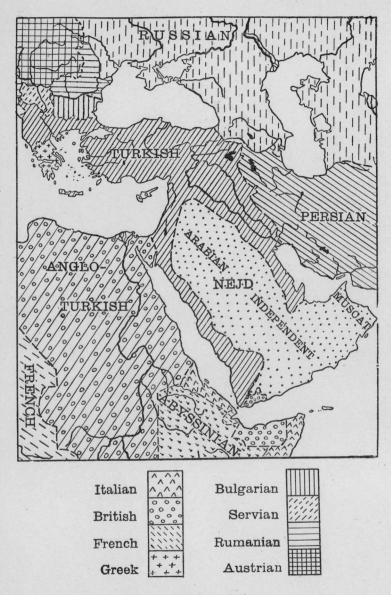

Italian	^ ^ ^	Bulgarian	
British	o o o	Servian	
French	\ \ \	Rumanian	
Greek	+ + +	Austrian	

FIG. 41.—Political Allegiance.

the 25,000 souls of the Metuali, and the far fewer Hashashim or Ishmaelites, direct immigrants from Persia, are too small to be taken into serious account.   Certainly they would not save their individuality for another generation, were it not for the guarantee against Sunni interference which they owe to the efforts of their hated Christian neighbours.   The Druses, however, since the migration of most of the race to Jebel Hauran, find themselves withdrawn from the active influence of serious Sunnism ; and their Incarnationist creed may long resist contamination by a Semitism, so weak and unstable as that of the Bedawins who range about their present retreat.

At least three denominations of Christians must be added to the West Syrian medley, each tending to group itself with the European Power which stands in the East for this or that dominant western Church.   And, finally, not taking account of numerous representatives of the western peoples themselves, we must mention, ere we pass on to Arabia proper, the increasing body of Jews, who, typical Semites that they are, tend to group with the Semitic type of Sunni, and to become, if Sephardim, who have long resided among Arabs and even Turks, hardly distinguishable from their neighbours in tradition and hope.

A singularly chaotic region this, where the governing Turk is out of sympathy with all the governed, and has much to do to keep one sub-group from the throat of another : where, in Jerusalem, all the religious *imperia in imperio* that he has created by his Edict of Toleration are concentrated in internecine rivalry ; and where in the Lebanon a territorial reservation has been made where he must abrogate the essential prerogatives of sovereignty.

III. While the physical character of the great Arabian expanse that these Fringes enclose, by producing a common type of creed, causes the population to fall within one great group, it does not serve to knit it together.   The absence of oases in the Hamad, compelling society to be purely nomadic, is almost as fatal to community of interest as the most rugged features of a highland country.   The

northern desert region is the most distracted by the enmities of tribes, families, and individuals that exists in the
Arabian area.   Nominally parted between the great clans
of the Shammar and the Anazeh, it is in reality divided
infinitely more variously into ill-defined *diras*, or ranging
grounds, of sub-tribes separated not by their indifferent
religion, their race, their speech, or their tradition and
hope, but by ill-blood aroused in the secular struggle for
water and pasture in a lean land.

South of the Nefud the cohesion of society is the closer
for the existence of large oases.   Not that the Nejdean
oasis-folk may maintain themselves, as in Central Persia,
apart from the desert about them ; for the fertility of their
homes is of too thin a quality.   But the large oases serve
to anchor even the nomad, and to suggest to him the idea
of unity.   In so meagre a region as Nejd, where the several
thin oases are divided only by narrow desert strips, while
all are shut off from the rest of the world, there is a
natural tendency not to multiply unities, but to form a
single, if a loose-knit, group.   And the present day, which
finds all the high-lying oases, and the steppe between and
around, under the single control of the Emir of the vigorous
southern Shammar, only repeats, after a short period of
disintegration, a state of things which, under the Wahabite sultans at Riad, subsisted far back into the eighteenth
century.[1]   If the Bedawin element is dominant, as now,
the union appears simply political : formerly when an oasis
element was the stronger, then the union took a religious
colour.   Religious, however, perhaps more in appearance
than at heart.   For good authorities (*e.g.* Guarmani, Pelly,
and Halévy) have always doubted if Wahabism, which is
only an expression of Shafei orthodoxy, was ever more
than a means to a political end.

The outer desert ring has up to now proved effective
to separate this loose unity from the Fringe populations.
These remain apart, isolated one from another by broad
tracts of desert and retaining, not only on the Gulf side,

[1] Most recent events seem to show that the Shammar dynasty, since the death
of Mohammed ibn Rashid, is less universally recognised.

but in Nejran, Yemen, Asir, and, to a less degree, Hadramut, primitive beliefs of Iranian colour, but more compatible with the Bedawin Indifferentism of Nejd, than the
stern Theism of the Turk. Indeed, the Jews, of whom
thousands dwell prosperously in Yemen, and the Britons,
known not only at Aden, but in Oman and Bahrein, are
more tolerable to the Fringe Arabs than the true Sunni.

It is only in the Hejaz that cosmopolitan influences
and the political preponderance of a Sunni Power have
produced what now passes for orthodoxy in Islam. The
populations of Mecca and Medina, though not without a
tinge of Zeidist Quietism, alone group with the Turk ; while
the rest of Arabia at the present day almost equals Persia
in its indifference or enmity to the successor of the Arabian
prophet.

The geographical uniformity of the Nile valley is
so complete, and the singular character of its life is
impressed so inevitably on all men alike, that there is
a unity here independent of and transcending Religion ;
while the formation of sub-groups among the indigenous
population is out of the question. Physical uniformity
overrides creed in the case of the seven peasants in a
hundred who are Coptic Christians ; it overrides that
racial variance which distinguishes the Barabra above the
cataract from the usual valley type, as clearly as from
their kinsfolk in the Eastern Desert ; it overrides the
differentiating influences of climate, and of exposure to
Mediterranean and Arab contamination which modify the
type in the Delta. Even the social distinction which, with
mutual contempt, is claimed equally by the Arab of the
Desert and the *fellah* of the fertile lands, is easily converted
in the life of a single generation to community of tradition and hope. If no account be taken of the numerous
resident aliens drawn from Mediterranean lands and the
British Isles, the only population, that within the limits of
Egyptian territory groups apart from the unity of the
valley, is the oasis-folk of Siwah. Of this a large part
holds aloof from the Egyptians, making common cause

with the great Senusi body in a profession of ascetic religion and display of fanaticism expressly designed to exclude the subversive social ideas of Europe from the slave-owning oases of the eastern Sahara.

I note that "Odysseus," the author of *Turkey in Europe*, implicitly follows a system of Creed classification throughout. The difficulty, however, is to find out of what creed large groups of the population are. For example, in Macedonia the church school statistics issued from Sophia, Belgrade, and Athens are utterly irreconcilable. Compare the Greek map, issued by Stanford in 1876, with that emanating from Sophia in *Geog. Rundschau*, xxi. For Asia Minor, W. M. Ramsay's *Impressions of Turkey* is very valuable, as are Sir C. Wilson's notes on populations in Murray's *Asia Minor*. For Persian groups Curzon, as usual, is compendious ; but Browne and Gobineau should be read for the more philosophic creeds, Sufiism and Babism. On the Bakhtiari creed, see Layard. On the little Sabæan group, Ainsworth (*Euphr. Exped.*), and Blunt (*Bedouins*, &c.) ; but better, an article quoted by Zwemer (*Arabia, Cradle of Islam*, ch. 28). On the Yezidis and their neighbours, Layard (*Nineveh*), and Parry (*Six Months in a Syrian Monastery*). On Ansariyeh, Ainsworth. On Lebanon creeds, Gobineau. On Arabian faiths, Robertson Smith (*Religion of Semites*). But on special groups, *e.g.* the Wahabis, see Burckhardt and Palgrave, and compare Halévy and Guarmani ; on the Omanis, Wellsted and Palgrave ; on the Carmathians, Palgrave ; and on all purely Bedawin beliefs, Doughty.

CHAPTER XII

PRODUCTS

THE produce of a geographical area, so far as it affects locally the life of considerable groups, may be divided broadly between Food Products and other Products. Items in both of these main categories may excite the influence of commerce ; and certain items in the last, if worked up on the spot, create a mechanic class. But in respect of all products, it must be borne in mind that man has nearly always modified them and sometimes introduced them, and therefore he himself is responsible to a large extent for the modification which they exert on his present state.

The grains, forming staples of food, distinguish certain belts. Where the rainfall is abundant, but the climate, owing to high relief or other causes, is temperate, we find a wheat-growing and wheat-eating people. Albania, Macedonia with the Thracian littoral, northern and central Greece (the latter region being not free from the necessity of importing), together with the Ionian Isles, the larger Ægean Islands, excepting Crete, the west, north-west, and central plateau of Asia Minor, the upper valleys of the Mesopotamian rivers, Azerl aijan, the littoral of Syria with the Lebanon, the Orontes valleys, the Hauran, and most of Western Arabia — these districts are consumers of wheat above all other grains. Barley is grown in every part of the region where corn may sprout at all, but chiefly for the feeding of the more valuable live stock ; it forms a staple of human life only in the south of Greece, in the smaller Ægean Isles, with Crete, and, allied with millet, in Armenia, in the middle valley of the Tigris, in Persia, and in parts of Western Arabia ; that is to say, in the poorer temperate lands. The intermediate grain of maize, difficult to cultivate successfully except where the possibility of adequate irrigation coincides with warm air, prevails over wheat in the south of the region, the Nile valley, and the central and south-eastern Arabian oases, and also, owing to some accident of introduction or the demands of the great capital city of the region, along the less suitable northern coast of Asia Minor from Ismit to Trebizond, and in the great Rumelian Plain. It is only in lower Mesopotamia and on the steaming shores of the Persian Gulf that rice is to the population what it is further east, although all over our region it holds a far more important place than in the west.

So much for the staple grains. Their geographical distribution has, of course, been too broadly sketched to be exact in detail. Millet and barley, for instance, prevail over wheat in the ruder hills of the wheat-eating districts, as in Northern Albania, Eastern Macedonia, and the Taurus and Hakkiari mountains ; millet rivals maize among the poorer Nilot *fellahin;* and maize competes with other grains wherever there are well-watered lowlands. But the classification stated above is sufficiently precise for our purpose. Before, however, proceeding to estimate the relation, if any, that difference of staple grains bears to difference in human character and life in various localities, we must bring into the account certain other food products, so largely consumed as also to be of the rank of staples.

The first and most important of these is milk, hardly ever taken in its natural state, but boiled, curdled, churned, or otherwise treated. The second is the fruit of the date palm, usually cooked. The third is olive oil, the fourth wine, and the last fish. Flesh of animals is throughout the region a luxury.

Milk and dates together are responsible for human life over an immense area, not included in our distribution of grains, namely, the Syrian and Arabian deserts. The milk is mainly that of home-bred camels. The dates are obtained from the oases and the Fringe lands. Milk without dates is a staple in a large part of all the

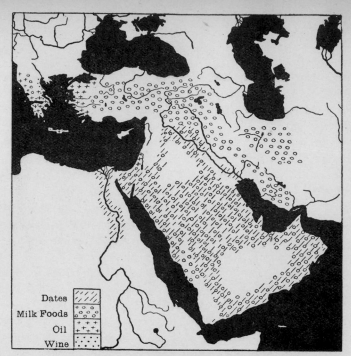

Dates
Milk Foods
Oil
Wine

FIG. 42.—The Chief Food Products other than Cereal.

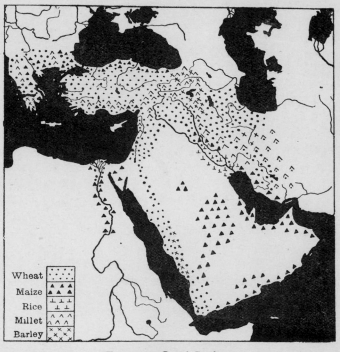

Wheat
Maize
Rice
Millet
Barley

FIG. 42a.—Cereal Products.

higher lands of the region, in Northern and Eastern Albania, in Eastern Macedonia and Rumelia, on the Anatolian Plateau, in Armenia, Kurdistan, and the Persian border ranges. Dates, without milk, are added by the Mesopotamian Arabs to their rice, and, in less degree, by the poorer Egyptian *fellahin* to their *durra*.

Olive oil and wine play an enormous part in the economy of all the Greek lands that are not predomi- nantly Moslem. In Crete the first commodity may even be said to be more of a staple than any grain ; while in that island and in all the considerable Cyclades and Sporades, in Cyprus and in all parts of Greece and Southern Albania but the most rugged, no peasant grudges wine more than bread. No other district of our area either produces or consumes these products on a com- parable scale, except the Lebanon. Fish is of far less moment. Though it is a conspicuous item in the meagre diet of the Ægean Isles, it forms a staple of life only on the more barren parts of the southern coast of Arabia.

With food luxuries we need not deal, although there are some so generally consumed in certain districts, as almost to be local necessities, for example, coffee by the southern Arabs and sugar cane by the *fellahin* of the Nile flats ; and we will pass at once to the main question of correspondence between staple foods and human char- acter and life, not forgetting that the products of a region often owe their nature as much to the character of the inhabitants, independently formed, as the character of a folk may be owed to the products.

The Albanian and the Greek populations have the same broad characteristics. As a whole they are distin- guished by physical and mental alertness and agility. They appear as do very hardily trained athletes, fine- drawn in body and mind, ready for instant action or thought, but not capable of sustaining thought or action strenuously or for long. Looking at their food, one re- marks that it is small in quantity, but of a kind which is quickly assimilated, and, for its bulk, sustaining. Olive oil has no superior in its rapid capacity both to satisfy and nourish. Milk is hardly its inferior, and what bread is consumed is chiefly wheaten, and the wine pure and light. With such staples the Albanians and Greeks readily satiate appetite without repletion, and their temptation to treat meals as occasions of dallying pleasure is small. No races that so generally eat to live, live as well as they ; and their failure to comprehend the European demand for complicated, varied, and abundant foods is as often expressed and as profound as the European's surprise that he cannot obtain a full meal in a village of vigorous and healthy Greek peasants. The animals seem to require as little as their masters. They bear a starved aspect from one end of the Balkan Peninsula to the other, but, working all day and every day, are rarely sick or sorry.

On the eastern side of the Spine, however, the general character of the peasantry in the Macedonian basins and the Rumelian Plain changes as the food changes. Where the heating grain of maize largely replaces wheat, and meat, vegetable soups, and butter have to do what oil does alone in the west, we find a slow and heavy farming folk, incapable of very rapid action or thought, but enduring long with both body and mind. The Bulgar-Slav race rivals the "Turk" in its excellence as military material. The Sultan has no steadier infantry than in the Fourth Army Corps, stationed in Armenia, but recruited in Europe ; and, at the same time, the professors of Robert College at Constantinople state that, of all the races they train, the strongest intellect is the Bulgar's. With him the future of the Balkans seems to rest. The Greek has, and will always have, a present.

In almost all Western Asia, north of the Arab area, we have to deal with peoples of a similar character to the Balkan folk, but less well nourished. The plateau folk of Asia Minor, whether Indo-European or Turkman, who still eat wheat, but worse prepared, and add to it only milk as a staple, have like endurance and depth with the Slavs, but more than their slowness and stupidity. The

Anatolians make the admirable infantry of the First and Second Army Corps; and they supply to Islam its most steadfast and pure-living adherents. But where the quality of the food seriously deteriorates, as in the western hill districts, we find nothing better than the crass, unstable, and profitless Yuruk; and in the eastern mountains the meanest and least profitable of the Kurds and Armenians. These people, unsatisfactory enough in their own highlands, are capable of much when surrounded by better life conditions. The Armenians of the eastern plateau are a worthy peasantry, which, trained and encouraged, comes to show a ready intelligence and enterprise equal to the Greek; while the rival race, which produced Saladin, appears to great advantage in the low, fertile tracts south of the Armenian mountains, e.g. the district north and west of Urfa, and the smiling left bank valleys of the Tigris basin, as far south as the Lesser Zab.

Conditions very similar to those of the Anatolian Plateau recur in Azerbaijan, and, with a repetition of the same foods, one is not surprised to find a folk which can contribute really good infantry to the Shah's army, but is not conspicuous for quick intelligence. The same generalisation covers all the tribesmen of the long border valleys, Kurds, Lurs, and Bakhtiaris, until pure nomadism gains the upper hand in Laristan. But as the food of these well-circumstanced mountaineers is of better quality and more varied with vegetables and fruits than that of the mass of the Turki husbandmen of the Azerbaijan shelf, they must be compared for energy and intelligence rather with the tillers of the Urmi strand than with those of the Kizil Uzun valley. Mrs. Bishop bears eloquent testimony to the plenty prevailing among the Kurds between Hamadan and the Great Lake; De Morgan found Pusht-i-Kuh a garden fenced about against the Persian publicans; and every traveller in Bakhtiari-land, from Layard to Sawyer, has spoken of the superior standard of life prevailing in the intra-mural valleys south of the Kuh-i-Rang.

On the Persian "Plateau," however, special physical conditions, as we have seen, divide life into two categories.

N

On the one hand there is found over a vast majority of the area a sparse folk living very poorly on barley, millet, and thin milk foods, at best feeble villagers, at worst mean nomads. On the other hand, a population, collected into towns whose life is governed by trade and the issue of trade, a population which feeds on such various products of many lands that it cannot be said to owe its general characteristics to food staples. But where all nutritious food, and especially grain, is scarce and dear, through bad government, lack of means of transport, and a short-sighted intelligence which for momentary gain replaces useful cultures over large tracts by luxurious products, it may be said truly of the population that it is physically and mentally unstable and unsound.

There is no folk whose capability varies more directly with its food supply than the Arab. Over the immense area of south-western Asia, where grain can be cultivated so little as to be in no sense a staple food, and the date fruit, heating and satisfying, but not of equal nutrition, takes its place, we find one character of man, restless and alert, but incapable of sustained action or any but the most superficial and conventional thought. If the Albanian or the Greek is the hardly trained athlete, the Bedawin is the athlete over trained. There is a common element in these two groups, and where the " Arab " (to use the ethnic widely) lives under conditions similar to the Greek, he resembles him at many points, both physical and mental. Witness the inhabitants of the Lebanon and the Syrian littoral, where wheat and olive oil are once more the staples of life, with milk and wine added. There is no more enterprising, no keener intellect in the Nearer East than the Syrian of the Fringe, capable of the highest Levantine civilisation and triumphant competitor with the Greek in the latter's chosen field, the marts of Alexandria and all Lower Egypt.

But the Syrian littoral is the garden of the Arabian area, and there are many lessening gradations of capability and character between its best inhabitants and the lowest

Bedawin, such as the Gara of Dofar and the fish-eating Mahri. The sturdy, independent cultivators of the high-lying oases of Nejd, to whom corn, dates, and milk are staples in about equal degree, and luxuries little known, are one sort; another, the equally independent and sturdy, but less austere, husbandmen of Yemen, over addicted to the coffee berry. Another, again, the softer dwellers in Hasa, a paradise of dates and all fruits and vegetables, tolerant, artistic, easily subdued, not unlike the Omanis; another, the men of the Hejaz oases, keen to use the food products of other lands, cunning, corrupt, and false. Yet another sort are the rice and date eating Arabs of the Mesopotamian delta, weak and degraded, but more stable than those who live on dates without grain in the desert. These are capable of being good tillers of favouring soils, while their northern neighbours, the Ánaze and Shammar, seem to become no better husbandmen, however greatly encouraged, than the wanderers on the Libyan waste. But where soil does not favour them these Irak delta dwellers are as unstable as the desert men, without their saving simplicity. There are no Arabs of worse repute than the Beni Lam, except, perhaps, those tribes which live under not dissimilar conditions on the opposite fringe of the Syrian Desert.

The wanderers of the Egyptian wastes, and the oasis dwellers on the south-western limit of our region, owe their slight deterioration, as compared with Bedawin and oasis folk in Arabia, to causes stated in an earlier chapter, not to food, for that is practically the same in the two regions. And the folk of the Nile trough, whose life should repeat most nearly that of the inhabitants of Hasa and Hadramut, have the considerable physical endurance and intelligence which go with their diet of maize, millet, milk, and cane, tempered by peculiar physical conditions not germane to our present subject.

This influence of food-staples, however, is not the only influence of products considerable enough to be taken into account in treating of the life of large groups. There

are certain raw materials proper to this region, the
culture of which (and in a few cases the manufacture)
modifies life and character in a marked degree (Fig. 43).

In Albania nothing such is worth mention, and in
Greece we find only products very local in their effect.
The currant vine, being valuable for export only, raises
the standard of living and diffuses that humanity, which
results from cosmopolitan relations, over the Achæan and

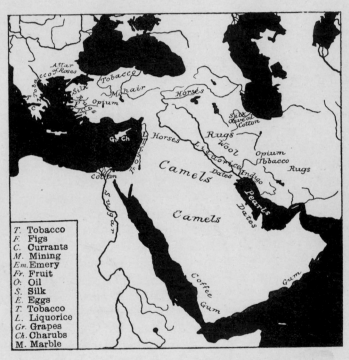

T. Tobacco
F. Figs
C. Currants
M. Mining
Em. Emery
Fr. Fruit
O: Oil
S. Silk
E. Eggs
T. Tobacco
L. Liquorice
Gr. Grapes
Ch. Charubs
M. Marble

FIG. 43.—Various Products.

Corinthian littoral and the adjacent Ionian Islands, Zante
and Kefalonia; and tobacco, demanded by Egyptian
manufacturers of cigarettes, performs a like office for
the districts of Agrínion and west Thessaly, for the lower
Macedonian basins and the Thracian littoral in the east
country. What profitable mining may yet do for mainland and isles may be judged at the iron and lead

workings of Lávrion and the emery beds in Naxos ; and to this is likely to be added presently a great extension of marble-quarrying to satisfy the artistic world's demand, inadequately met by Carrara. Both industries are of a kind to modify the general fault of Greek character, disinclination for regular, continuous, and disciplined labour. In the east of the Balkan Peninsula, beside tobacco, there is only to be chronicled, as a modifier of life, the unique rose cultivation of the northern Rumelian plain and valleys, which creates a wealthy peaceful community where brigandage might have been most to be feared.

In Asia Minor, however, we note three cultures in the coastal districts and two industries on the plateau. The raising of "Samsun" tobacco has made the peasantry, mainly of Greek speech and sympathy, which lives about the mouths of the Yeshil, Kizil, and Sakaria rivers, the most solid of the Anatolian farmer folk. But the good effect is being impaired there, as all over Turkey, by the action of the tobacco monopolists and the undue incidence of taxation. Silk has created a large and well-to-do class, half agricultural, half industrial, farther west in the district of Brusa ; and the cultivation and preparation of fruits for export, in particular figs, has a like effect on the folk of the lowlands of the Gediz and Menderes basins. Cultures like these, which demand attention all the year through, and when successful give the peasant a serious stake in the land, furnish the best of inducements to peace and progress in a mountainous land containing many unsettled elements. And if Islam is bound to discourage the grape, wherever Moslems form an important element in the population, it should have no feud with the olive, the valonia oak, and the charub—less indeed than with opium. There is no reason why the Anatolian coasts should not hereafter export a larger bulk of the product of those three trees than the islands from Mitylene to Cyprus and Crete, in whose abundant wealth and well-being not only these but vineyards and mastic trees may claim a large share.

The two important industries of the plateau are the

breeding and care of the famous mohair goat, of which the Angora province alone contains above a million, and the making of "Turkey" rugs and carpets for all the world's need. By introducing this species of goat, the pastoral intruders have done much to repair their "nomadisation" of Asia Minor. The breeders and herdsmen of the provinces of Angora, Konia, Kastamúni, and Sivas may claim to be ranked with the Arab camel and horse breeders, as the best experts in live stock that the Nearer East contains. If the demand for the Anatolian variety of mohair declines (as it has threatened to do in the face of South African competition), it will be an irreparable misfortune for the plateau folk. For their goats, which have already destroyed the last vestiges of the former forests, can alone turn to profitable account the immense bared tracts on the higher shelves and ridges of the land. The makers of carpets and rugs, as an organised industrial class, belong to the west of the plateau only, and feed Smyrna from such provincial centres as Ushak and Kula. This industry has not only brought into existence a class of skilled and disciplined workers in every village, compelled to consult and obey the taste of the outer world in design and colour, but, to a great extent, it governs the culture of wide lands which must be devoted to producing vegetable dyes, especially the madder root.

Among non-agricultural products none are of much account here except the sponge, which is to Symi and the smaller East Ægean Isles what the pearl is to Bahrein. Minerals, though abundant, are so little and ill worked that their quest scarcely affects life. The only district which has anything like a mining class is the province of Trebizond, whose Greeks are in request to work lodes all over Turkey. True that two deposits, one of emery near Smyrna and another of magnesium silicate (*meerschaum*) not far from Kutáya, furnish the chief supplies of those minerals to the world; but they have to meet a very small demand.

The extensive breeding of horses by the Kurds of the Armenian highlands leads to the perpetuation of nomadism, with all its attendant evils. The breeders of these animals, compelled to seek low ground in winter, choose for the most part the southern plains of Eastern Cilicia and the desert fringes of the Urfa and Mardin districts. Not only, therefore, do they "nomadise" these plains equally with their native mountains, but they cause, by their passage, recurring friction and unrest in the intermediate districts. The Ottoman officials have been trying for years to combat these evils by prohibiting migration. But they must take account of the fact that their prohibition will be enforced at the price of eliminating a hardy type of horse, excellent for military purposes; even as the measures taken to make *fellahin* of the Syrian and Mesopotamian Bedawin camel-breeders threatens to diminish seriously the supply of the one animal which at present renders transit possible over vast tracts of the Empire. Probably it is the effect already produced by such measures that has led the Administration absolutely to stop the exportation of horses from any part of the Ottoman Empire.

In Persia, for reasons already given more than once, no influence has universal range. The Gilani is an enlightened farmer, thanks to alien encouragement of his cotton-plants and mulberry and olive trees; but none of their products vitally affect the plateau. There we have to consider in chief the poppy culture, ever expanding to meet the larger demands of Indian smokers, content to inhale a drug so greatly adulterated by arts, first known in Isfahan, but learned by Yezd, that opium makes barely a sixth of its bulk. This lucrative crop has ousted grain from large parts of the oases, causing great distress among the poorer folk. For the ground available on the Persian Plateau for raising food supplies is strictly limited, and while roads remain as they actually are, it is impossible to import on a large scale or at cheap rates. Yezd and Kerman starve, while surplus grain is rotting at Kermanshahan. A large culture of fine tobacco, mainly designed to supply the needs of the *kalian* or waterpipe, does not mend matters for the poor.

But, on the other hand, it must be admitted that the commerce thus excited between the Gulf ports and the Iranian Plateau exerts on the fanatical south Persians a humanising effect whose strength may be judged by the continued failure of Russia, supreme in Teheran, to diminish British Indian influence at Isfahan, however ill promoted be the latter by British merchants and political authorities. Moreover, a certain chief industry of the plateau must be taken into account here, as in Anatolia, which supplies a western rather than a northern market. This is the manufacture of rugs and carpets, which has exercised in the Kerman district less good effect than in the vicinity of Ushak, only because it is not as yet so well organised or so directly in touch with western customers. But its development will strengthen that influence of the commercial nations on Persia, which may already be illustrated by some of its wilder districts. No Persian weapons are so effective to tame the Zagros Kurds, the Feili Lurs, or the Bakhtiaris as the refusal of the authorities and merchants on the west to facilitate the disposal of their surplus wool, which, to the annual value of a quarter of a million, must pass through Baghdad.

What the pearl fishery means to the Gulf folk has been implied already. There is no better index of its import than the social condition of the population of Bahrein. This is entirely Arabian, but as greatly superior in civilisation to the populations of the mainlands on either hand as inferior in its turn to that of the true metropolis of the Gulf, Bombay. What, moreover, pearls mean to one Western nation, into the hands of whose Indian subjects they come each year to the value of nearly a million sterling, may be judged from the power that Great Britain reposes in the hands of her representative at Bushire ; and from the fact that, whatever be the international status of the Gulf shores *de jure*, no one is permitted to doubt the fact that the Gulf itself is a British sea.

The palm culture on the banks of the Shatt-el-Arab and lower Euphrates supplies the most striking example in the Nearer East of the rapidity with which an agricultural industry may modify manners. A generation ago, as Layard's early adventures prove, the lower Muntefik and Kab Arabs were as hostile and treacherous a set of half-settled Bedawins as existed then in the Arab area. There were no towns in their territory, except the moribund Basra, and huge tracts of marsh, fed by the annual overflow, fringed all the river. Since then, thanks largely to the Ottoman Government, and especially to Midhat, when *vali* of Baghdad, these neglected swamps have become the richest date garden in the world. Half-a-dozen flourishing towns have sprung into existence, and the villages have swollen many times over in number and size. The southern Muntefik are become a laborious industrial people, occupied all the year with the care of their trees, and the gathering, packing, and exporting of fruit worth a quarter of a million sterling ; and are now as unlike their tribal kin on the lower Tigris as once they were unlike the *fellahin* of the Nile valley.

Among less fortunately placed folk a word too must be said as to the influence of liquorice. The search for this root in the arid soils it loves, since it requires no agricultural skill, attracts the needy Bedawins of lower Mesopotamia, as it does the Yuruks of the Menderes basin, and the Fringe folk of the lower Asi valley in North Syria ; and trade in it instils into the finders, as traffic in desert salt, or the esparto grass of the Tripoli shore instils into the nomad gatherers, the first beginnings of a commercial instinct, and the idea of labouring for money. The liquorice trade, as a serious factor in Mesopotamian life, is, like the date industry, a thing of yesterday, for the present demand for the root is almost entirely American.

On the stock-breeding of the Bedawins we have already touched. Camels come mainly from the Hamad and from Nejran. So far as concerns horses, breeding affects the northern Arabs more than the southern ; but neither one nor the other group has now as much to do with the production of what is commonly reputed the "Arab" breed as have aliens, Turks, Egyptians, and Indians. For the rest of the area we have only products of the Fringes to consider.

Some are increasing in importance like the orange and
lemon culture of the Palestinian and Phœnician littoral,
which every year widens the oasis of Jaffa, and bids fair to
redeem the Holy Land ; or like the egg and tobacco production of Latakia and Tripoli, and the oil and raw silk
of Beirut and the Lebanon. These cultures have the
usual civilising effect, here intensified through easy relations
with Lower Egyptian markets. Other products, again, are
declining, and of such are the long famous Damascene
fabrics in metal, leather, and threads. And of such, again,
are the two cultures that have made Yemen known all the
world over. Hardly any export trade in the coffee-bean
remains to Loheia and Hodeida, still less to Mokha.
What Sana will not consume is carried to Nejd and filters
thence a little further overland, while Jidda has to import
from Brazil and Ceylon to meet the needs of Mecca.
Nor is frankincense in much better case, either in the
Yemen or on the south coast. Perhaps the modern world
cares less for perfumes than the ancient. At any rate, it
can make or find them elsewhere than in Araby the Blest.
No wonder there is growing distress and continuous
unrest among the Yemenis under the Turkish yoke.

The Nile valley, once the chief granary of the civilised
world, now buys grain, but sells two commodities, neither
of which was produced by its soil a century ago. The
culture of both cotton and sugar has altered the conditions
of *fellahin* life more than anything in six thousand years,
except those railways, which the profit of the new cultures
has made possible. For the sake of the feathery seed half
the Delta has been reclaimed from saline marsh ; by the
continuous labour of tilling and irrigating cotton fields, in
addition to other crops, the *fellahin* of Lower Egypt have
been weeded out, till only a thickset sturdy race prevails ;
and, to sell the produce, a village has grown into a town
at every few miles between the Rosetta and Damietta
horns of Nile. Alexandria, which in 1805 held a bare
five thousand souls, is become a city of three hundred
thousand, and once again the first port of the eastern
Mediterranean after nearly two thousand years.

Sugar has had an effect on Upper Egypt, not entirely of the same kind and not so beneficial. Like cotton, it increases wealth and attracts the apparatus of civilisation ; and more than cotton, since it is worked up on the spot, it creates a class of skilled mechanics, where nothing was before but a very primitive peasantry. Furthermore, it must be conceded that it has added to the slender *fellahin* diet a most nutritive food, to which, as much as to anything, is due the rising natality and vitality of the race. But while the large flooded areas of cane both impair the health of the neighbouring peoples, and offer effective shelter to criminals, they do greater harm even than cotton by rendering *latifundia* the rule. Crops that demand continuous irrigation are not to be grown by small holders, who cannot raise water by manual labour all the season through. The small freeholder is dying out in Egypt, and recent local authority asserts that nine-tenths of the actual *fellahin* are serfs of the soil.

The authorities for this chapter are in the main H.B.M.'s Consular officers stationed in the area. Their little read but most interesting Reports to the Foreign Office supply sounder geographical, as well as historical, material than most travellers. Cuinet's tables for Asiatic Turkey inspire little confidence, being based on customs returns. They represent, no doubt, products on which the Imperial Government profited, but not all products on which profit was made. Villiers Stuart's report on Egyptian Regeneration (State Papers, 1895) is instructive reading.

CHAPTER XIII

COMMUNICATIONS

THE natural routes of communication have so important a bearing on local life that they call for separate treatment, although often incidentally mentioned already. Their existence, or absence, felt most acutely in time of war, modifies the character of a country no less in time of peace, both by determining the measure of commercial and social intercourse, and by increasing or lessening the persistent possibility of invasion.

A glance at the map of the Old World will show that the only great natural through routes, wholly by land or wholly by sea, which touch the southern Balkan Peninsula, are, first, the diagonal land road from Europe to Asia, which enters our Region at the pass of Ikhtiman and traverses Eastern Rumelia; and, second, the sea track from the Mediterranean to the Black Sea. These, crossing at the Bosphorus, confer on Constantinople not only its peculiar external importance, marking it as the inevitable capital for two continents, but also its internal political and social condition. Not only are all sorts and conditions of men and all influences of divers latitudes brought thither, not only is it a great port as well as a great city, but its most private and internal affairs are not merely the concern of its own rulers and ruled, but equally of the great Christian nations of the West who hold all ends of the cross roads. Their representatives, using an authority, originally conceded to their weakness, but now asserted by their strength, modify by an *imperium in imperio* the local relations between rulers and ruled in Constantinople as they are modified nowhere else in the world. It results that

the city is as thoroughly denationalised and demoralised
as the most virulent anti-Semite could assert of a Jew-
ridden society.

The trunk land route between east and west, however,
in these days of steam navigation has lost an importance
which it will only partially regain when the diagonal
trans-continental railway is prolonged to the Persian
Gulf. The trunk sea-route passes at present well to
southward of Crete, and even if Suda Bay should offer
special advantages to shipping under the new political
order, is not likely to be more seriously diverted than it
has been by the Corinth Canal. The present decay of
Syros shows that what importance the Balkan ports of
call once possessed in relation to the Black Sea and
Levant trades, has greatly declined since modern steamers
developed their greater speed and coal-carrying capacity.
And, in short, on all accounts one must not look in
the Balkan Peninsula and isles for much influence of the
through traffic of the world.

As to its eastern part, however, the Peninsula lies
open to attack by land through the passes which lead
from the Danube basin into the long and gentle valleys
of the Vardar and Maritza. The readiness with which
the Austrians can enter Macedonia is a constant factor
in the unrest of its inhabitants and its rulers. And how
little the Balkan avails for a scientific frontier was demon-
strated by the Russian armies in 1876, and again more
patently by the easy fusion of Eastern Rumelia with
Bulgaria. As to all the southern and eastern part of
the peninsula, with its immense development of coast line,
the readiness of sea access accounts equally for the western
tendencies of the inhabitants of the Hellenic kingdom,
and the uneasy seat of an Oriental Power at Stambul.

Communications, however, of more local relation are
not without their influence on the several districts of
the Peninsula. Even North Albania, one of the most
isolated tracts in the Old World, with no good ports
and only two difficult approaches from the east, Albania,
which neither buys nor sells in the world's markets, is

kept in continual fear by the ease with which the Slavs of Montenegro can raid round or across the Skutari Lake ; even as Montenegro in its turn is in fear of the Austrians who command the avenues of its external food supply. The vale and hill folk of the White Drin basin, on the other hand, are kept not less restless by their hopes. For by way of the two depressions in the Balkan water-parting they can descend at will into Old Servia to the north, or the Uskub and Tétova valleys to the south. In a land so rugged and broken by long spurs of high ridges, such a road of transverse communication as lies along the gorge of the Black Drin from Prisrend to Skutari is apt to be treated by the tribal groups as existing rather for their common plunder than their common trade ; and indeed little or no traffic passes by this road, now that the railways descend from Mitrovitza and Nish to Salonica, and all attempts to establish a regular service of steam navigation to Skutari by the Boyana channel have been abandoned.

None of the many paths which cross the Spine, south of the Shar, would be regarded as easy elsewhere, not even that Egnatian highway which, ascending from Ochrida, was once a great thoroughfare for Roman armies and trade, but is now compounded of short lengths of decaying *chaussée*, alternating with tracks along which a loaded mule can just pick his way. But, such as these passes are, they combine with the port of Avlona to modify considerably the ferocity of the Albanian of the centre, and to accustom him to intercourse with men alien to his particular tribe. Indeed, Berat is said to be the town of most European aspect west of Monastir. And as the easy road by the Zygos pass comes in, and the sea access is improved by the sheltering line of Corfu and the deep inset of the Arta Gulf, the character of the Toskh softens apace. Long used to the passage of traders through his country and the spectacle of Italian civilisation in Corfu and his coast towns of Butrinto and Parga, the Epirote has a more open and receptive mind than his northern brother, and is much given to seeking to improve his fortunes by temporary sojourn in the Greek lands of the Levant. In the years of Ali Pasha's tyranny and of the Greek Revolution, there was a considerable exodus from Epirus, which has left its trace in the Greek adoption of the Toskh national dress. But now the most of these voluntary exiles return after short absences, bringing with them the spirit of the southern civilisation, and working effectually towards the complete Hellenisation of their native land. Janina is immensely in advance of any other Albanian town, and ranks indeed with Brusa as one of the most enlightened and attractive cities in the Ottoman dominions.

There are only two practicable mule-passes across Pindus other than the Zygos road, and those are summer paths only; while through the southern continuation of the Spine, the *col* north-west of Karpenisi, admitting to the head-waters of the Spercheios or Helláda river, alone gives easy passage between western and eastern Greece. In all the southern extension of the Peninsula the natural communications are by way of the sea. The 3000 miles of road, mostly, it must be confessed, of indifferent quality, and the fast-growing railway system which the Greeks have made—they have done indeed far more to open land communication than might have been expected from inhabitants of so difficult a country— supplement but do not supersede the waterways, by which more foreign influence reaches the body of the people over this small area than in all the rest of the Peninsula. And the effect of cosmopolitan commerce on the Greek people is the more marked, since, owing to the ready access to her seas, the place of production is usually hard by the place of export. British steamers may be seen moored within a hundred yards of the vineyards which produce their freight of currants, and Ergastéria or Lavrion is at once a pit-village and a port. The Achæan shore and island of Zante, and southern Attica, are, with the ports of Piræus and Hermoupolis, the parts of Greece most obviously affected by intercourse with the outer world; but marble quarries and tobacco planta-

tions are introducing a strong element of foreign influence elsewhere, and especially into Eubœa, Thessaly, and
Ætolia.

Yet, as has been said already, the Greeks themselves
make remarkably little use of their matchless sea-ways.
There is much conveyance of passengers and cattle from
one locality to another. More craft, large and small, are
said to fly the Greek flag than any but the British, and the
number of little steamers plying about the coasts increases
apace. But very small bulk either of the exports or the
imports of Greece is conveyed in Greek bottoms; and even
fishing is a surprisingly feeble industry, perhaps because it
receives so great discouragement from a Church which pro-
hibits fish as well as flesh and fowl during two hundred
days out of three hundred and sixty-five. The population
of Patras and Piræus appears, from consular returns, to
satisfy its appetite for fish mainly with smoked New-
foundland cod.

Even the Ægean islands are less affected by their relation to sea-ways than might be expected. For the most
part scantily clothed rocks, they support such exiguous
populations that the possession of fine natural harbours,
such as those of Milos, Seriphos, and Amorgos, gives them
no important part in the economy of the Levant. Only
one port is frequented by international shipping, that of
Hermoupolis in Syros, thanks not to nature but to a political accident ; and all decaying as its importance may be,
that little barren island still stands to its larger and better
endowed neighbours as a capital city to rustic communities.
Only two of the other isles may be called distinctively
maritime at all, and those not less barren than Syros, and
not less indebted to political accident. Hydra and Spetsæ
owe their large Albanian population of sailors and fishermen to the Ottoman incapacity to control the sea. Long
ago they became a ready refuge for recalcitrant members
of a long-settled and energetic Toskh colony, which still
holds the southern part of Argos, and speaks its own
tongue in the large communities of Kranídi and Hermióne.
Once these Albanians had established themselves on the

barren islands, piracy offered an obvious resource. But
the nobler spirits among them succeeded in turning their
predatory energies into the stream of the Greek Revolution, to which they contributed its first navy, and
signal and bold service, if sometimes with a temper
more befitting corsairs than disinterested champions of
freedom.

The small effect of sea-traffic on Greece needs no
better illustration than the miserable failure of Corinth to
rise out of the condition of an Albanian village ; and at
present, after nearly ten years' working, the Isthmian Canal
has not only created no considerable settlement on either
shore, but barely pays its expenses of maintenance.

While defect of through land communication, largely
due to physical difficulties, but in part also to human
action and inaction, keeps all north-eastern Greece and
southern Macedonia in a very primitive state (and that
despite local railways and a matchless port in Thessaly),
western Macedonia, north of the Vistritza, is in much
better case. Its three plain tracts are strung on the
one line of the Vardar : they are all in common touch
with Austrian Europe on the north, and they all have a
common outlet for their superfluous wealth in Salonica, a
sure port in almost all weathers, and now in process of being
converted into a first-class harbour. Such advantages,
were political conditions less unfavourable to peace and
repose, would make Macedonia the garden of the Balkans ;
and even as it is, with a road-system far less developed
than that of the Lebanon, the agricultural, commercial,
and general social standard of the Vardar basin is much
superior not only to the primitive state of the more secure
Pomaks, who have yet to feel the effect of the railway
newly opened to the south of their hills, but to the condition of the nearest plains of emancipated and settled
Hellas.

The political conditions, and long process of unrest
already described in Eastern Rumelia, compel a similar
reserve in speaking of the beneficial effect of the great
through route which passes diagonally over the plains.

O

Nevertheless that benefit is already obvious. Stagnant though its trade seems for the moment, the upper plain has developed apace ; and the Greeks of the lower plain and the Marmora coast, while perhaps the most steady and least political of the Hellenised communities, are by no means the least well-to-do or progressive. For not only

FIG. 44.—The chief routes in the Balkan Peninsula and Western Asia Minor.

the railways which connect them with Europe and Constantinople, but also the great international sea-road which lies along the southern coast, are influences of cosmopolitanism more powerful than are experienced by any other Greeks. The most numerous element in the capital city, the Hellenic, is seen to better advantage nowhere but in Alexandria.

But Constantinople is really a port of Asia, and partakes of that greater plenitude and range of traffic of which the traveller is sensible so soon as he begins to advance up a trunk road of Asia Minor. Nor is that merely a result of the greater bulk of the continental mass, stretching eastward. For Anatolia by itself matters to the world in respect of production far more than the whole Balkan Peninsula, and that although her vast mineral wealth is not better developed.

The influence of great caravan roads, certain of which are being (or are about to be) laid with rails, is shown conspicuously along the northern avenues, which lead either directly to the Bosphorus or to Black Sea ports on "half-sea" routes, by the development of urban centres far more frequent and displaying more movement in their *bazars* than is consistent with the numbers of the local population. These towns should grow rapidly when steam causes a fall in the present ruinous disproportion of freight to value. Transport from Sivas to Samsun trebles the initial price of commodities, but nevertheless there is a continuous passage of caravans over the road ; and no one who visits the province of Trebizond will fail to remark, in its developed road system and general air of superior civilisation, the effect of the transit of Persian caravans which annually carry goods to the value of nearly a quarter of a million sterling to and fro over the long track from Tabriz. The southern districts of Asia Minor, on the other hand, lie off all through routes, and are given up to village and nomad life; and even Cyprus is not better off for being an island. But over all the west country, since the extension of the Smyrna railways to the edge, or in one case to the actual crown, of the Plateau, a similar state of things has resulted as in the north (Fig. 44).

The development of Hellenic civilisation in the interior is the measure of such progress. The valley of the upper Menderes has become a focus of Greek life in the past half generation ; and even more significant is the rapid process of re-Hellenisation now being experienced by those Orthodox communities, scattered farther inland, which owed their preservation to the enlightened policy of the Seljuk sultans of Konia, and had long been lost to Greek ideals and even to Greek speech. The group of Christian villages, to west and north of the lake of Egerdir, of which Isbarta and Olu Borlu are chief, have become themselves missionising centres of Hellenism. The Cappadocian and Pontic groups are still too far out of hearing of the locomotive to have experienced anything like the same modification ; but the Orthodox Church, having taken up vigorously the education of priests and laity in the rock-hewn villages south and west of Kaisaríyeh, is being rewarded by a great increase in the knowledge of Greek among the rising generation.

The possession, however, of the most accessible seaboard in the eastern Mediterranean, of a central plain which can be traversed easily in any direction, and of not difficult approaches to the central Iranian Plateau or the Mesopotamian plains, does not make always for the peace and prosperity of Anatolia. A non-maritime dominant race watches the harbours with a jealousy which seriously interferes not only with their trade and development, but with the comfort of the local population, as the Greeks of Rhodes know to their cost. To its central levels, to the many not arduous Tauric passes from the Cilician gates to the defile of the Upper Tigris (through one or other of which the Baghdad Railway will be laid), and to the long and gradual northern road which, by way of the upper valley of the western Euphrates, crosses easily to the head-waters of the Aras, and descends on Transcaucasia or Azerbaijan, Anatolia has owed more or less directly the constant passage of devastating armies, has owed subsequent nomadisation with all its grave economic consequences, and still owes a sense of local insecurity, which increases from the Axylon to the Armenian highlands. It owes further a certain persistent uneasiness in face of the great aggressive Power which holds the north-eastern approach, and has only to trundle its guns down the long westward slope to decide the fate not only of Anatolia but of Constantinople. For that city will be strategically and economically untenable whenever an enemy shall be seated on the Asian shore of the Bosphorus or even of the Dardanelles. Ottoman nervousness on the score of an inferior strategic position about the head-waters of the Euphrates is largely responsible for the policy pursued towards the peoples of the highlands. *Quidquid delirant reges plectuntur—Armenii!* (Fig. 45).

For the rest, the crown of highland Armenia and

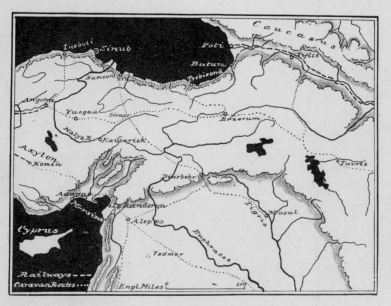

FIG. 45.—The chief routes from the Levant eastward.

Kurdistan lies as a rugged island, closed during several months of the year to the highways which skirt it on the north, the south-west, and the east. So far, however, as it has any ready communications with the outer world, it should be observed (as a key to the recent history of all this region) that they conduct south ; and that the Kurds, who have come up from that quarter, have the south country most at their mercy. The slopes, which fall to the upper shelf of Mesopotamia, suffer from lying in the annual track of the migrating Van, Hakkiari, and Tiári tribesmen ; and it is the quarrelling of these with the half-bred Arabs, who dispute their pastures, that serves to keep all northern Mesopotamia insecure.

Into the north-western corner of Azerbaijan enter an overland trunk road from the Bosphorus and the half-sea road by Trebizond, after their junction at Erzerum. These are joined at once by the great route from Trans-caucasia, which crosses the upper Aras at Julfa ; and all together proceed to Tabriz. Thence the immemorial way to Central Asia lies open along the Elburz flank ; or the Tigris basin can be readily entered, *pace* predatory Kurds and Lurs, by passes leading to the head-waters of the Lesser Zab, the Diyala, and the Kerkha.

Azerbaijan, therefore, experiences to the full the advantages and disadvantages of being a meeting-place of roads by which many nationalities have entered and can enter again ; and under existing political conditions the disadvantages prevail. In its north-western and south-western parts live many incongruous races of men. The weak Power, which holds it, governs nervously for fear of a strong Power at the northern gate, which can pass in at its own good time. The great trade route which crosses it, goes far to cancel its civilising influence on the towns by encouraging a predatory spirit in the rural districts. This is no uncommon effect of roads in ill-governed lands. The extension of railways in Anatolia has always meant at first the extension of brigandage.

But the balance against advantages is likely to be re-dressed ere long. The intimate relations, which Azer-baijan has had so long with western Turkey, through the influence of the Trebizond-Tabriz road, are giving place to a Russian connection promoted by the extension of the trans-Caucasian railway to the Aras. And the great mart of Tabriz, which has hitherto radiated something of the atmosphere of western Europe through the province, will in future be an east European centre. In any event,

Azerbaijan is destined less and less to be bound up with Persia, and under another rule to become a mining as well as an agricultural land.

The fact that from the flanks of Elburz, between which and the Caspian lies little but mountain and marsh, there stretches to the southern ocean a chain of impassable salt swamps, and hardly more passable sands, which large caravans can cross by only two routes, is less of strategic value to western Iran than a source of political and economic disadvantage. The " Medic Isthmus " has not been used by a large body of troops since Nadir Shah repulsed the Afghans in 1722 ; and modern armies directed against Irak from the north-east or east, would probably never attempt to operate from their land bases at all, but would turn one flank or other of the desert belt by sea. And it has exercised a separatist influence so powerful, that up to twenty years ago Persian authority, based on Isfahan and Teheran, was unable to secure its footing on the plains of Khorasan, and could even now be dislodged thence without the slightest difficulty, were there a strong ruler in Kabul, or did Russia choose to advance her posts to Meshed and Herat. As a trade route the Medic Isthmus has too little amenity to enable it to compete with the modern steam routes across the Turkman steppes and the Indian Ocean.

The natural access to Iran is from the north, north-west, and south-west. Russian influence comes into Teheran by the new cart-road from Resht, and to Azerbaijan by the Julfa ferry. Influences of British India enter from Bunder Abbas and the Karun, and reach Yezd and Kerman by the Laristan tracks, or Isfahan by the new Shuster-Ardal mule-path. Since, however, the western provinces of Persia are not less disjoined one from another than all are from the eastern, these influences hardly clash as yet, each observing its peculiar province, north and south. For no city has ever succeeded in being an effective centre to Iran. The position of the present Kajar capital, while it keeps Irak better in touch with the two important outlying provinces,

Khorasan and Azerbaijan, and also with Europe, than Isfahan, the Sefavi capital, could do, leaves the latter city with Shiraz, Yezd, and Kerman, not to mention the district of Khuzistan, to a half independence, which from time to time causes serious qualms to the central government. And little is done to bind together provinces where Nature opposes no serious obstacle to the engineer but the not prohibitive difficulty of saline steppe. No railway is in working order except a few miles of local line near Teheran ; and the only *chaussées* connect the capital with Resht and Kum. The other post-roads are mere mule-tracks, of which only that from Teheran to the Caspian at Amol, and the path from Isfahan to the Karun, have been modified to any serious degree by man.

Persian communications, in short, are still those of an undeveloped country. They follow the lines of Nature's least resistance, and are actually less good at this moment than when Shah Abbas built his causeway through the coastal swamps of Mazanderan. And even had they been no worse absolutely, the increase in speed and ease of locomotion in neighbouring lands would make them worse relatively.

Those Persian towns, which derived importance from their relation to natural avenues, retain it impaired only by general decay, not by such diversion of traffic as the nineteenth century order of road-making has occasioned elsewhere. Teheran gathers to herself the trans-Elburz tracks, and the traffic over the Medic Isthmus. Tabriz, as we saw, is the meeting-place of two or three great roads. Kashan will always be the point of division for the southward-tending traffic. Kerman and Yezd collect caravans to cross the desert belt, and there goods are " trans-shipped " from camel to camel for the mid-Gulf ports. Shiraz is the goal of the paths leading from northern ports of the Gulf, but it is doomed to wane, while Isfahan may wax again through its nearness to the terminus of steam-navigation on the Karun. But for the moment neither one nor the other

sees so much traffic pass through its streets as does
Kermanshahan, where Nature has carved the easiest of
her ways through the western chains.

There are, however, signs of better things at hand.
The enterprise of the Russian capitalists who have
widened the entrance to the Énzeli lagoon and made
an easy cart-road from Resht to the capital will restore
to Teheran some of the trade which passed through its
bazars, and those of Rhey before it, ere the " Medic

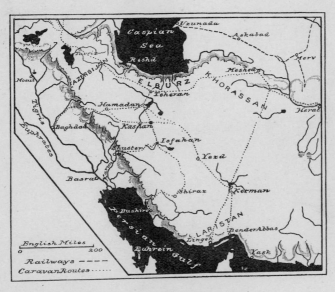

FIG. 46.—The chief routes in Persia.

Isthmus" ceased to carry the trunk road from west to
east. And the improved mule-road from Isfahan to the
Karun by way of the Ali Kuh pass and Ardal should
not only arrest the decay of the great Sefavi city, which
was once the Eye of Asia, but civilise further that section
of the border mountaineers who show most trace of
having been exposed in olden times to the humanising
influences of the west country, attracted up the lines of
traffic between Susa and Persepolis.

For the rest of western Asia Nature has restricted the modifying influence of through communications to a few well-defined lines. In the eastern part of the great southwestern area the heads of all important land roads must be upon the waterway of the Tigris. The great cities of Mosul and Baghdad mark points at which the chief natural avenues from west to east strike the river. Mosul is the terminus of those main tracks from the Mediterranean lands which avoid mountain or desert, and on their course make the prosperity of Urfa and Mardin; and of the direct route from the Bosphorus. And this convergence of roads has probably conduced to bring to the middle Tigris valley the motley assortment of religious communions that now inhabit it. Baghdad receives through the Kermanshah gap the Persian traffic, swelled to great proportions by an influence of which much account must henceforth be taken in this matter of communications, namely, religious pilgrimage. Nearly 100,000 of the Shiah faithful, carrying some 60,000 of their dead, resort annually to the gold-domed tombs of Ali, Hussein, and the Imam Musa at Nejef, Kerbela, and Kasimin; and to spoil them and their followers the Hillah Jews still sit by the waters of Babylon. For much trade accompanies this pilgrimage, going and coming over the farther land route, which crosses Arabia by way of Hayil to Mecca. And Baghdad is at present an emporium of inner Nejd as much as of inner Irak Ajemi, a thoroughly Arabised city, in which the Turk is more a stranger than the Wahabi of Riad.

If the projected German railroad to Basra be constructed by way of Mosul, it will develop the great resources, and settle the Kurds, of the Erbil district. If it follow the Euphrates, it will revive a route, which the energy of the Ottoman government, shown in recent years by the constitution of the *Mutessariflik* of Der and the policing of the right bank, has failed to develop. Should the Shah at last concede the Khoremabad-Dizful line to a powerful syndicate, and take a short way with the predatory Feili Lurs, Baghdad will suffer while Dizful and Shuster will increase.

As for the three great waterways, much of their useful-ness is in embryo as yet. The navigation of the Karun has been as much impeded by the unsettled conditions which prevail on its banks, as by the obstructions in its waterway. Indeed, the lukewarm attitude of the Teheran Government in this question of opening the Persian stream, has possibly been due in some measure to consciousness of inability to control the peoples among whom the steamers must be navi-gated. And as for the Tigris and Euphrates, Irak Arabi is much more affected by the pilgrim land-route than by through navigation. For the Baghdad steamers make only three or four halts on the lower Tigris, and the service is much hampered by the Ottoman policy, which discourages an effective British line of steamers in favour of a slow and irregular Turkish company. The development of regular navigation on the reaches above Baghdad by anything but rafts or *keleks* has not yet been effected, though the water-way is possible up to Jezire and even to Diarbekr. On the Euphrates there is now no regular steam-service at all. Thirty years ago it was hoped that Aleppo might be brought within five days of Baghdad by water transit from Méskine. To-day the stream is not considered navigable above Rakka, and is not, in fact, ascended above Hit.

Nevertheless the potential value of these waterways must not be minimised. They have shown their local power in the creation of the date-growing industry of the Muntefik country, and by calling into existence half-a-dozen towns like Kut-el-Amara ; and they have yet to develop an immense influence on Persia.

Weigh the physical features of the Gulf coast, together with the nature of the mountain roads that lead to Shiraz and Kerman, against the Shatt-el-Arab and the water and land-ways that open upon it, and the meanest intelligence can decide wherein lies the importance of the Persian Gulf as an avenue to the inland East. Is it, however, to be also a link in a great through route from the Far West to the Far East ? Is there ever to be a " Euphrates Valley " line, lying chiefly through deserts, for the use of the lords of India ? Or is a German line to be constructed down the richer

Tigris basin to develop in the first place Turkish, Armenian, Kurdish, and Persian local trade, whatever ulterior object there may lurk in the mind of its promoters? Or will the Russian locomotives arrive first from the Urmi basin? The near future will know.

No one of the tracks across the Hamad can be said to be frequented sufficiently to exercise even a local influence on the tribes. For since the opening of the Suez Canal, trade between east and west has deserted the painful Euphratean routes as completely as the Medic Isthmus. And the present policy pursued by the Ottoman Government towards the Anaze Bedawin, if it prove as successful as with the Shammar, will end by consummating the abandonment of the desert roads. For the nomads supply the only life which makes the passage of a large part of the Hamad possible, and to settle them as *fellahin* in the Euphrates trough is to make a solitude where peace should be. Already the oasis of Tudmor has lost even the shadow of that greatness which was once Palmyra's, when she gathered the caravans bound to and from the Euphrates ; and Damascus is become of far less consequence on account of its relation to the routes which cross eastward to Der and Hit, than as terminus of railways from the Mediterranean shore.

The powerful influence which steam should exercise on the Syrian Fringe is not yet developed. Rails have not been laid from Iskenderun to Aleppo or from Tripoli to Homs, and very little progress has been made on the natural and easy route from Haifa to Damascus by way of the head of the Ghor. The two completed railways, Jaffa-Jerusalem and Beirut-Damascus-Mzerib, are financial failures, the one because it is too short, the other because, the better to serve political interests in the Lebanon, it has been laid on an unnatural and too laborious line. But while the first has contributed towards the trebling of the population of Jerusalem in the past decade, and the colonisation of central Judæa with Jewish settlements, the second has realised Midhat's project of opening out the Lebanon, and made the volcanic plains of the Jaulan and western Hauran bear one of the largest wheat crops in the Nearer East. When fully developed and resting on protected harbours, this system of railways, cutting across the general direction of the geographical features of Syria, will serve to neutralise the immemorial tendency of this Fringe to display upon a superficial area, hardly larger than that of Greece, a *congeries* of human groups bitterly antagonistic in tradition and hope.

The influence of communications in the Arabian Peninsula is identical with the influence of the main pilgrim roads. And nowadays, indeed, hardly of more than one of these. For steam navigation in the Levant and Red Sea has seduced the great majority of the northern Sunnis from undertaking the painful tramp to the Hejaz, whether from Damascus by way of Man, or from Egypt round the head of the Akaba Gulf. From Man to El Ala the tanks and *kellas* are falling to decay. In the trans-Jordan country Circassian colonists have replaced the Albanian and Móghrabi garrisons, once maintained in little forts along the *Derb-el-Haj*, and they are found far more effective agents of civilisation.

The Shiah route, however, though not what it was a generation ago, is still of sufficient importance to make its control the key to supremacy in Nejd. In the palmy days of the Wahabite empire of Riad, the pilgrim caravans, with their following of merchants, traversed southern Nejd, coming from Nejef or the Gulf ; and the most serious blow struck at the dynasty of Ibn Saud was the diversion of the Haj from the Aflaj-Hanifah road, which lies within the range of Wahabi insolence, to the more northerly line of wells in the Rumma basin, which are under the more immediate control of Rashid's dynasty in Hayil. On that line the heretical Haj still marches twice a year, though in decreased numbers. Not that in this case, the sea has seriously diverted the pilgrims, for, unlike the Sunnis, Shiahs assemble at inland points, Kerbela and Nejef, hardly less holy than Mecca, whence there is transit neither easy

nor rapid to the sea. But the Persian *haj* is sharing the
decline which seems to be affecting all streams of the
Mecca pilgrimage alike.[1]

With the fate of that great Moslem institution, the
Mecca pilgrimage, is bound up the fate of a most important
part of Arabia, nay, in a sense the fate of the whole Moslem
world. The pilgrim routes alone have made Mecca and
Medina centres of trade. Only the importance of Mecca
and Medina has raised Jidda, Yambo, and El Wij from
collections of beach-combers' huts to the estate of towns.
The natural outlets of Nejd are on the side of the Gulf.
But for the route taken by the Persian *haj*, after visiting
the Euphratean shrines, no merchants from the farther
East would ever cross Nejd at all. The steady decline of
the pilgrimage, therefore, is a very serious matter for the
Hejaz. For some years past the land routes have been less
and less frequented, the old line of the Sunni *haj*, always
unsafe, especially where controlled by the Harb tribes,
being hardly used at all ; and this falling off, while in any
case seriously affecting such road stations as Tayif or the
oasis of El Ala, whose negroid folk grow dates for the
pilgrims, and even Medina, has not been compensated by
an equal increase in the numbers of the sea-borne devotees.

The Hejazis have indeed good cause both to bemoan
and to bestir themselves, sending their *dellals* out year by
year to the four quarters of Islam. As it is, Mecca can
no longer boast any secular industries of importance, and
is filled with little more than a collection of miscellaneous
caterers for the annual religious influx. The population
indeed is almost as little Arab as that of Jidda, and
equally increasing in fanatical hatred of the European
influence, to which, not without reason, is ascribed the
drying of the source of wealth. What effect this decline
will have on the inwardly heterodox population of the
Peninsula is obvious. But the effect, in a much wider
world than Arabia, of the discontinuance of a practice

---

[1] The decline seems real and continuous ; but much fluctuation is caused in the
not too reliable statistics by the operation of quarantine in Egypt, Kamaran, and
India ; and by occasional restlessness of such tribes as the Harb on the inland roads.

which has long been almost the only influence for unity exercised in common upon divers sections of Moslems, is less easy to estimate.

For the rest, there is little to be said about communications in the Great Peninsula. Hasa profits by the traffic which finds its way from Nejd over the narrow northward tongue of the Desert to Katif ; but its rulers shut it, equally with Katr and the Yemen, to the outside world. The inland districts of Kasim and Woshm owe their populousness not only to the drainage that their low basins collect, but also to the absence of difficult desert between them and the oases of the central Hejaz. Oman communicates readily with India, so readily that her merchant class is mainly Banian, and her politics are never allowed to be independent of the British *raj*. The

FIG. 47.—The chief routes in Arabia.

south-western ports, as far as Saihut, have become more African than Asiatic by constant intercourse with Somaliland ; but Aden is the only point at which the high sea road of the Old World affects the Peninsula, within sight of whose shores it passes for nearly a week of rapid steaming (Fig. 47).

Nevertheless, despite difficult sea-access west, south, and east, despite guardian Nefud to north, and inner ring

of sand defence, the communities even of inland Arabia
are troubled by a sense of their thin and dissipated organisation in the face of external foes ; and a nervousness of
strangers, often expressing itself in terms of a religious
fanaticism foreign to the real character of the people, is
characteristic of all Nejd, which, like half Africa and
Asia, fears lest influences from without should subvert
the slavery which is the basis of its social system.

The use that the Ottoman Power, which by the
treachery of the Koweit Arabs has seized Hasa, Katif, and
Katr, might make of the eastern approaches from the
Euphratean country and the Gulf shore is the present
ground of alarm.[1] To the north the Shammar feel safe,
for no armed force but the Emir's own camelmen who
took Jauf has ever crossed the Nefud; and from the south
it is not conceivable that any should ever appear. Nor
do they seem to apprehend invasion from the west as
much as from the east, partly because of the longer waterless marches (though these did not stop Ibrahim Pasha),
but more because they know the " Turks " to have enough
to do to maintain their own position in the Red Sea
countries. The *Daula* may stretch forth a weak arm
from Medina to Kheibar, even on occasion from Tebuk
to Teima ; but no one but the terrible Egyptian has ever
marched to Nejd, and even he did not touch Hayil.

The Persians had ceased to be a bogey, even when
Palgrave was in Riad. But the British are become hardly
less a source of uneasiness in Nejd since the suppression
of the Gulf Pirates, and the rapid increase of Aden, than
they have long been to the Omanis, to the hidden population of the Hadramut, and to the officials at Sana. For
to no part of her Empire does Turkey apply so vigorous
and so energetic a policy as to the Yemen. Her recent
reinforcement of the administration there, and her bid for
Bedawin support has been prompted not by fear only of
the implacable Carmathian peasants of the central Plateau,
but of possible support that might be extended to them by
the great European fortress which dominates Lahej.

[1] Justified, since the above was written, by a retaliatory attack made on Hayil
by the Sheikh of Koweit.

The Nile Valley is at once the most difficult region in the Nearer East for a Mediterranean power to enter against determined resistance, and the easiest to traverse, once the gates are forced. Of such gates there are, for important strategic operations, only two,—on the east the narrow tongue, half desert, half cultivation, between the Menzaleh marshes and the high Arabian waste, which the British army forced at Tel-el-Kebir; and on the north-west the still narrower interval between the Mariut and Burlos swamps, which Arabi closed at Kafr Dauar. European armies have been led into Egypt round the desolate western marge of Mariut, and by the Wadi Hamamat, but with great pain, and not a second time. The bars at the Nile mouths, and the wastes which stretch away right and left

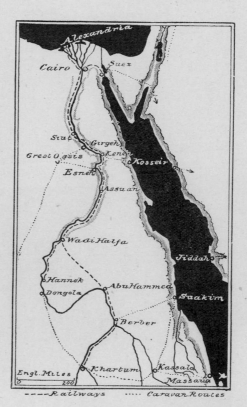

FIG. 48.—The chief routes in Egypt.

for many days' march, close above a thousand miles of the valley to serious invasion from any other quarter (Fig. 48). From the two gates, however, one of the easiest waterways in the world leads without interruption through all of the land that is to be desired of man. Hence the life of Egypt has been throughout her history

P

uniform in the intense individuality maintained under native rulers, uniform in the rapid modification experienced under aliens. All is secluded, or all is exposed.

The modification exercised on Egyptian life by communications other than this Nile waterway—the Suez Canal excepted—is not great. In other days the points of issue of caravan routes from the desert determined the position and importance of the provincial urban centres, even as the apex of the Delta, where control can best be exercised over the divergent waters, has determined the sites successively of Memphis, Babylon, Fostat, and Cairo. Aswan stands not only at the head of the uninterrupted riverway, but of routes to the old harbour of Berenice and to Dongola and Berber. From Esneh and Girgeh the roads start for the Greater Oasis. Keneh is what Kuft and Kus have been, the outlet of the short route to the Red Sea. Siut, most important of all, used to be not only in communication with the Greater Oasis, but the goal of the long track from Kordofan and central Africa. Mállawi and Beni Suef are still the trysts for caravans bound to Farafra and Baharia respectively. The only important exception to this rule for the growth of settlements to first rank in Upper Egypt is Minieh, which owes importance to its central position in that area of the Upper Valley, where irrigation is most developed, namely, the strip enclosed between the main river and the Bahr Yusuf.

The development, however, of the Nile Valley by the new railway, will probably be found to have destroyed the importance of all these desert roads, the eastern of which had already suffered by the cutting of the Suez Isthmus. And with their decay will vanish not only such external relations as the stoppage of Sudan trade by the Dervishes had left to these towns for the past fifteen years, but also most of the importance of all the western oases except Siwah. That oasis alone collects roads from a region of Africa to which the Nile Valley gives no access, namely, the fertile pans in the *hinterland* of the Cyrenaica, and the chain of oases which divide the

Libyan Desert from the high western Sahara. And since these (*pace* the Senusi Sheikh and the Wadai Sultan) favour the passage of the feather and ivory caravans, and now and again of slave convoys from Chad and Borku to Bengázi, Siwah is an African outpost towards Asiatic Egypt, and such a constant source of trouble, that, alone among the oases, it is excepted from the provincial divisions, and placed under the immediate control of the Minister of the Interior.

The past century has wrought many changes in the world's ways of communication, but none more radical than in Egypt. Before steam navigation was introduced to her great waterway, the best *dahabíya* probably ascended the river no faster than those Twelfth Dynasty boats that were dug a few years back out of the sands of Dahshur. Now the steamer has not only made rapid and sure the water-transit, but it has brought a most important new influence to bear on the peasantry. The immense tourist traffic upon the Nile is a modifying agency not to be ignored. It has raised Luxor from a small hamlet to be a centre of European civilisation, and it has altered, it must be confessed not outwardly for the better, the character of thousands of natives at different points on the stream. The indubitable increase of their wealth and the educating influence of the practice of alien tongues and of familiarity with the apparatus of a higher civilisation may be set against the loss of self-respect which the weak Nilot's nature, like the Bedawin's, often suffers when it is brought into intimate contact with luxurious Europeans.

But modern methods of communication in the Nile Valley have had an effect yet more subtle and farther reaching. The locomotive has transformed in a decade the way of life which the Nilot farmer had lived unchanged since days when the Pyramids were not. By main lines of rail, and in the Delta and Fayum by lately constructed light iron roads bridging the canals, which once were sufficient to keep him in his own island, the peasant visits every week three or four markets that his father hardly saw once in a lifetime. Ideas of locomotion, based since the dawn of time entirely on slow water transit, have given way at last to familiarity with rapid passage by land. The *fellah* takes to railways with a child's pleasure ; and he who was once the most stagnant of beings is fast becoming mobile, enterprising, and of wide experience. Even in the rural districts the old Egypt is passing away hardly less rapidly than right and left of the Muski in Cairo.

Special works on Communications need only be mentioned in a few instances. The Vardar route is very fully described by A. Tuma, who deals also with all roads in the western part of the Peninsula. On the Durazzo-Monastir road see also V. Bérard. For all roads in Asia Minor, see W. M. Ramsay's *Hist. Geography*, and for south-eastern roads and passes, R. G. S. Suppl. Papers, by J. A. R. Munro and myself. The sum of all our routes is in Murray's Guide, with those of British military consuls. On Persian routes, besides Curzon, see *Hauptverkehrswege Persiens*, by Rausch von Traubenberg (1890). On the Karun route, Ainsworth (*Karun*, 1890) and Curzon are full. On Mesopotamian waterways, see Ainsworth (*Euphr. Exped.*). The Pilgrim routes from Damascus, Egypt, and Persia to Mecca are described by Doughty, Burton, Keane, Snouck-Hurgronje, Palgrave, and Blunt. Finally, for all routes of commerce by land and sea it is essential to study the Foreign Office Consular Reports, sent from such places as Piræus, Salonica, Smyrna, Angora, Trebizond, Tabriz, Resht, Isfahan, Baghdad, Basra, Bushire, Jidda, Damascus, Beirut, Alexandria, and Suez.

CHAPTER XIV

LIFE UNDER BALKAN CONDITIONS

SINCE the Shar range permits no passage of loaded animals, while, on the other hand, the hills fall toward a prohibitive belt of malarious swamp, and a sea destitute of safe harbours; since also there are to be reckoned into the account such inner influences of separation as the numerous torrential rivers, fed by a copious rainfall and flowing in deep limestone troughs through hills of very steep incline, it need surprise no one that the highlander character is developed in its extreme form in north and central Albania. Instinct of clan exclusiveness; absence of common sentiment or authority, resulting in the glorification of fighting; devolution of all peaceful drudgery on the shoulders of women or slaves; most rigorous enforcement of that inevitable police measure of primitive clan societies, the blood feud; disinclination for urban life; and all the jealous individualism, superstitious imagining, primitive conservatism, and barbarous habit of an exclusively pastoral society—these are characteristic.

That the life led by the many small clans of the Gheg population of North Albania is largely due to the peculiar relief of their country, is proved in part by the fact that, as the geographical conditions grew gradually less arduous south of the Skumbi, so does the life of a folk, speaking the same family of language and presenting a facial type of the same class, change gradually to a less fierce and barbarian sort. But it is even more significant that Ghegs themselves, who in their own hills are used to despise any profession but armed idleness, when they emigrate elsewhere (as do many for long terms of years to Constantinople and other places in the Levant) become comparatively industrious and useful members of society, given to seafaring, skilled labour, and even the learned professions. Not that heredity and tradition ever permits an "Arnaút" from the North to be a model of a peaceful citizen or the most hardworking of his neighbours ; but abroad he can at least be not a savage.

Gheg character cannot, however, be entirely explained in terms of geography. The deliberate purpose of man has something to answer for. The Ottoman Turk has two ways of dealing with wild tribes, whom he would put under his heel, the one making for barbarism, the other for civilisation of a certain sort. He applies the last where the fighting character of the tribes is not deep rooted, and he has nothing to fear from their learning to combine, or (the greater danger) to look to foreigners ; and accordingly he disarms the Bedawins of Mesopotamia and forces them to settle and become *fellahin* or traders. But the Gheg, on the other hand, he arms, he trains in war, he encourages in tribal animosity and religious hate, and he dissuades from agriculture or trade. His own supremacy he secures by kidnapping and exiling the Albanian clan chiefs, but he makes no effort to civilise the people, to open out their country, to make roads or ports.

With the passage of the Skumbi river we leave this home of primitive barbarism for a gentler order of things. But there is gradual development, not radical change. For there runs southwards, through the Toskh Albanians of Epirus and the Vlachs of Pindus to the mixed population of Central Greece and the Morea, a certain solidarity in the manner of men's life and ethical custom. The highland ferocity of the northern Ghegs is only the extreme expression of a spirit, whose degeneration may be detected in the southernmost Greeks.

All travellers bound for Berat, who have come across the Skumbi, note a change in the attitude of the Toskh of the long river valleys, as compared with that of the dreaded Gheg. The former is not so confident, and is more individualist than clannish. Fighting less, he herds his flocks more, and will sulkily admit strangers in his midst, giving them his *bessa*, or plighted word.   For there are true Turki folk settled all down the Skumbi as far as Pekini, and a large group of sedentary gipsies are found in the plain of Musakiya.   Where conditions are easy, as in the rich basin of Goritza and on the coast plains, some attention is devoted to the soil ; and indeed forty years ago the English occupation of Corfu caused a market-gardening industry to spring up about Avlona.

There are, of course, certain isolated fastnesses, where a fierce clan-exclusiveness was maintained against Ali Pasha, and still is maintained by Toskhs in a manner worthy of any tribe of Ghegs, and every extreme feature of mountain society is in evidence.   But in general it is truly said of southern Toskhland, that in the genial climate of the westward Adriatic slopes, blessed with a copious winter rainfall and refreshed in spring and summer by the melting snows of the high central peaks and those frequent thunderstorms, which once were placed to the credit of Zeus of Dodona, the peasant finds a profit in cultivating his upland plains ; and the merchants of Janina, placed between an easy eastward pass and an accessible western sea, find themselves invited by Nature to traffic with the outside world.

The ruder physical conditions of the Spine below Goritza are not reflected, to the extent that might have been expected, in the character of the mountaineers.   The anomaly, however, is readily explained by the peculiar circumstances of their origin.   For they came, as we have seen, at no distant date from the plains, and still in the mountains maintain the characteristics of plainmen, a sturdy steadiness in battle, a talent for agriculture, and a great aptitude for trade.   Ere the blighting Ottoman rule was firmly established in Macedonia and Albania, the Vlachs of Moschopolis, controlling the great Zygos road, prosecuted a most lucrative commerce ; and they have given to both Turkish and Greek armies their most reliable fighters, and to liberated Hellas its best element of stability and progress.

Central Greece, a lean land elsewhere than in the

Ætolian lake basins, has few agriculturists and fewer traders, for its formation permits of no easy roads east of the lakes. Except in small and isolated coast plains like those of Missolonghi and Itéa, its sons, who are not shepherds, become sailors, repulsed by the inhospitable hills, and enticed upon the sea by the safe boat harbours that indent the shore from the Bay of Arta round to the recess of the Corinthian Gulf.

The folk of the Ionian Isles are Epirotes modified rather by the accident of insular position and intercourse with the foreigner, than by any peculiarity of physical conditions. Such modification is most noticeable in Corfu, whose inhabitants, to judge from their ancient history, had once no small share of the fierce mainland character. Ithaka, Paxo, and Santa Mavra have hardly more than peasant populations, for the most part pastoral ; but Kefalonia, ample and of varied relief, claims the most enterprising of the islanders, and more than the rest has maintained the standard of well-being to which the British advanced the Seven Isles. But for native riches Zante bears the palm. An acre of agricultural land fetches there a higher price than elsewhere in the Levant ; it lies in the Currant zone ; and its population, generally of northern origin, whether Slav or Toskh, has developed out of its natural resources, despite the discouragement of frequent earthquakes, a considerable commerce and a culture as high as, and more indigenous than, that of Corfu.

Facilities for navigation, the mountainous and beautiful nature of the land, and the keen bracing air of the most part of it, have been the chief formative influences on Greek life in all ages. The highlanders' restless individualism, intense local feeling, love of independence and imaginative habit, modified and softened by the civilising influence of the element which chiefly draws men together, assimilates and makes them know, and borrow from, the world about them—these are at the root of Greek character ; and the result has been sharpened and refined by a singular fortune of climate. The essential influences are the same now as they have always been, and they produce the same general order of intelligence, of greater or less energy ; but the channels into which that intelligence is directed have always depended on other influences, not physical, and mostly acting from without.

In a land of mountaineers and sailors it is to be expected that agriculture will not greatly flourish. The Greek soil is thin, stony, and seldom easy to work ; the draught cattle are of a weak breed ; water is scant in most of the land, and the population, for reasons often political, is thin even in such favoured districts as the Thessalian plain. In the great semi-island of the Morea, the radiating focus of Hellenism, is found the Hellenic population at once the most diverse in origin, the most completely unified, and the least affected now by outer influences. In general the Peloponnesian folk, though insular, are not distinctively maritime ; and it has been acutely pointed out that only when the Morea has been in the hands of an external sea-power, like Venice, have the centres of its life been ports. It is true that, deeply indented as are the coasts of the Peninsula, it has no perfectly sheltered and conveniently deep harbours, except perhaps the bay of Navarino, which has difficult communications with the interior. But when we observe the same character in the folk of certain of the largest islands of the Levant, notably Cyprus, Rhodes, and Crete, we must ascribe the blunting of the natural maritime instincts of the Greek in the Morea to that anarchy of the sea, already mentioned more than once, which has been the continual curse of the Levant. The eastern basin of the Mediterranean is studded and fringed with such rocky refuges as Psara, Kasos, and Hydra, whose inhabitants, having nothing to gain and nothing to lose on their own shores, have pursued with single minds the trade of corsairs wherever and whenever no strong power maintained a police of the sea. Living in their ships these pirates could prey on the surrounding coasts, where inland wealth existed, secure from suffering any loss equivalent to their gains.

Agriculture, where possible, and the herding of flocks are the pursuits of the Moreote. Rich marble veins and

mines have yet to be reopened for him, and he manufactures little but dairy produce. His is the low standard
of living which characterises pastoral folk, and his their
vices of idleness and indiscipline. But his also their
virtues of sobriety, frugality, agility, and consequent healthy
morality ; and oppressed though he was for centuries by an
alien domination, fixed in his very midst, he has preserved
the spirit of highland independence. A worthy, dignified
folk, mostly small peasant holders on the old "Timariote"
system, the Moreotes impress the traveller more favourably than do the Ionian, Attic, or northern Greeks.

Of the smaller important islands that hang on the
Morea, the two which prolong the Argolid, Hydra, and
Spetzae, being utterly barren, are inhabited entirely by
maritime folk. But the island of Cerigo is of a softer
aspect, as befits the seat of Kytherean Aphrodite, and
being broken up into small and fertile plains, supports a
peaceful and intelligent population.

The self-sufficing and continental character of Crete is
reflected in the jealous and exclusive independence of its
inhabitants. Of homogeneous type, with a common refinement of feature which attests purity and antiquity of race,
the Cretans are divided only in creed, and that owing
ultimately to physical conditions, to the contrast, in fact,
that exists between the tremendous relief and inaccessi-
bility of most of the island, and the openness of a few
plain districts, where a defenceless population, with much
to lose, found that it had all to gain by identifying itself
with the dominant alien. Although Crete has one first-
rate harbour and many that will shelter small craft, the
natives, as distinct from their alien rulers, have retired
inland, attracted by the rich lacustrine basins, which open
within their hills, and either contract to very narrow guts
on the sea side or are completely closed ; and in these
the Cretan dwells to-day, as the old proverb said of him,
"ignorant of the sea," poor, and rooted to the soil.

Nor are the islanders of the larger Cyclades much more
maritime. Through the possession of small fertile plains
or mineral wealth, Naxos, Paros, Santorin, Milos, Tinos,

and Andros have always been self-supporting, and have
left enterprise upon that sea, which few Greeks roam by
choice, to the men of the barren rocks, Kasos, Syros, or
Psara. Betwixt and between lie such as Siphnos, Serpho,
Zia, Thérmia, Amorgos, Ios, and their like, as aloof as their
larger and better endowed neighbours. And therefore
there survives, even in this day of steam navigation, a most
remarkable variety of custom and aspect in the several
members of the Cyclad groups, the most of which, though
within sight of mainland, are the most "isolated" islands
of the Mediterranean. Each suffices barely for itself, compelling simplicity and frugality of living on its naked calcareous slopes, which yield no agricultural surplus for
exportation, and indeed little that in any case would find a
market abroad.

Not only great tradition, but physical character and
environment, marked Athens for the one possible capital
of new and centralised Hellenism. No other spot, except
Corinth, is so situated that it can hold the same relation
to highland and to lowland Greece. Had the capital
been chosen in the Morea, new Hellas had been a little
mountain republic. Had it been fixed in Bœotia, as
under the Frank Dukes, then a tiny State of farmers,
at war with surrounding highlanders, would have been
called into being. And not even Corinth, on her two
bays, would have so effectually done for new Greece
the further and greater service of turning her eyes to
the sea. As we have observed, the majority of present
Greeks are, strange to say, not distinctively a sea-folk. The
particular hills or plains of each several locality hold chief
empire in their minds, and all the national tendency is
towards a provincial subdivided society, taking little account
of the outer world. But alike to those internal divisions
and their common exclusiveness the sea is the essential
antidote. It is not only her matchless harbour of the
Piræus, but the barrenness of her land, that makes Athens
maritime. The Attic hills are too ill watered and too ill
clad for highland refuges ; the Attic plain is ungrateful
soil. By the sea Athens must live, and by the sea in a

certain measure she makes all Greece live, with a bond
of internal union, an encouragement to external relations,
and a possibility of being centre of a Greater Hellas,
which no other capital would have given her (Fig. 49).
The city stands, morever, on undulating ground in a singularly beautiful, dry, and healthy situation, open both to
sea-breezes and the purifying northern airs, admitted
between Hymettus and Pentelicus. And such advantages
must be held to outweigh the difficulty of providing a
water-supply, the dusty nature of the soil, the lack of
surrounding vege-
tation, and the un-
fortunate fact, that
the town lies apart,
and at a distance
both from the most
productive areas of
Greece, and from
the main track of
commerce.

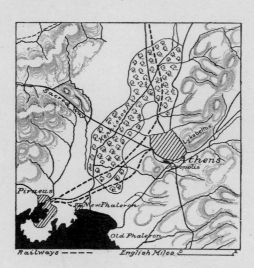

FIG. 49.—Athens.

Attica is Athens
and its environs,
and the rural
population, except
in one district, is
a thin Albanian
farmer and shep-
herd-folk of no
great account.
The exception is the single considerable mining district of
Greece, that lead and iron-veined hill country at the point
of the Attic peninsula, where a singular apparition of tall
chimneys, slag-heaps, mineral railways, rows of grimy
cottages and knots of grimy men, recalls a pit district of
North Yorkshire.

In the chain of broad and low lacustrine basins, parted
and enclosed by high and narrow ridges, which succeed
one another up to the Vardar head, a rude population of
shepherds and woodcutters is sandwiched between larger

communities of agricultural plain-dwellers ; and the mountain element is made the more restless by the neighbourhood
of political frontiers, and the competition of racial rivals.
The southernmost basin, the Bœotian, lying farthest from
any frontier, is the least disturbed, but at the same time its
population is the most primitive. For the barbarising
influence of a numerous Albanian folk, settled on the
fertile adjacent slopes, has to be added in modern times to
the stupefying effect of the Copaic marshes, long notorious.
Until the draining of some 60,000 acres through the
reopened *katavothrae* was accomplished, enabling Bœotia
to take front place among Greek agricultural districts,
the great island of Eubœa, or Negroponte, which lies
along the Bœotian coast, had been in advance of the
mainland both in productiveness and in civilisation.
For under other political conditions Eubœa has derived
a certain advantage from the very fact that it is an island.
Furthermore, it is an island fronting to a tranquil land-
locked sea ; its high ridge catches great part of those
north-easterly rains that would otherwise drench Bœotia
and Attica, and is able to retain snow ; and, also, like
the small but well-conditioned isle of Skyros, which lies
off its eastern coast, it is singularly rich in marbles and
minerals. A long-settled farming population, which used
to cultivate the cornlands and vineyards of the feudal
Turkish gentry, is now being reinforced by a growing
element of quarrymen and miners ; and its well-being and
wealth, of which Eubœa imparts a sense to the traveller
more than any Greek mainland district except Messenia,
is steadily on the increase. Good roads, made at very
great cost, mineral tramways, and trim port-villages, are
outward and visible signs of what has always made this
isle desired by the dominant race of the mainland,
Athenian, Frank, or Turkish.

The natural advantages of the Thessalian basin have,
however, long been impaired by insecurity of public
peace ; and it has come about that, although Thessaly
is the granary of Greece, well supplied with railways,
and in parts of a soil very favourable to the culture of

tobacco, cotton, and the mulberry, land there at present
is not worth on an average the fourteenth part of its
value in Zante ; and there is no more poverty-stricken
and rude population than that of its less grateful soils, such
as the slopes of the Khassia mountains on the northern
border.

Against the physical conditions favouring the development of a higher local civilisation in Macedonia, must be
set others which, given a weak or ill-intentioned Government, exert serious counter-influence. Not only are the
basins backed everywhere by the pastoral wilds of Albania,
but they are outlined and traversed by shaggy lateral ridges
of the Spine, apt to foster a rude shepherd folk. The
wolf can keep the flock always in sight, and if hunted, retire
up the buttresses of the impenetrable mountains on the
west. To the chronic evil of brigandage falls to be added
the degrading influence of the undrained deltaic marsh of
the Vardar and Vistritza, which affects all the southern
district, even the great city of Salonica, and of the
northern lacustrine basin and coastal swamps of the
Chalcidic Peninsula. The political influences, which make
for disturbance from without, are not therefore the only
agents that deprive the Macedonian valleys of the peace
which should follow on their comparative plenty.

The frequent occurrence, however, of large and busy
urban centres in the Vardar basin speaks to a general well-
being in advance of the Greek ; and the greatest of these,
the Jewish city of Salonica, is a thriving port despite all
disadvantages. It has the fortune to be situated about the
middle of the European coast-line of the Ægean, on the
deepest and best protected of its inlets, and at the mouth
of the easiest road to the fertile districts of the interior.
Moreover, most other ports, which might compete with it,
are blockaded by mountains, or by unsettled populations.
Thus its collecting radius is very wide. It is better to
send goods from north-eastern Epirus to Salonica than to
Avlona or Durazzo ; and even for the products of the head
valleys of many Danubian tributaries the first named is still
the most accessible port. Want of drainage and security

in the surrounding district, however, prevent Salonica
from being not only a great port, but the centre of a
highly productive agricultural area.

Inland eastern Macedonia is suited in the main to a
pastoral and wood-cutting folk, living retired in glens of
the hills. On the Upper Struma a series of upland basins
gather these hillmen into groups rooted to the soil and
capable of some sort of economic unity ; but in the wild
and strait Mesta valley they remain detached and semi-
nomadic. Yet the coastal strip of this rude zone, as we
have seen already, is physically so circumstanced as to
favour agriculture above any other Balkan tract ; and,
developed by a railway and improved ports at Dedeagach
and Kavalla, it must modify sensibly ere long the highland
wildness of the Pomaks.

The islands, that lie off the west Thracian shore,
sharing its copious rainfall, are distinguished from other
Ægean isles by the wealth of vegetation which springs
wherever the gradients of the emerged peaks are gentle
enough to retain their soil.   Thasos and Lemnos, the latter
blessed with rich volcanic earth, have a numerous agricultural population, while the huge peak of Samothrace
and rocky Imbros maintain only sparse fishers, shepherds
and burners of charcoal.

In the last zone of the Peninsula—those lowlands
that open beyond the Despoto range—the physical conditions, so far as they go, make all the population alike
farmers, cultivating vineyards and rose-plantations under
the shelter of the Balkan and the Sredna Gora ranges to
the north, cereals in the bare wind-swept plains of the
centre, and market - gardens over a wide radius about
the capital. A densely-grouped, peaceful, and well-to-do
people should fill therefore the upper and lower Thracian
plains. But, in effect, owing to causes not physical, all
these qualifications apply only to the folk of the upper
levels ; and the low scrubby hills which fringe the plains
on the east continue, hardly less than the huge mountain
system on the west, to shelter rude pastoral communities,
hardened by a singularly inclement and variable sky.   In

the intervening plains are no urban centres of the first
rank. The capitals of the two levels, Philippopolis and
Adrianople, have a local importance only, and the former,
enjoying better political conditions, is fast outstripping
the latter. The difference in the shelter and accessibility
of the coast makes the inhabitants of the Marmora littoral
active sea-traders, while those from the Bosphorus to Burgas are of the lower grade of fishermen, when not merely
shepherds or cultivators of the lower seaward slopes.

The condition of Rumelia has always been profoundly
modified by the fortunes
of the great imperial city,
which stands partly in it,
but is of world-wide im-
port. For geographical
purposes Constantinople
is all that agglomeration
of habitations which
covers not only both
banks of the Golden
Horn, but both shores
of the Bosphorus for
many miles, and shelters
a million souls (Fig. 50).
It is really a city and
port of Asia as much as
of Europe.   Attention
has been called already
in the chapter on Com-
munications (p. 204) to

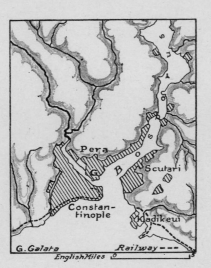

FIG. 50.—Constantinople.

the unique importance of its position, astride on the
frontier of two continents, where the greatest trans-
continental road crosses one of the most frequented of
the secondary sea routes, the only one giving access
to Russia throughout the year. No other site in the
world enjoys equal advantages, nor perhaps ever will
enjoy them.   For the isthmus of Suez is beset by deserts,
and that of Panama has a climate not to be compared.
Constantinople not only has an open and most fertile

environment and easy access to the interior of both
Europe and Asia, but its position between two seas and
exposure on the side of Russia give it an almost northern climate.   Add to this a dry, sloping site, a superb
harbour, an admirable outer roadstead, easy local communication by way of the Bosphorus and inexhaustible
water supply, and it is easy to agree that those who
founded Chalcedon, but left Byzantium to others, were
indeed blind.

Unprejudiced appreciations of the character of South Balkan peoples
are very rare.   The Greek character, especially, is seldom treated justly
by a northern observer, apt to remember the ancient Hellene too much
or too little.   The Oriental element does not give endurance and dignity
to Latin decadence in Greece as in Spain, because it is not due to the
intrusion of a strong Oriental race.   To be fair, the Briton must overcome his strong aversion to ideas without works.   In his aloof manner
" Odysseus," the author of *Turkey in Europe*, takes an unusually judicious
view of all the constituents of the Balkan population.   Next to him
among recent observers I should place M. Victor Bérard (*La Macédoine
et l' Hellenisme Contemporain*).   In published accounts of the Greeks one
has usually to do with social, religious, or scholarly idealists with little
knowledge of the realities.   To their views a course of Byron's letters
from Greece and Finlay's final volume supplies a salutary corrective.

CHAPTER XV

CROSS from Europe to Asia by way of Bosphorus, Dardanelles, or Ægean Archipelago and you will observe no greater degree of immediate change in the character and life of the population than in the nature of the Relief. But as the physical conditions of all the Asia Minor coasts occasion a more genial climate, greater fertility and less unquiet seas, so the folk of this littoral are of a softer temper, more rooted to the soil, richer and less warlike, and more prone to and deeply involved in maritime trade. But their commercial instinct is developed, and their wealth and with it their standard of living are heightened rather by an accident of position. For unlike the coasts of south-east Europe, which, being less favourably circumstanced than other coasts of that continent, attract only a local trade, those of Asia Minor have at their back half a continent, selling and buying through their ports.

While, therefore, the affinities of the Anatolian islanders and west coast dwellers are essentially with the inhabitants of the opposing shores, the Asiatics have in all ages been more highly developed than the Europeans. When history begins to know anything of their condition, they were held to be of one racial family with the inhabitants of European Greece, and to look to that land as the origin and focus of their civilisation. But they and not the western Greeks were the " eye of Hellas."

The degree of civilisation among the Greeks in the several localities of the Anatolian islands and coast does, however, vary relatively, as physical conditions favour or discourage, and the political action of alien rulers has or has not hampered agriculture and trade. The ports of the western mainland command the larger arable areas and lie at the issues of continental trade routes ; and Smyrna, the city most favoured in both these respects, in virtue of its position in relation to the Menderes and Gediz valleys, is therefore the greatest and richest of all Anatolian communities.

Of the group of great cities which once competed for the commerce passing on Nature's road to the East, Smyrna has long borne off the palm, leaving Miletus and Ephesus to sink to villages. This success it owes to the single fact that no river of any volume falls into the head of its deep gulf. While Miletus and Ephesus have been choked by pestiferous deltaic deposits, Smyrna on its high, warm and dry site still overlooks a deep sea. But while the head of its gulf remains clear, the mouth is already threatened by the output of the Gediz : and at the same time Constantinople is developing, thanks to railway construction, a dangerous rivalry. As the Bosphorus port can command overland traffic, while Smyrna must always be on a half-sea route, it is probable that no extension of the Menderes railway will ever restore the latter to the same relative position that it occupied at the beginning of this century.

Not only have the physical advantages of many of the western mainland ports been thus impaired by the silt of neighbouring rivers, but they have also lain always more open to racial contamination and political oppression than the neighbouring islands. Mitylene, Chios, and densely - peopled Samos owe the comparatively greater energy and peaceful enterprise of their citizens not to any advantages that climate or soil possess over the mainland, but to an accident of position which has enabled them largely to escape counter-influences. Rhodes, not less blessed by nature, but exposed to successive alien oppressions, is the exception which proves the rule. While the large Greek population of her broad slopes continues to be almost exclusively of a primitive agricultural and pastoral sort, the Samiotes,

with far less territory, have ten times the export trade of
Rhodes, the Chiotes form the most liberal of all Greek
communities, and Mitylene has the largest turn-over of
any island port in the Levant. The rest suffer by their
unproductivity, like Patmos or Leros, or the want of
good ports as Astypálæa and Nikaria ; and only Symi,
the headquarters of the sponge harvest, and Tenedos,
which manufactures a rough red wine for export, can
boast much wealth. The people of the less favoured
islands are greatly given to emigration, and Leros,
Kálymnos, Nisyros, and Khalki are the motherlands of
most of the keen progressive Greeks of Lower Egypt.

On the Black Sea coast the nature of the relief
and the rigour of the climate have retarded the development of the population, except in the low region over
against Constantinople, where a heavy rainfall is turned
to account in the cultivation of orchards to supply the
bazars of the capital. The heavy seas, which the steppe
wind drives on shore, discourage small navigation ; and,
though the mass of the population from the Sakaria to
the Russian frontier is of the same stock, creed, and
speech as that of the west coast, it makes little use of the
sea. The most of these northern coastal folk abide
in the deltaic strips, industrious enlightened agriculturists,
interested in tobacco culture, to the exclusion of the
political ideals of other Greeks, by whom their speech
is hardly to be understood. But in certain localities, for
example, the Bafra and Charshembe plains, where five
hundred villages live on the fat of the land, the Greeks
find themselves so seriously harassed by Caucasian
new-comers, that they are losing their quiet and con-
tented habit. If the relief of the coast be arduous, the
same population takes up readily the trade of wood-
cutter, contrabandist, and brigand ; and wherever mining
operations have been undertaken, it is they who supply
the miners. The extent of the workings (now for the most
part intermitted) in the silver-lead and iron veins of the
hills of Pontus behind Kerasund and Trebizond, compared
to the neglect of metals in the rest of Turkish Asia, has

caused the Trapezuntine Greeks to be regarded as the professional mining population of Turkey, and to be transported wherever a lode is to be worked, whether at Bulgar Maden in the Taurus, or Arghana on the upper Tigris ; and their Bishop of Gumush-Khane has civil jurisdiction over all the Christian mining folk wherever found. Finally the same people supplies an element to the composition of the wild Lazis, once robbers by sea, but now confined to the Pontic Alps on the confines of Transcaucasia.

The southern coast of the Peninsula, as we have seen, is very thinly inhabited in its western part. The great harbours of Marmaris and Kekova can show no habitations but a few Greek hovels and Yuruk booths ; and what considerable longshore settlements are found now in Lycia seem to have grown in modern times from a very humble state, thanks to colonists attracted from the Greek islands of Rhodes and Castelóryzo to become orange-growers in the little warm deltas, and woodcutters and charcoal-burners on the shaggy shoreward slopes. The warmth and fertility of the littoral from Adalia to Aláia have caused it to be re-peopled by successive bodies of refugees, mainly Greeks, formerly drawn from the Morea, but latterly from Crete, who may there develop their natural bent for tillage ; and the same phenomenon is to be observed in eastern Cilicia, but with colonists of another sort, a leakage from semi-nomadic peoples of Inner Asia, whose education in agriculture is recent and greatly retarded by the marshy character of all the coastal plain and much of the inner level. All the south coast has passed through a period of desolation, thanks to the long anarchy of the Levantine sea. Where the mountains fall to the waves it is still No Man's Land ; in Cilicia it is in process of resettlement ; in Pamphylia it has resumed lately its earlier settled aspect.

The insular position of Cyprus has modified its case. More thoroughly Hellenised in antiquity, more easily protected by the Byzantine emperors, and longer preserved from Moslem invasion, first by the concentrated strength of crusading Christendom, and later by the occupying forces of Genoa and Venice, it has retained its settled agricultural population, tilling a plain which, despite droughts and locusts, is among the richest of Levantine levels, and hillsides, which produce the finest grapes of the Mediterranean. Even the Baffo and Tillyrian hill districts produce but a mild type of turbulent highlander, easily controlled and quickly modified by the agents of a western administration, as the speedy efficacy of the recently promulgated Arms Act has proved.

The ways to the central Plateau are for the most part so difficult, and the climatic and other conditions of the two regions are bound to be so diverse, that we shall expect to find that there existed, in ages when man had not much mastery over Nature, little communication but rather sharp distinction between the communities of the coast strip and the interior. And the former, being everywhere an alternation of deltas and sea-washed mountains, whether lying broadside or end on to the waves, is not less sharply divided into small territories with only a sea outlook. In this respect it reproduces on a somewhat larger scale a leading feature of Central Greece and the Morea ; and it has combined with those lands and the Archipelago islands to implant in Greek minds that tendency towards small independent groups, each imbued with its own intense local patriotism, which characterised the ancient Hellenic peoples and breaks out still, despite vastly improved facilities for intercourse.

The main agent in the differentiation of life on the Plateau is Nomadism in varying degrees of survival. The wandering habit, a direct consequence of certain physical conditions, is proper to those vast tracts which are found in all continents, undulating plains, which are neither always verdant nor always brown, being destitute neither of arable soil nor of water, but possessing the latter nowhere in sufficient abundance or sufficient permanence to render agriculture remunerative, and to maintain stationary animal and human life all the year through. Immense areas of such country exist in central and south-western Asia, containing a large aggregate of communities, constantly on the move. But since these tracts are unable to support the natural increase of their communities, a constant tide of migration sets out of the steppes towards the lands which still have room for more life.

Asia Minor has been for many centuries one of these. In no part, not even the Axylon, unfit for settled life, it was once thickly peopled, but had the misfortune to become the main stage on which the struggle between Islam and Christianity was fought out during seven hundred years ; and partly by the destruction of life, partly by the emigration of the Christian peasants, partly at last by forcible deportation of large bodies of its Moslem converts, destined to garrison Macedonia and Thessaly for the Turk, the Plateau of Anatolia had lost the half of its original population ere the Byzantine Empire finally fell. The vacuum so created has hardly yet ceased to draw a current from inner Asia. Hordes of Turkman nomads followed the Seljuk and Ottoman conquests as closely as the kites and crows ; and by the eleventh century were become old inhabitants of the eastern Taurus. Other Turkmans, Afshars, and Kurds followed in succeeding centuries, and refugees from the Caucasus come in still. The region to be first and most seriously affected has naturally been the east of the Plateau, those exposed downs of Cappadocia and the Axylon, which were never so populous as the west country, and suffered continual devastation during centuries of frontier warfare. Indeed, much of their older settled peasantry was driven westward to fill up whatever vacuum existed beyond the central plain. And the camel triumphed over the wheel.

Large tracts of the east country, therefore, are now in the hands of people, who have the habits of wandering society to forget, and in many cases have not had much time in which to do it. But the plains and lower valleys of the west are filled with concentrated survivals of elder populations which were never nomadic, leavened only to a slight extent by the descendants of the earliest Turki intruders, now so long settled and given to agriculture as to retain very rarely even the custom of migrating to a summer camp. The secondary waves of migration have not passed the Axylon, and the new elements for which room has of late been made in the west, Circassian and North Balkan refugees, do not come of true wandering stocks. The nett result is this. That the purely communal village-life of the western Plateau is modified upon the eastern downs by some vestiges of the camp. The traveller, having passed the centre, will note that he is lodged no longer in a common house of entertainment, but in the private guest-room of a chief, as it might be in the tent of a *sheikh*.

For the rest, the uniformity of Plateau life is affected by no serious physical changes but of altitude or exposure to the cold air currents. As the 4000 feet mean is reached, the peasants are found to be dwelling for the most part in houses half hollowed out of soft rock or hard earth, and their long hibernation and painful effort to utilise a short and inclement summer are reflected in the low standard of their living.

In a land like "Armenia," lying far in the interior of a continent, a land whose plains are set so high that they are snow-bound for four months of the year, while the passes leading from them are blocked still longer, one would not look for much commerce or productivity even were public security assured. As matters stand, the hills are in possession of some of the most subdivided, uninstructed, and unproductive clan societies in the world, under no control of religion, whose nomadic instinct leads the units to be for ever clashing with one another, with the plain dwellers and with the Ottoman posts, which have enjoyed as yet only about sixty years of precarious and doubtful dominance in the Van and Hakkiari countries. The plains are mostly occupied by an almost equally rude race of Christians, themselves in many cases refugees in their present holdings, who, now that tax-gatherers of the Ottoman Government have reached them, create fresh trouble by natural efforts to evade old established payment of blackmail to the hillmen. Without security of tenure and life, means of transporting or possibility of exporting produce, the cultivators provide only for the narrowest local needs, making nothing from their grapes but a nauseous sweetstuff, growing a villainous tobacco, and herding in the most miserable of villages and small towns. Where is so little time for culture the plains remain largely pasture, inviting migration of the hill peoples in the cold season, and increasing unrest. The great altitude of the highlands makes it impossible to keep the more delicate stock, especially the horses, in the hills through the winter; but the summer heat of the upland plains in that clear air is hardly less severe, and prompts speedy return to the higher ground. Only the Kurd of the hills, however, who commands all approaches to the plains, can avail himself of every level, plundering and blackmailing as he moves.

On the farther slopes of Ararat the softening of both relief and climate is accompanied by a greater humanity in the constituents of society. Azerbaijan, easily undulating, warm and well watered, has attracted to it the laborious race which made gardens bloom in Turkestan; and even where this naturally agricultural people has not penetrated, circumstance makes of the Armenians to the north of Urmi, the Nestorians and Chaldæans to the west, and the Kurds immediately to the south-west, peaceful *rayahs* compared to their kin in Mush, Kochanes, or Hakkiari.

In its central relation to this favoured district lies the lesser reason for the long-standing importance of Tabriz. The greater is dealt with in the chapter on Communications. To gather up the caravan trade from Erzerum and Erivan and forward it to Irak, the town stands back from the lake on the less fertile side, *i.e.* the east: and according as the foreign routes have been open or not, so has the greatness of Tabriz fluctuated in all ages. The modern insecurity of Kurdish Armenia on the one hand, and Russian protective duties on the other, have combined with the competition of the Caspian route to depress the wealth and population of Tabriz to a low point. But as the centre of Azerbaijan, the best recruiting-ground in Persia, and as post of observation over against Transcaucasia, it will never lose its capital importance in the eyes of the Shah's government, until that government loses Azerbaijan.

As the country to the south of the lake passes into rolling pasture, a fiercer pastoral type of Kurd is encountered; and on the bare downs which bound the province on the south and look over the plain of Irak, even the Turks, mostly of the Afshar tribe, become an unsettled population whose social state is midway between that of the farmers of the northern province and that of the nomad *Iliats* of the centre and south.

The vigour of the Turk of Azerbaijan is present in far less degree to the Medo-Tatar-Turkman of the Caspian shore. In the north-western part of the littoral, Talish, where the peasant is mostly a Tartar, he makes no effort to combat the evil influence of marsh and forest, and remains in a very primitive state. The Gilani, who appears to retain the handsome Medic type, has been civilised by the influence of a great highway of trade, leading from Resht to the Plateau, and by the foreign enterprise that his rich delta has attracted. But Nature resumes the upper hand in Mazanderan, and water and wood become too much for the peasants, who evidently share the languor which all travellers feel in the district. The south-eastern littoral is a land of human decay, that has lain long at the mercy of the vigorous Turkmans of the not distant steppes, stragglers from whose body roam everywhere over the mountainous region behind ; and it now lies an easy prey to the Power which holds Ashurada.

The disproportion of villages to towns in Irak, which we have already noted briefly in speaking of Distribution, is due, of course, to peculiar climatic conditions. Water is hardly obtainable on the Iranian Plateau, except in the neighbourhood of mountains, and must then be collected in underground conduits, which call for the labour of large communities. And since in consequence salt is everywhere, Irak and Fars, in spite of the great variety of their Relief, are largely steppe of the kind which is almost desert and will only support a very thin and constantly moving population. The rare oases collect the most of the inhabitants into restricted areas ; and there their quickness of intellect and capacity for refined civilisation will depend on the character of the oasis. The Shirazis, for example, being better circumstanced than the Teheranis, are much in advance.

Having brought about this result, the climate accentuates the effect on the national character by its saline dryness, stimulating a lively intelligence to which rural life is irksome. The typical Persian has much the same quality of mind as the Attic Greek. He is ἀστεῖος in the same not too satisfactory way, loving to be where he can display his quickness of intellect before his fellows, a prey to mordant vanity and incurable superficialism, persevering only in talk. Hence that oft-noted contrast between the standard of intellectual and the standard of practical life in Persia. The keenest appreciation of refinement in thought and literary expression, and a taste for the most subtle transcendentalism, are not in the least incompatible with the most squalid social existence. The further result of this overstimulating climate is seen in the rapid exhaustion of the mass of the population of whatever origin its units may be. The Turkman element, though dominant under the present Kajar dynasty, seems to hold out no better than the Farsi. And the gathering of all into towns accelerates the melancholy process ; for it is an axiom that in cities of the East death prevails over birth.

Finally, a region consisting so largely of oases isolated by arid steppes or utter deserts must possess but a loose-knit society. Azerbaijan has little in common with Irak, and Khorasan, beyond the salt pans, is still less in union with what lies to west. But it is not only provinces, but urban centres, that under present circumstances are detached one from the other ; and the traveller who, passing from Teheran to Kerman or Shiraz, seems to cross a frontier every three or four days, will understand why provincial governors, who obtain real power over more than one great city, are so rare, and so disquieting to the Shah-in-Shah.

Teheran, however, the existing capital, as has been already pointed out (p. 216), is the one possible point of concentration. On the threshold of the narrow passage between the Elburz and the Kavirs, along which the one road to the East must pass, and commanding the Elburz defiles, a great city has always stood, although there is no amenity in the locality, and no rich environment. Teheran is modern, and its great size largely artificial ; but before its day Rhey or Rhagæ had existed a few miles south even to a dim antiquity. That the capital of Persia should so long have been fixed in Fars, first in the Shiraz region, as Achæmenid Persepolis and later as Sefavi Isfahan, is due to the fact that the modern conception of Empire, as implying centralised administration of a territorial realm, was not present to Shahs before the Turkmans. While kings or governors of outlying satrapies were uncontrolled, so long as they fulfilled certain obligations, the capital was naturally selected as much with a view to amenity of environment as to central position : and the waters of the Murghab or the Zendeh counted for more than a trade route. Under modern conditions Isfahan is probably doomed to an inevitable decay, which will only be checked awhile by improvement of the very difficult roads to the Karun or the Gulf ; and future railways appear likely to avoid it, passing far to northward from Kashan to Hamadan and Baghdad, or to eastward by Yezd and Kerman to Bunder Abbas. In the local distribution of influence in Persia the past is with the British: the present and future with the Russians.

As the general elevation rises towards the western edge of the Iranian Plateau, and the oblique ridges draw so close together that their intermediate furrows cease to be open plains, the character of the people changes with the changed climatic conditions. The invariable tendency of inhabitants of mountain valleys towards clan organisation is exaggerated in Luristan by the peculiar disposition of the hills in parallels, tied together at intervals by such knots as the Kuh-i-Rang, and split by transverse clefts or *tengs*, only to be crossed with infinite labour. And to other influences, which render highlanders an unsettled folk, the great extremes of summer heat in these latitudes add the necessity of shifting quarters twice a year.

But be it observed that neither the Persian Kurds nor the Lurs are true nomads, though perforce given to periodic migration between certain fixed points ; and that, since their range extends into the very fertile lowlands on the west up to the point at which those difficulties of desert are encountered with which it has been given to the Arab alone to cope, and since also their upland valleys are mostly spacious and easily irrigated, both races are disposed to temper their nomadic habit with considerable practice of agriculture. The yield of grain from the Kurdish valleys, north of Kermanshahan, far exceeds local consumption ; while the cow-keeping Bakhtiaris have long sought distant markets for their varied produce, and M. de Morgan found even the fierce Feili Lurs of Pusht-i-Kuh treating problems of irrigation as their primary concern.

The less accessible country to the south is more exclusively pastoral. Laristan is the principal nomad district of Persia, better clad and of more genial climate than the central plains, but too ill-watered to support large settlements. Its life is of the most primitive and gipsy sort that is to be found within all the borders of Iran, capable of too little combination for serious assertion of independence, and of too little repose for civilisation to take root and grow. As the ridges sink into downs the tribes grow less jealous and aggressive. The Mamasenni Lurs of the North, though broken by Ferhad Mirza some years ago, are still robbers in grain ; while the Turkman wanderers about the Bunder Abbas roads are a simple and peaceful people.

I know no truer summary of Anatolian characteristics than Sir C. Wilson's in the introductory matter of Murray's *Guide to Asia Minor*. On the west country Prof. W. M. Ramsay writes in his *Impressions of Turkey* with unequalled knowledge and sympathy. Estimates of the

Persians, as of the Greeks, vary greatly with the innate sympathies of particular observers. To a practical mind like Morier's, or still more Curzon's, their life appears a hopelessly unsatisfactory compound of pretension with ineffectiveness ; to a speculative intellect, with a leaning to transcendentalism, like Browne's, they are the most gifted of God's creatures. Morier is the more convincing to any one acquainted with any part of the Nearer East, but his bitter satire must be adulterated with Browne's enthusiasm.

CHAPTER XVI

LIFE UNDER SOUTH-WEST ASIAN CONDITIONS

In the vast region, which remains, all mountainous country is confined to the Fringes, making an almost continuous hedge to an immense expanse where the chief agent of popular separation is altogether wanting. For mountain ranges, in which races abide and take a certain character, distinguish peoples far more drastically than either rivers or deserts, which can only be man's thoroughfares, and do not greatly interrupt the main climatic currents which modify his life. The uniform character, now degenerating into that of sheer desert, now improving to the condition of *savannah*, which Nature has imposed on the main part of this region, meets no counter-influence which can radically disturb its effect on the population ; and so greatly does it prevail, that it makes its influence felt, not only in the isolated oases, but far into the fertile outer Fringes, to the great detriment of their productivity and social state. A certain degree of similarity in human character and an even · greater similarity of language prevails over an immense area, where races of most various origin have all been assimilated more or less by the one, which occupies the healthy crown of the land, the Arabian of Nejd.[1]

Differences there are many and obvious among this widespread people, differences due to the local circumstances of their habitation, whether steppe, or desert, whether in the neighbourhood of oasis, or in an oasis itself ; differences due to the elevation of one district compared with another, to latitude or to exposure to particular climatic influences ; differences due to the

---

[1] I make no attempt to give a special sense to " Arab " or " Arabian," as distinct from " Bedawin," nor to be over precise in the use of the latter, *e.g.* I do not deny it to some tent-dwellers as the Sleb or Sherarat, and allow it only to the Nejd tribes.

proximity or distance of a non-Arabised section of the mountainous Fringe, or to communications with the civilisations of Persia, or India, or Egypt, or Europe ; and finally differences of less moment, due to race. But through all persists the uniformity of that Desert life, which is the same to-day as when the Beni Israel were wandering in a corner of this wilderness. For of all physical conditions which mould the character of man, those of the Desert suffer least reflex modification at his hands. This only must be reserved, lest all should seem to be credited to physical causes, that the " Arabisation " of the north of the area, though it dates from long before the Hejra, was increased and widened by the great Arabian religious revival, and in the past two centuries it has received a further impulse from migrations of Bedawins, who, upon the withdrawal of Ottoman authority during the wars of Mohammed IV. in Europe, swarmed across the Nefud. The ground thus lost two hundred years ago, the powers that be at Stambul are engaged in retrieving at this day.

The product of the Arabian type of steppe is the Bedawin type of humanity. Bedawins may be, and are, of many racial families, but the uniformity of physical conditions over all this area and the absence of the strongest natural influences of separation, cause their life to be organised on such similar lines that they have all come to take something of a common national character from the most vigorous, because best circumstanced, of their kind. Hamite in the south-west, Mongol in the north, Iranian in the south-east, all have been Arabised by the Semites of the centre. Oases which they completely envelop, or narrow river valleys which flow through their steppes, can only to a small extent modify the influence exercised by the vast circumjacent area upon the inhabitants. Those adjacent regions alone, which, being themselves of a physical character in strong contrast to the steppe, are in immediate touch on another flank with the vigorous influences of settled civilisation, resist the Arabising influence. Of all the fertile tracts of the Fringe, only the mountain system of the Mediterranean littoral as far south as the Lebanon has been able altogether to withstand Arabisation, and that in virtue of its abrupt relief, its high fertility, and its intimate connection with eastern Europe and Anatolia ; while the Nile valley, for all its immemorial civilisation, its rooted peasantry, its immense productivity, and its exposure at one extremity to direct influences of the Mediterranean, has not been able to counteract the slow but sure effect which the drying Sahara had been exerting long before Islam appeared in the Delta.

The distinguishing Bedawin characteristic is, in a word, that of his land, Meagreness. Meagreness of osseous starved frame, short of stature, and doomed to early decay ; meagreness of sensory faculties, ears and eyes dull of hearing and sight, except in tracking a foe ; meagreness of mental qualities, issuing in unstable shifty conscience, in easy cowardice, in absence of religion, in gusty passions, and in swift deterioration upon contact with civilisation. The man of the Arabian desert is an ineffective animal, bad shot, bad rider, bad fighter, bad breeder, and when brought out of his steppes, as bad a cultivator as a citizen. But, for all that, an attractive animal. Take him on his own high and open desert, the product of its keen air and clean, non-verminous soil. He has all the outward charm which purity of race and freedom from servitude and menial toil through many generations confer all over the world. His shape, his bearing, his social code are alike noble. A guest need not ask what relation there may be between his theory and his practice, nor try him long or hard. But wandering as the Bedawin does, he may admire the simplicity, frugality, and patient obedience of successive camps, himself possessed by the indefinable exhilaration of the Waste. And should he wish to stay long in the Desert, he must be sure he has in his own nature more than a little sympathy with indolent, unreflective quietism, the Eastern, not the Western, type of mind, which can empty itself at will of all thought and all desire of action.

Within the broad uniformity of Bedawin life, one leading difference of geographical circumstance distinguishes the human groups. Is their portion of the Desert interrupted by oases, or does it stretch unbroken from Fringe to Fringe? Such is the poverty of even the most favoured parts of the high Arabian steppe that none of the nomad peoples can remain altogether independent of some more fertile land. Dates and tobacco, at the least, are required even by the most savage ; and no Bedawin of higher development than the Gara of the south Arabian coast, will dispense with cotton clothing. If his deserts enclose large oases tracts, the Bedawin depends upon a civilisation of which he is master ; and under such self-sufficing conditions of autonomy his life is seen at its best. Independence confers dignity, the thin fibre of the desert nature is not tried by influences, before which, however high in themselves, its rootless virtues fade and perish ; and the man of the steppe, graduated insensibly into the oasis *fellah*, has a various experience of life, and the chance of developing wider interests in a civilisation of his own making.

Where, however, such large oases do not exist, the Bedawins, so long as they remain in the steppe, must be simple nomads of the most primitive kind ; and when they communicate with fertile regions, those will be on the Fringes occupied by the civilisations of other races. Herein, of course, lies the secret of the control, which Governments like the Ottoman and the Egyptian can exercise over the bird-like inhabitants of the wilderness, without attempting the impossible task of establishing administrative centres in their midst. The Bedawins must bring their bred stock to the markets of the Fringes, and buy certain necessaries there ; and they can easily be headed away from those markets if taxes be in arrear, or too many couriers have been robbed on the Desert roads. By-and-by their flocks increase and the mid-steppe pastures do not suffice them through the year : then must they come again and for longer to the outskirts and lease grazing, which the administration can withhold, or if granted, police. By one way or another a hold is obtained which will not only ensure safety of transit across hundreds of miles of unpoliced waste, but will give a

Government, which is desirous of breaking down the existing semi-independence of Bedawins, a lever for gradually imposing on them a sedentary habit of life.

The Arabian Wilderness is distinguished into two portions, the north and the south, by the presence or absence of such oases. The Bedawins of Mesopotamia and the Hamad—in fact, all north of the Nefud, if Jauf be reckoned in the latter—have no choice but to maintain relations with the Fringes which are in Ottoman hands. They are nowhere independent, and, on the whole, either are of the most primitive rudeness, or will display every stage of contamination down to uttermost depravity. It is true that the northern Waste is divided by the green line of the Euphrates Valley. But that attenuated belt is more adapted for a thoroughfare, than a seat of independent civilisation. And while the first effect of the great migration of the Shammar tribesmen from Nejd, and their collision with the Anaze, was to destroy all civilised life over hundreds of miles of the middle valley, no new *fellahin* were supplied by the steppe tribes, and the riparian flats relapsed into tamarisk-jungle to which nomad shepherds brought their herds for grazing and water. Of late, however, the Shammar of the western half-tribe have been induced by the Ottoman Government to adopt the life of cultivators in this valley. A similar policy used towards the eastern half-tribe has largely failed simply because the Tigris trough affords much less favourable agricultural conditions.

The Fringes of the northern waste have been Arabised much, little, or not at all, according to the nature of their relief. Irak Arabi, low, easily accessible from the southwest, and bounded on the farther side not by hills, but by plain, is wholly Semitised. The population between the rivers presents one of the lowest types of Bedawin. The curse of Babylon seems to have fallen on this land of broken canals, irreclaimable marshes, and dusty mounds of dead cities. The *fellahin* between the rivers are enfeebled and depraved by the malarious heats ; the nomads, half settled on the outer western Fringe, have that degraded character which the unstable Arab displays when he has tasted a lowland civilisation and imbibed discontent of himself. For of all the Bedawin kin it is said by the western traveller who has known them best, " this is nigh all that serves the nomad for a conscience, viz., that which men will hold of him." It should be admitted, however, that of late years the spread of date-planting has converted great part of the southern Muntefik to a *fellah* life more worthy in its kind, but still impeded by bad government.

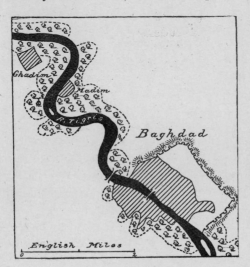

FIG. 51.—Baghdad.

But the same beneficent influence has not yet been extended to the Shiah tribesmen of the eastern flats, the northern Muntefik, ruined by the bursting of the Kerkha bank in 1837, the Kab and the Beni Lam, who remain Ishmaelites among Ishmaelites, and repay the malign influence of Nature by making waste her face ; until now the desert licks the very walls of Baghdad (Fig. 51).

The ruin of the immediate environment cannot, however, entail the complete ruin of that city, still the most important in Turkish Asia, though much reduced. Certain geographical conditions render necessary the existence of a very great urban centre near the confluence of the Mesopotamian rivers. Baghdad has succeeded to Ctesiphon, Ctesiphon to Seleucia, Seleucia to Babylon. The site has shifted from one stream to the other, and from one bank to another, but it has remained always in touch with both great waterways and the land routes which follow their valleys, always in command of the Babylonian garden, and always the outlet of Arabia on the one hand and western Persia on the other. Baghdad at this moment may be regarded more justly as a city of Nejd, or the Persian borderland, than of Turkish Arabia. When the city was chiefly a local centre it was situated on Euphrates. When it was to be a focus of continental trade it was removed to the better waterway of Tigris. Had Alexander lived longer, he would have treated Babylon as his successor Seleucus treated it. As the centre of an empire, originated in the east, it was transferred to the left bank : when a new imperial power appeared out of the west it was shifted back again, and became the Round City of Mansur. As that empire lost its hold on the west and came to have closest relation to Persia, the left bank suburb grew into the modern city of Baghdad. And there a railway will ultimately reach it, and, for want of a good port on the Gulf itself, once more make it the great emporium of West Asia.

North of the Kerkha the accidented character of the eastern Fringe has suited the Kurd better than the Arab, and in the rich, well-watered valleys from Sherizor to Amadía, the former folk are firmly established as prosperous husbandmen, who keep the Shammar mainly on the farther bank of the Tigris. The more gradual and less well irrigated slopes of the north, by which the Mesopotamian steppe passes into the first Tauric uplands, have favoured the formation of a nondescript and shifty pastoral blend, more Arab than Kurd ; and the Yezidi cultivators of the Sinjar and even the Syrian Christians of the plains of Mardin, Diarbekr, and Urfa, are to some extent "Arabised" in character as well as speech.

Seated on the Tigris between these two areas of fertility, where the river has definitely left the mountain gorges, and not yet entered the desert, has always been a great city. Mosul faces the mounds of Nineveh. For at that point meet two great roads, the diagonal trans-continental route from Asia Minor to the Gulf, and the easier "half-sea" route from the Levant, which runs between

Taurus and the deserts : and here these routes fork east
to Hamadan or Ecbatana, south to Baghdad or Babylon.
But in the interval between the establishment of whole
sea routes to the east, and the inception of steam traction
on the old land routes, the overland traffic has declined
apace, and Mosul with it, waiting for the German engineers
to lay their rails from Diarbekr.

The desert influence, however, has little power in the
north-west and west.   A fertility, which in half a century
has civilised the Kurds, deported from the Giaur Dagh
to the plains at the root of Taurus, saves the character of
the Syrian basins north of Aleppo ; and thanks to that
fertility and the local importance of the district, Aleppo
itself still retains something of the importance which once
was Antioch's.   But those imperial considerations which
prompted the founding of Antioch, and made Aleppo a
great city in the Middle Ages, weigh no longer.   The
opening of the Suez Canal has given its death-blow to
the half-sea trade which long passed from Seleucia of
Pieria or Alexandretta to the Euphrates valley ; and the
hopes founded on the opening of the Euphratæan waterway up to Meskine, or the construction of a railway
down the right bank, have come to nought.   Aleppo
remains an important local centre of provincial administration—nothing more.

The rapid increase in the height and abruptness of the
Relief, as it trends southward to Hermon and the Lebanon,
has resulted in the development of a distinctive highlander
character in the jealously segregated groups of the " Fold "
ranges. Nor is the deep tilth of the Asi valley and the Syrian
littoral in danger of being possessed by any " nomadised "
folk.   What element of unrest there undoubtedly is in
the Syrian Fringe, if due to physical conditions, must be
ascribed to the natural division of the land into long vertical strips—mountain and Rift, and mountain and littoral-
plain—not traversed by common roads until builders of
railways and macadamised *chaussées* began to assail the
Lebanon in our own time.   These will bring the urban
centres of the rich eastern half of the Fringe into close

connection with the coast, almost for the first time. Hamath, Homs, and Damascus have had a history for the most part distinct from that of the Phœnician littoral. The last-named and greatest of them, for instance, owes pre-eminence to its relation with an overland route much travelled in antiquity, viz., that from Egypt and Palestine to the Euphrates, round the head of the desert ; and as the vogue of that road declined, Damascus has lived on as the most important gathering-point of other overland caravans, those of the northern pilgrims bound for the Arabian holy cities. Now that this road too is passing out of use, the town declines rapidly despite its paradise of waters, despite the adjacent corn lands of the trans-Jordan, despite the French railway to the west. Nor is anything that can be foreseen, not even the improbable construction of a railway along the Derb-el-Haj, likely to arrest

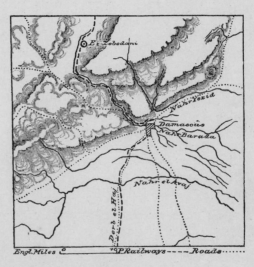

FIG. 52.—Damascus.

decay. Damascus is doomed to be nothing more than the capital of the oasis of Sham (Fig. 52).

South of the butts of the two Lebanons the desert men have overrun and largely wasted a land which, discouraged, readily relapses into naked aridity. The corrugated volcanic areas east of Jordan, and the not lofty but greatly broken hills of Moab and Seir have supplied a ready refuge for the worst Arab elements, and developed their predatory habit. All Bedawins, dwelling not in the open desert but in a broken cave country with hidden water-holes, to be kept from strangers' eyes, acquire a secretive and treacherous character. And it is from such undesirable tracts that the Arabs have spread on to the more open and fertile declivities of the Jaulan and Hauran and the denuded Palestinian downs west of Jordan. Indeed, for some centuries Palestine has been in the evil case of having to receive from time to time broken remnants of Hamad tribes worsted in desert warfare, who must perforce take up the uncongenial status of *fellahin*. Such have no skill in agriculture and no heart. They impoverish the land and lightly abandon it to denudation and sand-drift ; and it is largely due to them that Palestine, especially in the south of Judæa, is the waste that it is. The Bedawin, born of the desert, becomes in turn its creator ; and it remains yet to be seen whether the strangers, Circassian, Druse, and Jew who have fled, or been artificially introduced, of recent years into this region, will be able to reclaim permanently for agriculture what has so long been exposed to the worst neglect of nomads.

For the moment great change has been wrought both in Western Judæa and in Ammon, and it is worth remark, that the Jewish immigration has largely restored its artificial importance to Jerusalem. Artificial, because it rests on no natural advantages of situation, but not unreal, since sentiment modifies the life of peoples as profoundly, if not so constantly and permanently, as geographical conditions. Jerusalem is in the same class with two other important cities of the Nearer East, Athens and Mecca. All three lie off trade routes and in poor and unproductive lands ; and their sites would be occupied by villages were it not that the appeal that they make to sentiment is powerful enough to overbear all the economic influence of geography. Without foreign commerce or manufactures Jerusalem steadily grows ; and if the process goes on it will end, like Athens, by creating a local commerce of considerable importance to satisfy the demands of its own population.

The conditions of the Hamad hold in southern Arabia

with one important difference. In all the northern deserts
there are hardly a dozen settlements which can possibly
be called villages. In Nejd, however, there are hundreds.
For not half the high Plateau is desert at all, and indeed
in all the Peninsula of Arabia two-thirds of the soil is
capable of cultivation.

But it is thin and hardy cultivation in Nejd, such as
steadies the Bedawin, but does not make him a slow and
servile *fellah*. And the oasis feels always the keen dry
air blowing off the ring of desert, and the quickening
influence of the steppe-men who must usually be the
dominant class. Besides their enclosure by an outer
ring of deserts, the oases, large and small, are each
divided from each by strips of very waterless steppe,
often sheer sand. From Jebel Shammar to Teima, and
Teima to Medain Salih or Kheibar, from all these to
Kasim, from Kasim to Woshm, and thence to the
various provinces of which Riad is the capital, the
camel, or at least the ass, must convey the passenger.
The steppe-men, therefore, hold the keys of oasis life.
The *fellahin* have always had to submit to their terms,
to their assumption of greater nobility, and generally
to the domination of a Bedawin sheikhly family, which
leads a half settled life between a fortress in the oasis
and black tents on the steppe. From such families
have sprung the dynasties of Sultans or Emirs who,
alone able to combine one oasis with another in virtue
of their command of the intervening tracts, have collected a treasure sufficient to secure a standing force,
which may overawe other Bedawins, and more distant
oases, and often all the Plateau.

The Fringes of the Arabian Plateau are less clearly
to be distinguished from the centre than those of the
Syrian Plateau. Hasa is only a desert oasis, differing from
those of the uplands chiefly in the possession of a moister,
warmer climate, which makes its people a somewhat
enervated and commercially-minded folk, refined, luxurious, little given to fanaticism. The insalubrious flats of
Katif degrade the coast population, and all the enterprise

of this district seems to be developed in the fresher air of barren Koweit, on the edge of the northern desert, and in the low island of Bahrein, chief centre for the 50,000 pearl fishers of the Gulf.

The wild coast of Katr, with the Red Desert at its back, has only room for considerable villages in the small plains which lie between the spurs of the mountains. And since the sea on which these settlements look is traversed by fishers for the richest product of the deep, the formation of a series of little predatory maritime states was always inevitable. There are no wilder coasts of south Asia than the sea-face of the ridge which runs out in Ras Musandim, few more primitive races than the dying Negrito folk who hold the Cape.

Oman, out of reach of the Turk, and by reason of the Red Desert not readily accessible on the land side to any but the weak Bedawin tribes behind Jebel Akhdar, and moreover of abundant fertility, is the most self-dependent portion of the Arabian Fringe, and probably most nearly represents now what the best tracts of the Peninsula were before the preaching of Islam. It displays by favourable examples every modification that the national character undergoes in varying physical conditions. Bold and skilful navigators and fishermen possess the flourishing ports of Sohar, Barka, Maskat, and Sur ; laborious *fellahin* till the lands of a hundred villages in the Batna plain ; free-living, cultivated, and dignified are the folk in the inland oases and the palm-planted hollows of Jebel Akhdar ; and unspoiled the nomads on the inner swell of the land which skirts the great Desert.

The political influence of this favoured district extends over all Dofar, but the standard of life deteriorates considerably as the narrow southern littoral is followed westward to Mahra and the mouth of the Hadramut ; and the Gara Bedawins of the arid hills interposed between the isolated fertile patches and the sea-like expanse of the Dahna, which cuts communication with Nejd, are stunted savages hardly of higher development than bushmen. But both the Hadramut itself, and the coast villages south of it from Saihut to Makalla and the limits of the Aden Protectorate, are farther advanced in civilisation of the oasis type. And the Hadramut especially, low-lying, but saved by the vast dry areas about it from any suspicion of malaria, nourishes a sturdy folk of better physique and more robust and alert intelligence than most oasis Arabs.

The prosperity and strength of Yemen is confined to the central belt. The eastward slopes of the main chain behind the Plateau, which were once the headquarters of Sabæan power, have been largely reconquered by the sands and are now given up to the Carmathian Bedawins of Nejran ; while the western Tehama, cursed with a mean annual temperature of 85° Fahr., little and bad water, and a thankless stony soil, would be uninhabited except by mongrel nomads, were it not for necessary, but sorry ports, of which Mokha has decayed to nothing, and only Hodeida and Loheia, lying nearest to the administrative centre of the upland, retain importance. But the happy central Plateau is one long oasis of terraced coffee-gardens, broad ploughlands, and meadows, divided by running streams, and villages set in orchards. Every condition is favourable. Exhilarating airs of the great desert come with the north and east winds, but the sand is screened by a high range of hills ; the south-west winds blow from the sea, and twice a year bring sure rains ; days are clear and genial, and nights are cool. No wonder the Yemeni is of a race robust both in body and mind, addicted to peaceful pursuits, but impatient of subjection to masters less well endowed, and careless of his interests. The few Europeans who have penetrated in recent years to the plain of Sana are unanimous in comparing the indigenous folk most favourably with their Ottoman lords.

With the failure in the periodicity of the rains in the rough region of Asir, the population of the Western Fringe relapses into a primitive and unsettled state. And were it not for the economic and political influence of the Holy Cities, there would be little more civilisation in

the Hejaz. Religion apart, Mecca, Tayif, Medina, El Ala,
Kheibar had been all on a par, sparse and unimportant
oases, hidden among arid slopes, and possessing even less
power of modifying the meagre nomadic character than
the concentrated oases of Nejd.

The one geographical asset in the account of Mecca
is the fact that no sandy Nefud divides it from the central
Plateau, although east of Tayif there lies a waterless belt.
But this advantage is shared not only by Tayif, but by
the other oases just enumerated, and the access to Nejd
from the Hejaz is certainly in any case less easy than
from Yemen by way of Nejran and the Wady Dauasir.
The site of Mecca itself is in the last degree arid, liable
to floods, and intensely hot. It can hardly be termed an
oasis at all, and the richer Meccans in summer fly to El
Ain and Tayif. Unlike Medina, it has no agricultural
population, and no local life of the soil. Its inhabitants
are in part half settled Bedawins ; in part, a half-bred
commercial folk dependent on the traffic with the yearly
pilgrims. We have already compared it with Jerusalem
and Athens, but inasmuch as the sentiment which attracts
population to Mecca is in no sense national but the out-
come of individual superstition, its importance as an
urban centre may fairly be regarded as even more artificial and less stable than theirs.

North of the Holy Cities and their ports there are no
folk to consider but Bedawins. To the Billi of the northern
Tehama succeed the Howeitat who range over the whole
Harra and arid mountainous land of Midian, towards the
base of Sinai,—that Peninsula even more naked than
Midian, which Doughty calls the "worst grazing ground
in the wilderness." Here pure nomadism is no longer
possible. At no season is there any pasture at all upon
three-fourths of the soil, and the sparse Teháya and
Towára Bedawin only migrate quickly between fixed
points, and live the poorest kind of oasis life.

Natures of aristocratic sympathy in revolt against the restraints of
western society seem to find their most congenial refuge with the tent-
dwellers. These are apt to see Bedawin life through a roseate mist. In

appreciation and description of it, Doughty has no rival. His very inconsistencies reflect the character of the people of whom he treats. Next to him, *mea sententia*, but after a wide interval, stands Palgrave. Burckhardt is more conspicuous for his grasp of the conditions of Arab life than for his sympathy with Arabs. There is much sound appreciation and often candid criticism in the Blunts' two books on Arabia. Of most recent travellers, Huber won the confidence of Mohammed ibn Rashid, but has left too brief an account of life at Hayil and in the Emir's dominions. Snouck-Hurgronje is most accurate and informing, but writes by no means as an Arab with Arabs. W. B. Harris has the " Oriental mind," but not adequate power either of observation or description.

CHAPTER XVII

LIFE UNDER NORTH-EAST AFRICAN CONDITIONS

ON entering north-east Africa we find ourselves still under the social conditions of a " steppe and fringe " country, analogous to those of the Hamad and Mesopotamia, where divided by the Euphrates valley. A long and low ribbon of cultivation, expanding at last into a delta, is flanked for many hundreds of miles by vast tracts of such extreme aridity, that no posts of control can be fixed in them, and they must be abandoned to nomadic folk, of whose comings and goings it is far more difficult to have constant information than of the movements of sea-rovers. It is true that, on the other hand, this same arid character of the Egyptian steppes serves to mitigate the danger by making it necessary for the Bedawins to form very small groups, very widely distributed ; by rendering them physically a more weedy race than the wanderers of Mesopotamia and the Hamad ; and especially by compelling them to depend more or less on some fertile fringe. The object of all capable administrators of the Nile valley, therefore, has been, and must be, to obviate the possibility of the dwellers in the steppes to east and west knowing any resort but territory under control of Egypt. She and no one else must hold the whole line of the western oases, difficult to reach, unhealthy and unproductive as they are ; and it is not in order to have control only of the Nile flood, but also of the movements of the desert tribes, that she has reconquered the dreary and costly eastern Sudan.

The narrowness and sandy character of the Suez Isthmus has always prevented the disturbing influence of Nejd, and of the rude tribes of the southern Hamad and mountain country of Moab, Seir, and Midian, from having ready access to the East African steppe. But access to a certain degree there was and is. The Howeitat come and go in large bands, and range east of the Nile much farther south than Cairo ; and in former days these Bedawins could come to the Wadi Tumilat, and be off again to pastures beyond the control of Egypt, as secretly and easily as the Beni Israel made their exodus from Goshen. But now that the Isthmus has been cut, this may no longer be, and the tribesmen must squat on their haunches, and wait for the ferry at Kantara, watching with primeval eyes the slow procession of modern monsters of the sea.

Yet it will be long before the *fellahin* of the Nile valley cease to regard the east bank of the river as perilous. Indeed, since the Red Sea shore is practically uninhabitable by settled folk till near Sawakin (Koseir being just kept alive by its connection through the Wadi Hamamat with the Nile), and the oases of the northern Etbai will hardly support a starved Coptic convent apiece, the Egyptian can do little with the Howeitat and the Arabised Barabra nomads, unless these wish to draw supplies from the valley. The population, however, is very thin and little formidable. In the porphyritic high-lands of the north, to which some day the reopening of the Roman quarries may recall life, it keeps the secret of certain water-holes and strays by single families. In the south-east, where the Romans worked gold and emerald mines, there is more pasture, and tents often give place to huts ; but Mr. Bent doubted if there be more than a hundred families resident in that part of the desert. The most of the Ababde and the northern Bishrin hang about the skirts of the valley cultivation, where tourists admire the slender forms and too refined features of a race old as the Pyramids.

The western Egyptian steppe is likewise so utterly desert that the more numerous Bedawins, for whose exist-ence the large areas of intermingled waste and fertility, which the western chain of oases affords, are mainly responsible, must hang on the fringes of the Valley or the Basins. The southern oases, Khargeh, Dakhel, Farafra, and Baharia, are the most "nomadised," and by consequence the worst cultivated, least drained, and socially most miserable. Siwah, however, is a fairly compact territory, and its inhabitants, therefore, are of a much more settled and self-sufficing sort, living in large walled villages, and cultivating carefully the lands about the central marsh.

Waste to east and to west ; a ribbon of rich soil threaded by a continuous waterway, but interrupted in the direction of inner Africa by cataracts and an arid belt, while lying open to the Mediterranean sea,—such are the conditions that have made of the long-skulled population of the lower Nile valley an "Arabised" agricultural oasis-folk, Asiatic rather than African, and of remarkably uniform character. The climatic conditions, occasioning a fresh dry air in sub-tropic latitudes, compensate the low altitude of the valley, and endow the Nilot with much the same kind of activity and intelligence, that mark an oasis-dweller in Nejd. There would indeed be nothing in the physical conditions to distinguish the "Arabised" population of the Nile valley from those of other oases were it not for the peculiar action of the river.

The Nile inundation does much to neutralise the stimulating influence of the north wind and the desert airs. It is not that it makes for indolence. On the contrary, life is full of labour where is no sky-sent rain, but only irrigation from a river which will not do its part unless canals and drains be cleared annually with infinite toil of man and beast, and water be raised by hand through a twelve hours' day. And indeed in these times labour is become more and more the lot of the Nile peasant, when his land must bear two, if not three, crops a year, and cotton and sugar-cane are superseding the comparatively easy culture of cereals. But the Nile, crawling year by year over the flats, now a little higher, now a little lower, giving all the possibility of existence that there is, and admitting of no variety in the annual work of preparation for its coming, or of utilising what it leaves on going, makes life monotonous to a degree hard to realise in a zone of quick-changing skies. Despite all his physical energy, the Nilot is bound not only to lack enterprise, but to direct all his spiritual, as his physical vision, to earth. He takes no thought of the sky, nor of any God therein. The cult of the Sun in old Egypt was an exotic above the Delta ; nor anywhere does it seem to have had the usual characteristics, imagery, or consequences of a sky-worship. The real Gods were on the earth or under it, clothed with bestial or human forms, worshipped with myriad superstitious observances, but without reference to religious or social ideals.

With the oasis of the Fayum, the first trace of those influences, which gradually differentiate the Delta population from that of the Upper Valley, may be detected. Lying on the Fringe of the northern rains and projected far into the Desert, the Fayum has been considerably affected by nomadic folk, of whom those on its northern borders are more truly Arab than any of the southern tribes, except the Baggára, far removed in the Sudan. And the consequent improvement in the physical type of the alert Fayumis is accompanied by a certain improvement in civilisation, due to the superior productiveness of their low-lying and easily irrigated lands, for which the neighbourhood of Cairo supplies a market. Medinet-el-Fayum owes its singular prosperity as much to its fruit and vegetable gardens as to its situation at the parting of two desert roads, which, diverging to the oasis of Baharia and the Wadi Mághara, converge again at Siwah. With the increase of population, a steady attack is now being made on the edges of the Fayum wastes, and when the Aswan and Siut dams shall hold up the Nile waters, much of the low desert to the north-east and south-west will probably be recovered for the arable area, and the Wadi Rayan should become a dependent oasis.

Thereafter the change, which no traveller from the

s

south can fail to begin to notice in the valley population, is due at first only to the fact that he is nearing cosmopolitan Cairo—a capital whose effect on peasant life is the farther felt and the more conspicuous for the narrowness of the habitable area in which it lies. This, the most populous city in the continent of Africa (though to all real intents and purposes a city of Asia) affords as good an example as Baghdad of the constant effect of geographical conditions. There always has been, and always must be, a very great urban centre near, but outside, the apex of the Nile Delta. Cairo succeeded to Fostat ; Fostat, to Memphis and Heliopolis. It is not only because at this point the all-important Nile waters can be best controlled and the upper valley be commanded ; nor only because this is the true centre of balance between the long upper strip and the broad deltaic fan ; but also because the great land routes from Asia, whether by way of Kantara or Suez, must follow the eastern edge of the Nilotic water system up to its union in a single channel. The Nile is the true western frontier of Asia. The ground, upon which the bulk of native Cairo stands, is better chosen than that of Memphis. The citadel and Mokattam behind it are capable of being made stronger fortresses than any points behind the left bank city, and the site altogether is higher and more salubrious. It is significant of the European insensi-

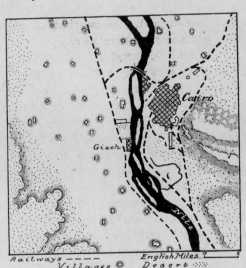

FIG. 53.—Cairo.

bility to the natural conditions of Egypt, that the alien community has been led to choose, instead of the slopes of Abbasíeh, the mud flat by the Nile for its new quarter.

As the Delta spreads fan-wise, the spare framed and alert type of the Upper Valley passes by rapid gradations into one more Bœotian, thicker-set and sturdier, till at Alexandria or Port Said one might fancy oneself among Turks. The sea, however, has little or no part in this modification. Egypt possesses the first port in the Medi-

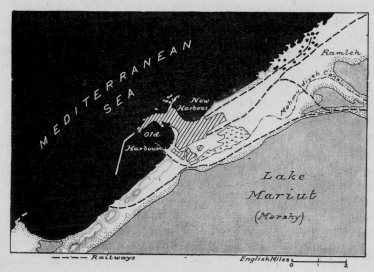

FIG. 54.—Alexandria.

terranean, but the Egyptians have not departed for that one hair-breadth from their habitual ignorance of the sea. The truth is, that the great city of Alexandria is not really of Egypt, and barely to be reckoned in it. The northern gate of the Nile land is at Kafr Dauar. Consequently Alexandria has always been, and still is, essentially foreign (Fig. 54). There is a large Egyptian element in it now as in antiquity, but one feels that this does not determine the character or civilisation of the city. In Cairo, on the other hand, however numerous and obvious the foreigners, the Egyptian element supplies all the essential colour. Whether the founder of Alexandria understood that, though the commerce of Egypt would flow through his new port, it was not a point from which the Nile Valley could be adequately controlled, and if therefore he must be held to have foreseen that it would become first and foremost a cosmopolitan mart, has been doubted. But the result was inevitable from the first. The site is admirably chosen, and penned between sea and marsh the city has remained on substantially the same ground throughout all ages. It lies in the only elevated sea-side locality within reach of a Nile canal, at a point where a low limestone swell pushes from the Libyan desert towards the Canopic mouth ; but it is far enough to west of that estuary to be free of the silt put out by the river. The only considerable island off the Delta coast (now joined to the mainland by an isthmus, originally artificial) protected the ancient harbour, and still in large measure protects the modern, but on another quarter. With all its drawbacks of shallow sea approach and inadequate shelter against the north, Alexandria is the one spot where there can be a great port in Egypt. But though Alexandria depends for its life on Egypt, and has decayed almost to nothing when the Nile Valley has been distracted and impoverished, as in the eighteenth century, it lives upon it as irresponsibly as a chartered Christian living on a Moslem state.

Whence then the modification of the Delta Nilot? Influence of race will not account for it, since in Lower Egypt the population has been recruited, far more than in Upper, from Nejd and the Hamad, homes of a fine-drawn type. We must look to physical conditions. Marshy soil and comparatively cloudy skies are the first causes which have adapted the physique of the Delta folk to the monotonous and continuous labour which modern irrigation imposes upon them ; and those responsible for the projected conversion of all Egypt into an area of perennial production, must consider how far either by physique or disposition the differently conditioned *fellahin* of the Upper Nile, not more than one-third of whose children reach puberty, are prepared to adopt the life which is now led in the Delta.

There is no very excellent book, that I know of, on the Egyptian Arabs later than Lane's *Modern Egyptians*. Many things in the Nile Valley distract attention from native life, and the kind of European, who goes thither, is seldom the best qualified to enter into it. The French and Italians acquire more sympathy with the native society than the Briton does. They can assimilate where the latter governs. The Greek excels all, being a Nearer Eastern himself ; there is no people which so easily obtains the confidence of the poorer *fellahin*, and so quickly adapts itself to Nilotic conditions. But such Greeks do not write about Egypt.

CHAPTER XVIII

WORLD RELATION

FINALLY, what place does this Region fill in the economy of the greater World? In virtue of its position or its features and character, how far does it matter to the corporate human body?

The very part which it has played in the development of civilisation in the past has altered the significance of its geographical position in the present. When the civilised world was smaller, what we now regard as the Nearer East contained in itself both East and West, and also a Debatable Land between. Now it is neither East nor West but become all Debatable Land.

Man attains to high independent civilisation only where natural conditions of climate and soil do not impose a severe strain on his infant powers; and, in fact, he has emerged unassisted from barbarism only in large and well-watered plain countries of great natural fertility, blessed with genial but neither damp nor torrid climes. These conditions cannot be found at once except in the warmer belts of the two Temperate Zones, and are found, in fact, only in the northern. For the most part of the southern Zone, where it is not ocean, has been condemned by special conditions of soil and climate to be desert, swamp, or forest. In the northern zone, however, there occur in succession from east to west four favourable areas, the great river valleys of central China, the plains of northern India, the lower basin of the Tigris and Euphrates, and the garden strip of the Nile. Here the seed of civilisation was encouraged to take root and able to grow to adolescence.

But that it may both come to full flower, and rise

superior to others, an adolescent civilisation must be able to pass beyond the narrow limits of its warm birthland into some larger area, where the conditions of life are less smooth and easy. In a word, it must find means of communication, ere the world be old, with other favourable regions such as do not entail passage over rugged or ill-watered tracts of land, or the open ocean. China and India, hedged by unfavourable environment, have been constrained to develop in and by themselves. Not so civilisation in the basins of the greater south-west Asian streams and of the Nile. The several influences, not precluded from contact with one another by any impassable barriers, have met on the shores of that sea which is the most favourable to rude navigation, and gives easiest access to a section of the northern Temperate Zone, where conditions of climate and soil, while stimulating to exertion, have not ceased to be kind.

Therefore, what was born in warm sub-tropic valleys has been able to pass to the cooler west and there attain full development. The ideas proper to the eastern contemplative nature have been brought to exercise their influence on western energy, developing their greatest excellence as ideas where the Jewish and Greek races, settled midway, combine characteristics of both types of nature, but their greatest effect on action among the younger and stronger races of farther Europe. While all the time the great civilisations of the Farther East have remained perforce in their closed sub-tropic cradles ; and their influence on the West and its reflex action on them have been hardly appreciable until these last centuries, when immemorial geographical barriers have been overcome by forces previously unused, and two extreme types of mind have been thrown into daily intercourse only that each may find the other too old and too rigidly set for sympathy or fusion.

Thus developed by the influence of the East, the pure Western civilisation is now found spread over a great outside area, which was once of no account to civilisation at all ; the East uncontaminated by reflex action of the

West, must be sought equally outside our Region. The
"Nearer East," therefore, is become all an Intermediate
Region, serving for the communication of the outer
West, that itself has created, with an outer East which
also owes it much. Birthplace of the Semitic and Greek
social systems and of their joint issue, the Christian code
of ethics, this Region has supplied the strongest influences
which have acted upon the Western type of mind. Birthplace of the religious system of Islam, it has modified only
less powerfully the Eastern type.

It is truly a strange irony of fate that a Region, which
has bestowed on the western nations the crown of their
civilisation, should have come in their age to matter to
them as a field of contention and an influence of uneasiness. But it was inevitable that this should be. As we
have seen, it is a Debatable Land, distracted internally by
a ceaseless war of influences, and only too anxious to lean
in one part or another on external aid. Therefore is it
always prone to involve in its own unrest those responsible
for the peace of the world, and ultimately to endanger the
balance of power in Europe. Needless to labour this
point. What has the " Eastern Question" meant in international politics these fifty years? And, even if this
"Question" has of late begun to be overshadowed by the
wider one which regards a Farther East, who, looking
closely at the actual constitution of society in the time-
honoured storm-centre of the eastern Mediterranean, can
suppose the earlier Question solved? There is hardly a
race in the Nearer East which is not divided against
itself, hardly a combatant who does not invoke alien
support against his fraternal foe. Local antagonisms in
this hot-bed of religions naturally express themselves in
terms of creed. Catholic Albanians count on Latin support against their Moslem and Orthodox compatriots.
Moslem Greeks of Crete, Cyprus, south-west Macedonia,
and southern Anatolia, of Hellenic speech and conscious
of community of race, are the most implacable foes of the
Hellenic unity. Macedonia has been torn this way and
that for half a century by an internecine struggle between

peoples indistinguishable in type, fighting under the irreconcilable banners of churches which cannot adduce an iota
of serious doctrinal variance to explain their schism. What
can come of Armenian national aspirations but sporadic
enterprises rendered futile and therefore fatal by discord
and treachery, while one part of the race, being Catholic,
looks to France ; a second being Protestant, to the Anglo-
Saxon ; a third is Moslem, and one with the Ottoman ;
and the mutual enmities of all three are only equalled in
intensity by the reciprocal antagonism of all to the
Gregorian residue ? The Syrian groups are in like case,
some looking westward, some eastward, but none to the
others. Copts, reinforced by the strong element of alien
Christians in Lower Egypt, permanently impair the growth
of a spirit of national unity in the Nile Valley. And we
have seen already what fierce and implacable hostilities
divide the world of Islam into two great camps, and how
hostilities, more covert but hardly more placable, under-
mine, and are likely further to subvert as time goes on,
the seeming unities of even the two main armies. If the
weak Imperial rulers in Stambul and Teheran have hitherto
found security in these divisions, they must set on the
other side of the account the fact that no alien Power,
which wishes to set foot in their respective empires, will
ever lack an invitation or an excuse.

Nor is it only as a Debatable Land that the Nearer East
has a disquieting influence on the outer world, but also as
an Intermediate Land, that is to say, a thoroughfare—the
region through which must lie, and by which can be en-
dangered, the communications between the West and the
West-in-East. It is only in comparatively recent times that
it has come to matter so greatly in this respect.

For in the process of the change in the significance of
its position, the Nearer East, shutting its door jealously
against the growing influence of the West, long ceased to
play any part in the development of civilisation. But
already ere the cutting of the Asiatic isthmus had brought
the trunk sea-way of the Old World through its midst, it
had accepted its inevitable rôle. And now, with the con-

struction of railways to the Bosphorus and thence to the
Anatolian Plateau, the main diagonal route of the Hemis-
phere, which has its half-way house at Constantinople, is
resuming all its old importance.

Every day it becomes less possible for Western Powers,
with interests in the Farther East developing till they bid fair
to become vital to their own national existence, to leave the
Nearer East to its proper devices, and least of all, at those
points which lie in most intimate geographical relation to
the trunk routes.   Neither the shores of the Bosphorus nor
Lower Egypt can hope ever hereafter to cease to be objects
of the most lively concern to the nations of Europe.   And
as railways are extended, and the speed of navigation is increased, a score of other points are becoming hardly less
intimately related to the great avenues of communication.
Salonica and Suda Bay ; the harbours of west and south-
west Anatolia ; Cyprus and the Syrian Fringe ; the Plateaux
of Asia Minor, Azerbaijan, and Iran ; the Mesopotamian
river valleys ; the Gulf ports from Bunder Abbas round to
Maskat ; blistered volcanic islets and coral cumbered promontories of the Red Sea ; one after another these are
being invested with an external importance very different
to that which their own products would confer.   In short,
the Nearer Eastern societies, which once mattered to the
universal Society as being the source of its most vivifying
ideas, have come, in the present state of the world's
economy, to matter mainly in proportion as they command or can trouble its routes of communication.

Probably most westerns who pass along these routes
take account of nothing less than the Societies through
which they fare.   By which neglect they render scant justice
to history and sentiment, but in all unconsciousness hardly
less than is after all the due of the Nearer East, as its actual
state might be regarded with merely utilitarian eyes.   For
thinly peopled as this region is, largely compounded of
steppe, desert, and mountain, and in great part dominated
by unprogressive systems of society, it cannot buy or sell in
the world's markets on a scale comparable with many other
regions.   And further, as so it happens, it is not the great

World's demand for necessaries, but for luxuries, that the productivity of the Nearer East in the main supplies. Natural geographical difficulties, lack of transport, lack of fuel, lack of hands, capital and knowledge, render the surplus cereals of the Region not worth export, the mines mostly unproductive, and the manufactures of useful goods unable to compete with those of other races. The cotton of Egypt, and, in much smaller bulk, of Anatolia, Syria, and Persia ; Egyptian sugar ; Greek iron and lead ore ; Anatolian and Greek emery ; coarse Cretan oil for soap manufacture; the charub bean of Cyprus, Crete, and other Levantine coasts, used for cattle food ; perhaps the stud horses of the Steppes ; these make up but a feeble list to compare with the long catalogue of articles of no necessity. Various coasts of the Balkan Peninsula, north and west Anatolia, Syria and Persia supply west and east with its favourite tobaccos. The opium of southern Persia, and that of Anatolia, are reputed best. Currants for all the world's consumption come from Greece, and the finest kinds of marble. Choicest of all dates are those of the Muntefik district in the Euphratean Delta and of the oases of Hasa and Siwah. The fresh oranges of Jaffa, the dried figs of Smyrna, and the crystallised fruits of the Syrian littoral are of universal renown. The Anatolian Plateau was the first source of mohair known to Europe. The Brusa district, where mulberries prosper more abundantly than in Europe, the Lebanon and the Caspian littoral export a great bulk of raw silk. Turkey, Persian and Kurd rugs have only to be mentioned ; Smyrna alone exports them to the value of a quarter of a million sterling. And numerous are the hand manufactures of embroideries, decorated leather, and metal work, now, alas ! failing fast. The pearls of the Gulf and the indigo of the lowlands east of Tigris ; bird wings and caviare from the Caspian coast : —these are main items in a total which still supports the ancient fame of the Nearer East as purveyor to the luxurious world.

But great Western Powers at the present day do not send armies, like emperors of old, to secure their luxuries;

and even necessaries must be of urgent necessity to entail serious interference with the social state of the producer. The products of Egypt were the primary attraction neither to Napoleon nor the British ; and the case of the Valley of the Lower Nile may be taken to exemplify a truth applicable to all the region.

Political and commercial considerations, however, do not now divide the whole kingdom of the higher western mind. The day is fortunately past when sentiment and emotion can be disregarded among the important factors in human action. To such emotion and sentiment, whether they vibrate to scenic or plastic beauty, to the mystery of antiquity or the mystery of religion, no region of the world appeals so variously as the Nearer East.

Antiquities and the sentiment of historic interest are no more to be ignored in estimating the degree in which this Region matters, than the historic and beautiful memorials of Italy in reckoning the assets in her economy. This needs no detailed demonstration ; but the matter may be dwelt upon for a moment under the utilitarian aspect only. We have seen already what important economic advantages result to various districts of our region from the pilgrimages to the holy places of Islam. Hardly less in quantity and far greater in quality are the benefits accruing to Palestine, Egypt, and Greece from those who visit the cradles of western faith and western culture. Expressed merely in terms of currency, the annual gain to Egypt from its winter visitors has been estimated at over a million sterling. Palestine has had its population doubled, and its wealth indefinitely increased by an Idea. Greece owes to the sentiment that her past excites, more than to anything else, the fact that she is free to-day. Like advantages will follow not less surely on changed political conditions, in Asia Minor and the areas of the Assyrian and Babylonian Empires. Nor do certain parts of the Region lack natural attractions. Egypt adds a matchless climate and a singular charm of scenery, and the Greek lands have a brilliance of atmosphere combined with grace of natural outline and seascape intermingled with landscape such as no other European country can offer. The Lycian is the grandest of Mediterranean coasts, and has matchless yachting harbours. The Lebanon is one of the world's gardens, and the vast sandy areas of all the Region are among the chief restorers of human vigour.

And since to profit by and enjoy these things is the privilege of the rich and powerful, the Nearer East must matter for its beauty and historic interest ever more widely to the western nations with every stage in the increase of their power or wealth. However little it may offer to their cupidity, it has still a part to play in the development of their civilisation.

INDEX

T

THE END

Printed by BALLANTYNE, HANSON & Co.
Edinburgh & London